FOOTBALL QUIZ BOOK

FOOTBALL QUIZ BOOK

PAUL DREW & COLIN JENNINGS

This edition published in 2009 by Arcturus Publishing Limited
26/27 Bickels Yard, 151–153 Bermondsey Street,
London SE1 3HA

ISBN: 978-1-84837-380-8
AD000191EN

Printed in the UK

Typeset by MATS, Southend-on-Sea, Essex

Contents

European Championship 2008

Quiz 1

1. Who scored the winner in the Euro 2008 Final?
2. Germany's top scorer, Lukas Podolski, was playing for which club before the start of Euro 2008?
3. Who was the Austrian coach that quit after his side's poor performances?
4. Who scored the last-gasp equaliser for Turkey in the quarter-finals against Croatia?
5. What was unusual about Slaven Bilic's goal celebration when Croatia had gone one-up against Turkey?
6. After the Czech Republic were beaten by Turkey, goalkeeper Petr Cech said, 'The only positive thing about this season is that it's over.' Why was he so downbeat?
7. Who scored Germany's late winner against Turkey in the semi-finals?
8. What was unusual about coach Raymond Domenech's interview shortly after France exited the cup?
9. Why was Lilian Thuram dropped from the French team that lost to Italy?
10. Which France player told the BBC the following: 'This tournament was my last. To have been allowed to wear France's colours, that's my trophy.'?
11. Who was Italy's 'under fire' coach following their defeat to Spain?
12. In which year did Roberto Donadoni miss a penalty in the World Cup semi-final shoot-out against Argentina?
13. Which player ran the Dutch ragged in their quarter-final against Russia and was credited as Man of the Match?
14. What nationality is Russia coach Guus Hiddink?
15. At the end of Euro 2008, which two players shared the same record, having made 16 appearances in European Championship Finals?

1. Fernando Torres 2. Bayern Munich 3. Josef Hickersberger 4. Semih Senturk 5. He ran on to the pitch to join a group hug that involved most of the Croatian squad 6. He dropped a clanger that allowed Turkey to equalize 7. Philipp Lahm 8. He proposed to his girlfriend on national television 9. He dropped himself by saying that he wasn't properly prepared 10. Claude Makelele 11. Roberto Donadoni 12. 1990 13. Andrei Arshavin 14. Dutch 15. Lilian Thuram and Edwin van der Sar.

Quiz 2

1. Edwin van der Sar finished Euro 2008 as the Netherlands' most-capped player, with 128 call-ups. In what year did he make his debut?
2. Who was the coach that picked Van der Sar for his first Dutch international?
3. Who was the Poland coach that blamed his side's Euro 2008 exit on 'nervousness'?
4. What nationality is he?
5. Who did he coach at the 2006 World Cup?
6. Why were the Portuguese Football Federation reportedly annoyed at Chelsea after the country's exit from Euro 2008?
7. Who coached Romania at the finals?
8. What was the score in the Russia-Netherlands quarter-final after extra-time?
9. Who scored the final penalty for Spain in the shoot-out against Italy?
10. Which Spanish player missed his penalty?
11. Which team were the first group-winners to reach the semi-finals?
12. Spain's semi-final appearance was their first in a major tournament since when?
13. After losing their shoot-out with Spain, Italy had lost on penalties five times. Whose record did they equal?
14. Italy hold the record for goalless draws in European Championship matches. How many was it after Euro 2008?
15. Which of the Italian players who missed a penalty against Spain also missed one for Roma against Manchester United in the 2007–08 UEFA Champions League quarter-final?

1. 1995 2. Guus Hiddink 3. Leo Beenhakker 4. Dutch 5. Trinidad & Tobago 6. They felt that Chelsea's announcement of Luiz Felipe Scolari as their next manager was premature and affected the team's performance 7. Victor Piturca 8. 3–1 to Russia 9. Cesc Fabregas 10. Dani Guiza 11. Spain 12. The 1984 European Championship 13. England's 14. Seven 15. Daniele De Rossi.

Quiz 3

1. Before Euro 2008, Germany's last European Championship meeting with Portugal was in July 2000. Who won?
2. Who scored a hat-trick that day?
3. After scoring against Portugal Michael Ballack became only the third German player to score in more than one European Championship Finals. Who were the other two?
4. Hosts Austria and Switzerland failed to progress beyond the group stages, eqalling the record of which previous host nation?
5. How many goals did Austria score in the tournament?
6. What was special about Luka Modric's winning penalty for Croatia in their first match against Austria?
7. Against which team did Lukas Podolski collect his 50th cap?
8. Who received Euro 2008's first red card during the Germany–Croatia game?
9. Who was the only German to have been sent off in the European Championships prior to 2008?
10. Croatia were the sixth team ever to win all three group matches at a European Championship. What differentiates them from the other five?
11. Who became the only Croatian player to have appeared in the 1996, 2004 and 2008 European Championships?
12. How many times had Turkey reached the semi-finals of the Euros prior to 2008?
13. Rustu Recber became Turkey's oldest-ever player in a tournament when he came on against Croatia. How old was he?
14. Which well-known manager engineered Turkey's success?
15. Turkey were given 17 cards at Euro 2008. Only two nations have ever received more. Who?

1. Portugal won 3–0 2. Sergio Conceicao 3. Jurgen Klinsmann and Rudi Voller 4. Belgium (2000) 5. One 6. It was the fastest spot-kick in the history of the tournament. Previously, that had been Zola's missed penalty against Germany in 1996 7. Croatia 8. Bastian Schweinsteiger 9. Thomas Strunz, during the goalless draw between Italy and Germany in 1996 10. The previous five all made it to the semi-finals or beyond 11. Dario Simic 12. None 13. 35 14. Fatih Terim 15. Greece (18 in 2004) and the Czech Republic (19 in 1996).

Quiz 4

1. What was unusual about the Swiss team that lined up against the Czech Republic?
2. Jan Koller and Marek Jankulovski equalled the record for most European Championship caps. Which three Czech stars had previously shared the record?
3. After scoring against the Czech Republic, Arda Turan and Nihat Kahveci equalled whose record by becoming Turkey's joint top scorers in European Championship history?
4. Turkey goalkeeper Volkan Demirel received a straight red card. Which two goalkeepers shared a similar fate at previous Euros?
5. Who became the oldest goalscorer in Czech Euro history when he struck against Turkey?
6. Who was the only striker at Euro 2008 to have more scoreless games than Nicolas Anelka?
7. Which match ended in the first draw of Euro 2008?
8. Romania's last win in a Euro Championship came against which team?
9. What was the score in that game?
10. The Netherlands hammered France 4–1 in the group stages. Who got their impressive goals?
11. Only one of those scorers had never played for a Premiership side. Which one?
12. True or false: no team has ever survived the group stage without winning a single match?
13. Netherlands' 4–1 win gave France their biggest defeat in the tournament. Their previous biggest loss was 2–0, against which team?
14. The Netherlands' biggest win in Euro history was 6–1, in 2000. Who did they beat?
15. True or false: the French team that lined up against the Dutch was their oldest in the history of the competition?

1. It was their youngest ever in the tournament (average: 25 years, 193 days) 2. Vladimir Smicer, Karel Poborsky and Pavel Nedved 3. Hakan Sukur 4. Filip de Wilde (2000) and Sergei I. Ovchinnikov (2004) 5. Jan Koller (35 years, 77 days) 6. Turkey's Arif Erdem 7. The 0-0 between Romania and France 8. England at Euro 2000 9. 3-2 10. Dirk Kuyt, Robin van Persie, Arjen Robben, Wesley Sneijder 11. Wesley Sneijder 12. True 13. Czechoslovakia in 1960 14. Yugoslavia 15. True.

Quiz 5

1. True or false: Italy's win over France was their first (excluding penalty shoot-outs) in 30 years?
2. When was Italy's previous win over 90 minutes against France?
3. In what country was Germany's forward Lukas Podolski born?
4. Who were Poland's first opponents in 2008?
5. Podolski scored two goals against Poland. Prior to this, who was the last German to do so in the Euros?
6. True or false: at the end of Euro 2008, Poland coach Leo Beenhakker had still not registered a win at a major tournament?
7. Against whom did Michael Ballack score a 30-yard free-kick – arguably the best in the tournament?
8. Which Portuguese star became the fourth player to score in three different European Championships?
9. Who, at 36 years, 264 days, became the oldest player to represent Sweden at the Euros, breaking Roland Nilsson's record?
10. True or false: Greece were the first defending champions to lose and also to fail to score in their opening two matches of the Euros?
11. Against Russia, Giorgos Karagounis received his fifth career yellow card at a European Championship. Which three players share the same record?
12. True or false: Karagounis broke the record for yellow cards in the Euros when he was booked and then sent off against Spain?
13. True or false: Holland's win over Italy was the biggest defeat ever suffered by the Italians in the tournament?
14. True or false: Italy's starting line-up against Holland (average age: 31 years, 52 days) was the second-oldest starting line-up in the history of the competition?
15. The Netherlands scored nine goals in the group stage, equalling the record set by which team in 1984?

1. True 2. 1978 World Cup (2-1) 3. Poland 4. Germany 5. Oliver Bierhoff (Euro 96) 6. True 7. Austria 8. Nuno Gomes 9. Henrik Larsson 10. True 11. Gheorghe Hagi, Pavel Nedved and Gianluca Zambrotta 12. False: he did break the record by being booked but was not sent off. 13. True 14. False: it was the oldest at that time 15. France.

Quiz 6

1. True or false: Guus Hiddink had never taken a team to the semi-finals of the Euros before 2008?
2. The last time the Netherlands had been knocked out in the quarter-finals Hiddink was the coach. Who beat them?
3. Ruud van Nistelrooy has six Euro goals to his name. Name the two players to have more.
4. Who scored Switzerland's two goals against Portugal in their 2–0 win in the group stages?
5. True or false: the defeat of Portugal was Switzerland's first-ever win in the European Championships?
6. Who became Switzerland's all-time record scorer in the Euros, with three goals?
7. Who scored Russia's only goal against Spain in the group stages?
8. Who scored a hat-trick for Spain in the group stages?
9. True or false: this player became the second Spanish player to score a hat-trick at the Euros, after Emilio Butragueno?
10. True or false: Cesc Fabregas' goal against Russia was his first for Spain?
11. Which player, then plying his trade at Liverpool, scored Spain's first goal against Sweden?
12. Prior to 2008, Spain's longest winning streak came in which decade?
13. Spanish coach Luis Aragones had his 50th match in charge against Sweden. What was the score?
14. What was the score at half-time in the Spain–Russia semi-final?
15. Which Spanish player went off in the semi-final to give Cesc Fabregas his chance to change the game?

1. True 2. France (on penalties) 3. Alan Shearer (seven) and Michel Platini (nine) 4. Hakan Yakin 5. True 6. Hakan Yakin 7. Roman Pavlyuchenko 8. David Villa 9. False: Villa was the first 10. True 11. Fernando Torres 12. The 1920s 13. 2–1 to Spain 14. 0–0 15. David Villa

Quiz 7

1. Which BBC personality retired from live commentary after the Euro 2008 final?
2. Which player finished as Turkey's top scorer?
3. Which player hit the post in the first-half of the Final?
4. Who was voted Player of the Tournament?
5. Name the goalkeepers in the UEFA Team of the Tournament.
6. Who was the only Turkish player to make the Team of the Tournament?
7. True or false: only Russian and Spanish players were picked as strikers in the Team of the Tournament?
8. True or false: Ronaldo was picked as a midfielder in the Team of the Tournament?
9. Despite their great performances only one Dutch outfield player made the Team of the Tournament. Who?
10. When did Spain first win the European Championship?
11. True or false: Spain did concede a single goal during all three knock-out rounds?
12. Before 2008, Germany had lost two Euro finals. In which years were these?
13. David Villa was the tournament's top scorer with just four goals. When was the last time someone won the accolade with fewer than this?
14. Jens Lehmann became the oldest player ever to appear in the European Championship final (38 years, 232 days). Whose record did he break?
15. At the age of 69 years, 337 days, Luis Aragones became the oldest man ever to coach in the final of a European Championship. Whose record did he surpass?

1. John Motson 2. Semih Senturk 3. Fernando Torres 4. Xavi Hernández (Spain) 5. Gianluigi Buffon, Iker Casillas and Edwin van der Sar 6. Hamit Altintop 7. True 8. False. He wasn't picked at all 9. Wesley Sneijder 10. 1964 11. True 12. 1976, 1992 13. 1992, shared by Dennis Bergkamp, Tomas Brolin, Henrik Larsen and Karl-Heinz Riedle (3 goals each) 14. Arnold Muhren (37 years, 23 days) in 1988 15. Otto Rehhagel (65 years, 327 days) who managed Greece at the Euro 2004 final.

Quiz 8

1. When was the first UEFA European Football Championship held?
2. The name currently used was adopted in 1968. What was it called previously?
3. Which team won the first Euros in 1960?
4. Why did Greece withdraw from the 1964 tournament?
5. Which country hosted the Championship won by Spain?
6. The host nation won in 1968. Who were they?
7. What was unusual about the semi-final of that year (1968) between Italy and the Soviet Union?
8. West Germany won the tournament in 1972 but where was it hosted?
9. In 1976, Czechoslovakia beat West Germany on penalties. Which player famously chipped the 'keeper with his spot-kick?
10. West Germany won the 1980 tournament which was hosted by Italy. Who did they beat in the final?
11. Michel Platini set the record for goals in a Euro tournament in 1984. How many did he get in just five games?
12. The 1992 tournament was won in Sweden, by Denmark. What was particularly surprising about the fact that they won the tournament?
13. What was unusual about the German side that year?
14. Germany won Euro 96 in England by getting the first golden goal in a major tournament. Who scored it?
15. Euro 2000 was the first tournament to be hosted by two nations. Who were they?

1. 1960 2. UEFA European Nations Cup 3. The Soviet Union 4. They were drawn against Albania, a team that they were officially at war with 5. Spain 6. Italy 7. It was the first and last Euro match to be decided on the toss of a coin 8. Belgium 9. Antonin Panenka 10. Belgium 11. Nine 12. Denmark were only in the tournament because of the withdrawal of Yugoslavia due to the conflict in the region 13. It was the first time they played as one nation in the Euros 14. Oliver Bierhoff 15. The Netherlands and Belgium.

English League Clubs

Accrington Stanley

1. In which decade were these Accies founded?
2. Name the ground where they play.
3. When Stanley gained league status in 2006, how long had it been since a club of this name had last been in the league proper?
4. True or false: Oxford, who lost league status in the same year Stanley gained it (2006), was the team that was elected to replace the former Accrington Stanley as members of the Football League in 1962?
5. Stanley's rise to the league was seen by some as a result of the windfall brought about by the sell-on clause of one of their stars. He was eventually sold on to Southampton. Who was he?
6. In 2006, Stanley won their first-ever League Cup match. Who did they beat?
7. The Accies were name-checked in a 1980s advert. Remember this: 'Accrington Stanley? … Who are they??!' What was the ad for?
8. Which defender in the 2008–9 side shares his name with a famous British pop star?
9. Which Stanley player was voted the club's most popular ever in a survey by the PFA, in 2007?
10. Which league title did Stanley win in 2002–3?
11. True or false: the entire 2008–9 squad is British?
12. Which manager led the club into the 2008–9 season?
13. Which former player returned to Sheffield United in 2003–4 where he teamed up with his brother, completing a mammoth jump from Conference to Premiership in one season?
14. Which pub is referred to on the club's official website as 'our very own pub'?
15. Stanley won the 2005–6 Conference League. By how many points?

1. The 1960s (1968) 2. The Fraser Eagle Stadium 3. 44 years 4. True 5. Brett Ormerod 6. Nottingham Forest 7. Milk 8. Robbie Williams 9. Chris Grimshaw 10. Northern Premier League 11. True 12. John Coleman 13. Stephen Jagielka 14. The Crown Inn 15. Eleven.

Aldershot Town

1. In what year was the club founded?
2. Where did the team play their home games in the 2007 season?
3. In which year did they win the the Conference National?
4. What is the team's nickname?
5. Who was the manager at the start of the 2007–8 season?
6. What nationality is he?
7. Prior to Aldershot FC folding, which club had been the last to do so?
8. Who was club captain during the Conference-winning 2007–8 season?
9. From which club did Aldershot acquire Dean Howell?
10. From which club did Aldershot acquire Chris Blackburn?
11. To which team was Joel Grant sold for a club record in 2007–8?
12. True or false: Aldershot's Recreation Ground had a capacity of 15,000 in 2006?
13. In 2008, the club signed a three-year kit deal with which company?
14. Which national side has Louie Soares represented?
15. Which national side has Junior Mendes represented?

1. 1992, just after the closure of debt-ridden Fourth Division Aldershot FC, who had been founded in 1926 2. The Recreation Ground 3. 2007-08 4. The Shots 5. Gary Waddock 6. Irish 7. Accrington Stanley 8. Rhys Day 9. Rushden & Diamonds 10. Swindon Town 11. Crewe Alexandra 12. False. In 2008, the stadium still held around 7,500 13. Carbrini 14. Barbados 15. Montserrat.

Arsenal

1. Which player scored the first goal at the Emirates Stadium?
2. Dennis Bergkamp was a boyhood fan of which rival club?
3. Who was Arsenal's youngest-ever goalscorer going into the 2008–9 season?
4. Which Arsenal icon has been involved in all three of Arsenal's 'double' successes, the last of which was in 2002?
5. Before 2008–9, which team provided the opposition for Arsenal's biggest league victory and their heaviest league defeat?
6. Liam Brady moved to which club from Arsenal in 1980?
7. In which area of south London was the club formed?
8. Why could Arsenal's 1–0 FA Cup Final victory over Southampton in 2003 be described as a 'first'?
9. What was Arsenal FC's original name?
10. Arsenal have not been relegated from the top flight since their promotion in 1919. What was unusual about this 'promotion'?
11. What was the original name of Arsenal tube station?
12. Who was Arsenal's oldest-ever player?
13. Against which club did Thierry Henry finally beat Ian Wright's all-time Arsenal goal-scoring record?
14. Which player scored in consecutive FA Cup Finals in 2001 and 2002?
15. What was the name of the 1940 British Film in which a member of the non-league 'Trojan' team dies in suspicious circumstances during a match against Arsenal at Highbury?

1. Klaas Jan Huntelaar (Ajax) 2. Tottenham Hotspur 3. Cesc Fabregas (16 years, 212 days) 4. Pat Rice (as player in 1971 and Assistant Manager in 1998 and 2002) 5. Loughborough Town lost 12–0 to Arsenal in 1900 but had won 8–0 four years earlier 6. Juventus 7. Woolwich 8. It was played 'indoors' (under a roof at Cardiff's Millennium Stadium) 9. Dial Square FC 10. They were elected members, rather than being promoted on playing merit 11. Gillespie Road 12. Jock Rutherford (41 years, 236 days) 13. Sparta Prague (October 18, 2006) 14. Freddie Ljungberg 15. *The Arsenal Stadium Mystery.*

Aston Villa

1. Which Irish defender was nicknamed 'God' by the Aston Villa faithful in the 1990s?
2. In which year did Aston Villa record their only European Cup win to date?
3. What was unusual about Aston Villa's first match against Aston Brook St Mary's?
4. What is the nickname of former Aston Villa chairman Doug Ellis?
5. Which American Football team is current chairman Randy Lerner associated with?
6. Which former Aston Villa and Ireland midfielder went on to become a regular TV pundit with ITV?
7. Which manager won the European Cup for Villa in his first season in charge?
8. Which player left Aston Villa to become captain of arch-rivals Birmingham before the 2007–8 season?
9. Which two former Aston Villa players have scored over 100 Premiership goals (up to and including 2007–8)?
10. At which club did Aston Villa legend Dion Dublin start and end his career?
11. Which former Aston Villa player was the first Peruvian to play in the Premier League?
12. The players of which cricket club formed the club which became Aston Villa in 1873?
13. Where did Aston Villa finish in the inaugural Premier League table of 1992–3?
14. Who, up to the end of the 2007–8 season, was Aston Villa's record transfer?
15. Who was the first sponsor on Villa shirts?

1. Paul McGrath 2. 1982 3. The first half was played using rugby rules and the second half using football rules 4. 'Deadly Doug' 5. He has owned the Cleveland Browns since 2002 6. Andy Townsend 7. Tony Barton 8. Liam Ridgewell 9. Dion Dublin and Dwight Yorke 10. Norwich City 11. Nolberto Solano 12. Villa Cross Wesleyan Chapel, Aston, Birmingham 13. 2nd to Manchester United 14. Ashley Young, £9.65m from Watford 15. Davenports.

Barnet

1. From whom did Barnet acquire Luke Medley in pre-season 2008–9?
2. Who did Barnet sell Jason Puncheon to for a quarter-of-a-million pounds?
3. Who started the 2008–9 season as manager?
4. Which two players were lost to Stevenage on free transfers just before the beginning of the 2008–9 season?
5. In what year were the Bees founded?
6. Which ground did the Bees play their home games at during the 2001 season?
7. In which year were Barnet on the verge of expulsion from the League for failing to pay players' wages as well as failing to meet a deadline for a fine, but nevertheless they managed to win promotion to Division Two?
8. Who was the colourful character who steered the club to promotion successes in the early 1990s?
9. Which of the club's former managers was a striking legend at West Ham, and later Everton?
10. In which season did Jimmy Greaves play for the club?
11. Against whom did the club set a record attendance of 11,026 in the FA Amateur Cup fourth round, in 1951–2?
12. Arthur Morris scored more than 400 goals for the club in a period spanning which two decades?
13. With which club did former player-coach Terry Gibson win the FA Cup?
14. What do the red rose, white rose and crossed swords represent in the team crest?
15. In what season did the Bees win the Conference National, with an impressive 86 points, to gain promotion back to League 2?

1. Bradford City 2. Plymouth Argyle 3. Paul Fairclough 4. Anthony Thomas and Andy Drury 5. 1888 6. Underhill Stadium 7. 1992-93 8. Barry Fry 9. Tony Cottee 10. 1978-9 11. Wycombe Wanderers 12. The 1920s and 1930s 13. Wimbledon 14. The 1471 Battle of Barnet, which was a pivotal battle in the War of the Roses 15. 2004-5.

Barnsley

1. Where do Barnsley play home matches?
2. How much did Blackburn pay for Barnsley's Ashley Ward in 1998?
3. What non-human creature features on the Barnsley Crest?
4. How old was Mick McCarthy when he made his Barnsley debut in 1977?
5. According to supporters, watching Barnsley in action is often just like watching which South American side?
6. Which team beat Barnsley in the 2000 play-off final?
7. Who holds the record for most league appearances for the Tykes?
8. Who scored the goal which won Barnsley's FA Cup quarter-final against Chelsea in 2008?
9. In what year did Barnsley win the FA Cup?
10. True of False: Barnsley have spent more time in the second tier of English football than any other team?
11. Who started the 2000-1 season as Barnsley manager?
12. In which country was Leonidas Bertos born?
13. From which Finnish club did Barnsley buy Janne Salli?
14. Who managed Barnsley from 1994-98?
15. Which club did Steve Parkin manage immediately before taking over at Barnsley?

1. Oakwell 2. £4.5m 3. Dragon 4. 18 5. Brazil 6. Ipswich Town 7. Barry Murphy - 514 8. Kayode Odejayi
9. 1912 10. True 11. Nigel Spackman 12. New Zealand 13. FC Haka 14. Danny Wilson 15. Rochdale.

Birmingham City

1. Who was the first Birmingham City player to have received a World Cup winners' medal?
2. When Trevor Francis left Birmingham City in 1979, he became the first £1m player. To which club was he sold?
3. When Karren Brady took over as managing director of Birmingham City in 1993, how old was she?
4. What was Birmingham City's original name when they were formed in 1875?
5. Why did City play their home games at Villa Park during the early 1940s?
6. Which team did City beat 5–1 in an FA Cup match in January 2007?
7. In which year did Birmingham City first win the League Cup?
8. As of 2007–8, which player held the club record for most league goals in one season?
9. Who was the first full-time manager of Birmingham City FC?
10. How many goals did Andrew Johnson score in his 82 games for Birmingham?
11. Which team did Birmingham beat on penalties in the final of the 2002 Division One play-off to secure promotion to the Premier League?
12. Birmingham became the first English club to play in Europe when they played against whom in May 1956?
13. Which ex-Villan scored on his debut for City in 2004?
14. Bert Trautmann famously continued playing in the 1956 FA Cup Final after breaking his neck in a collision with which Birmingham City player?
15. Which former World Cup-winner proved inspirational for City when he arrived on loan in 2003?

1. Alberto Tarantini of Argentina, in 1978 2. Nottingham Forest 3. 23 4. Small Heath Alliance 5. St. Andrews was hit 20 times by the German Luftwaffe 6. Newcastle United 7. 1963, their only victory in the competition to date 8. Joe Bradford scored 29 league goals during the 1927-8 campaign 9. Bob McRoberts 10. Eight 11. Norwich City 12. Internazionale 13. Dwight Yorke 14. Peter Murphy 15. Christophe Dugarry.

Blackburn Rovers

1. Who was Rovers' all-time record goalscorer going into the 2008–9 season?
2. Rovers' biggest League win was a 9–0 home victory in 1954. Who were their opponents that day?
3. In which season did Rovers first win a top-flight league trophy?
4. How much did Rovers pay Southampton for Alan Shearer upon their promotion to the Premier League in 1992?
5. How many Premier League goals did Benni McCarthy score in his debut season?
6. In which year did Blackburn Rovers win their first-ever League Cup?
7. Two old boys of which school founded Blackburn Rovers in 1875?
8. When did Rovers win their first-ever FA Cup?
9. Rovers' record attendance of 62,522 at Ewood Park in 1929 was against which club?
10. Who has made the most league appearances for Blackburn Rovers?
11. Which manager guided Rovers to their first and only Premier League title to date, in 1995?
12. Why did the club start their games later than the rest of the division at the beginning of the 1965–66 season?
13. Who was Rovers' first-ever 'seven-figure' signing?
14. In which season did Rovers record a club record eight hat-tricks?
15. Which player did Chelsea pay £17m for in 2003?

1. Simon Garner (1978–92) 484 appearances, 168 goals 2. Middlesbrough 3. 1911-2 4. £3.5m; an English transfer record at the time 5. 18 6. 2002 7. Shrewsbury School 8. 1884. They went on to retain it in 1885 and 1886 9. Bolton Wanderers 10. Derek Fazackerley (593 + 3 as sub) 11. Kenny Dalglish 12. Because of an outbreak of polio in the town 13. Mike Newell from Everton 14. 1963–64 15. Damien Duff.

Blackpool

1. How much did Blackpool pay Hull City for Steve MacPhee, their record signing?
2. In what year did 'Pool require re-election to the league after finishing in 21st place in Division 4?
3. Who was top scorer in the promotion season of 2006–7?
4. In what year did the club first start playing home fixtures at Bloomfield Road?
5. True or false: the capacity of Bloomfield Road is under 10,000?
6. Who do Blackpool play in the West Lancashire Derby?
7. Which club did Blackpool sign striker Ben Burgess from?
8. What sort of animal is the Tangerines' mascot?
9. What is Blackpool's record finish up the league ladder?
10. Who were Blackpool's first shirt sponsors?
11. Which side of Bloomfield Road stood as an empty space when the stand was demolished in 2003?
12. Where was manager Simon Grayson under contract prior to moving to the Seasiders?
13. In what year did Blackpool win the 'Matthews Final'?
14. How much did Southampton pay for Brett Ormerod in 2001?
15. Did footballing legend Stanley Matthews play more games for Stoke City or Blackpool?

1. £300,000 2. 1983 3. Andy Morrell 4. 1899 5. True 6. Preston North End 7. Hull City 8. Bear 9. 2nd in the First Division – 1955–6 10. Easywear 11. South/Bloomfield Road side 12. Blackburn 13. 1953 14. £1.75m 15. Blackpool.

Bolton Wanderers

1. What was significant about Bolton's FA Cup win in 1923?
2. Bolton's record goalscorer, Nat Lofthouse, played 33 times for England. How many goals did he score?
3. Bolton reached the Premiership by winning the play-off final in 1995, 4–3. Who did they beat?
4. Bolton's last trophy of the 20th century was the FA Cup in 1958. Who did Bolton beat in the final?
5. Which World Cup winner arrived at the Reebok in 2002?
6. What was Bolton's highest Premier League finish under Sam Allardyce?
7. Bill McAdams scored twice on his debut against which club?
8. El-Hadji Diouf was banned for three games in November 2004 after spitting at which player?
9. Who holds the record for most appearances for Bolton?
10. Despite losing 4–3 in the 'Stanley Matthews Final' of 1953, which Bolton player scored a hat-trick?
11. By what name was the club known before changing its name to Bolton Wanderers?
12. How many times were Bolton relegated from The Premiership during the 1990s?
13. How many times have Bolton won the FA Cup?
14. Who scored Bolton's only goal when they lost in the League Cup Final in 2004?
15. From which club did Bolton sign Jay-Jay Okocha?

1. It was the first final played at Wembley 2. 30 3. Reading 4. Manchester United 5. Youri Djorkaeff 6. 6th in 2004–5 7. Chelsea. Bolton won 4–1 8. Arjan De Zeeuw of Portsmouth 9. Eddie Hopkinson (519) 10. Stan Mortensen 11. Christ Church 12. Twice (1996 and 1998) 13. Four (1923, 1926, 1929 and 1958) 14. Kevin Davies 15. Paris Saint-Germain.

AFC Bournemouth

1. In which year was the club set up?
2. After which gym network was the club's stadium named?
3. Who started as manager for the 2008–9 season?
4. What was the Cherries' original name?
5. Which side did Bournemouth seek to imitate by changing to a red-and-black kit?
6. Which former Ireland and Charlton midfielder represented Bournemouth early in his career?
7. Who has been Bournemouth's most successful-ever manager?
8. At what age did Jamie Redknapp make his debut for the club?
9. Against which team did crowd trouble lead to Bournemouth having a de facto ban on Bank Holiday games?
10. The club have recently signed a new shirt sponsorship deal with Focal Point Fires plc thus ending a long association with which previous sponsor?
11. Which former England star scored a 40-yard screamer on his debut to equalize against Scunthorpe United, in 2006–7?
12. Against whom did the same player score his first hat-trick for the club?
13. Bournemouth's highest crowd (9,632) at their current stadium came in 2007–8 against which club?
14. Only one player in the 2007–8 squad wasn't British. Who was he?
15. What is the club's mascot called?

1. 1899 2. Fitness First 3. Kevin Bond 4. Bournemouth and Boscombe Athletic 5. AC Milan 6. Matt Holland 7. Harry Redknapp – he masterminded a shock 1984 FA Cup win over Manchester United and took the club into the second tier of the English league for the first time in their history in 1987 8. 16 9. Leeds United 10. Seward Cars 11. Darren Anderton 12. Leyton Orient 13. Leeds United 14. Jo Kuffour 15. Cherry Bear.

Bradford City

1. Give two of City's main three nicknames.
2. Where do the club play their home games?
3. Which former player managed the team at the start of the 2008–9 season?
4. In what year did a fire tragically claim the lives of 56 of the club's supporters?
5. True or false: the club was founded before 1900?
6. In which year did the Bantams win their one and only FA Cup?
7. After relegation from the old Division 1 in 1922, how long did fans have to wait to get back into the top flight?
8. In that first year in the Premiership, City stayed up with the then lowest number of points ever. How many did they have?
9. True or false: City avoided relegation again the following year (2000) with an even lower number of points?
10. In October 1998 Bradford's big new signing became one of the first players in history to prove negligence by an opponent who broke his leg in two places. Who was the Bradford player?
11. Who was the club captain that scored the winner when the Bantams won the FA Cup?
12. Which former England star scored directly from a corner against Huddersfield in 1997?
13. Bradford were surprisingly relegated from Division 1 in 1921–2 alongside which other surprise strugglers?
14. True or false: Bradford City is the only professional football club in England to wear a claret-and-amber kit?
15. Club scarf sales have allegedly spiralled due to fans of which series of novels?

1. The Bantams, The Paraders and The Citizens 2. Valley Parade (Coral Windows under sponsorship) 3. Stuart McCall 4. 1985 5. False. It was founded in 1903 6. 1911 7. 77 years (1999) 8. 36 points 9. False. They were relegated 10. Gordon Watson (he was awarded over £900,000 in damages after being hurt in a tackle with Huddersfield's Kevin Gray) 11. Jimmy Speirs 12. Chris Waddle 13. Manchester United 14. True (although there are other clubs in Scotland such as Motherwell) 15. Harry Potter (they are the magician's school colours).

Brentford

1. True or false: Brentford were founded before Barcelona?
2. Where do the Bees play their home games?
3. Which Englishman managed the side at the start of 2008–9?
4. In which decade did Brentford achieve Top 6 finishes in Division 1?
5. The club was founded to provide a winter pursuit for athletes of which other club?
6. During the war, Brentford competed in the London War Cup. They lost in the 1941 final at Wembley Stadium to which side?
7. They won it the following year. Who did they beat?
8. Which larger club almost took over Brentford in the 1960s?
9. Which team ended Brentford's great FA Cup run in the 1989 quarter-finals?
10. Name the only non-Englishman listed in the squad at the end of the 2007–8 season.
11. All but four of the Bees' managers have been English prior to 2007–8. What other two nationalities have featured?
12. Which famous rocker was an apprentice at the club before deciding to pursue a music career?
13. Which former Bees defender was once part of George Graham's miserly back four?
14. Name the Jamaican international who played for the Bees.
15. Which former Bee went on to play for Ireland and Tottenham?

1. True. They were founded in 1889. Barcelona were founded in 1899 2. Griffin Park 3. Andy Scott 4. The 1930s 5. Brentford Rowing Club 6. Reading 7. Portsmouth 8. Queens Park Rangers 9. Liverpool 10. Irishman Kevin O'Connor 11. Irish and Scottish 12. Rod Stewart 13. Kenny Sansom 14. Marcus Gayle 15. Chris Hughton.

Brighton & Hove Albion

1. Which Turkish international made 43 league appearances for Brighton and left the club in August 2005?
2. In which season did Brighton finish runners-up in the FA Cup?
3. Who were Brighton's opponents in that final and what was the score?
4. Who scored Brighton's goals in the first game?
5. One of these players also featured in the Scottish League Cup Final in the same year for which team?
6. What is Brighton's nickname?
7. Which legendary manager was in charge of Brighton for the 1973–4 season before taking charge of Leeds United?
8. Who did he replace as Brighton's manager?
9. Which famous DJ and musician sponsored the club through his record label, Skint Records?
10. Which comedian was once a director of the club?
11. Which manager bought Mark Lawrenson from Preston North End for a fee of £100,000 in 1977?
12. Who did he join in 1981 for £900,000?
13. Where did Brighton play their home games for two years before moving to their current stadium?
14. Why were they forced to groundshare?
15. Who did Brighton beat to win the Charity Shield (now the Community Shield) in 1910?

1. Colin Kazim-Richards 2. 1982–3 3. Manchester United. The final finished 2–2 and United won the replay 4–0 4. Gordon Smith and Gary Stevens 5. Rangers 6. The Seagulls 7. Brian Clough 8. Pat Soward 9. Norman Cook aka Fatboy Slim 10. Norman Wisdom 11. Allan Mullery 12. Liverpool 13. Gillingham's Priestfield Stadium 14. Brighton had to sell their Goldstone Ground to help pay off the club's debts 15. Aston Villa.

Bristol City

1. What were Bristol City called when they formed in 1894?
2. Who did City beat in the last game of the 2006–7 season to achieve promotion?
3. Who was the top scorer in the league for Bristol City in 2000–1?
4. In what year did City win the LDV Vans Trophy?
5. What is Bristol City's highest league placing?
6. Which club did Gary Johnson manage before joining the Robins in 2005?
7. Which club sold Andy Cole to Bristol City?
8. How much did Bristol City pay for Ade Akinbiyi in 1998?
9. Who beat City in the 2004 play-off final?
10. Which band released the record 'One for the Bristol City'?
11. Who put seven past the Robins to spell the end of Brian Tinnion's reign as manager?
12. Which Premier League manager played for Bristol City between 1985 and 1987?
13. Despite finishing fourth in the 2007–8 season, City's goal difference was fairly poor. What was it?
14. Which trophy did Bristol City win in 1934?
15. Which Bristol City player scored a hat-trick in the 3-0 win at Northampton Town in August, 2001?

1. Bristol South End 2. Rotherham United 3. Tony Thorpe 4. 2003 5. Second in the top division, 1907- 6. Yeovil Town 7. Arsenal 8. £1.2m 9. Brighton & Hove Albion 10. The Wurzels 11. Swansea City 12. David Moyes 13. +1 14. The Welsh Cup 15. Tony Thorpe.

Bristol Rovers

1. Who did Bristol Rovers defeat 3–1 in the 2007 League Two play–off final?
2. What was the club's name when they were founded in 1883?
3. What is the club's official nickname?
4. The club is also known locally by which name?
5. Where did the club play their home games before moving to the Memorial Stadium?
6. In which year did Rovers first play at the Memorial Stadium?
7. Which World Cup winner played 17 games for Bristol Rovers during the 1982–3 season?
8. Which father–and–son pairing made 526 appearances between them for the club ?
9. Which former Bristol Rovers player has been capped over 100 times for Latvia?
10. Which manager led the club to the Third Division title in the 1989–90 season?
11. Why were the club docked two points during the 1982–3 season?
12. Who was the player?
13. Who scored a club record 33 goals in one season during the 1952–3 campaign?
14. Which American folk and blues artist wrote the song 'Goodnight Irene' that was adopted by the club?
15. Which former Bristol Rovers goalkeeper became the first £1m 'keeper when he was sold by Crystal Palace to Leeds?

1. Shrewsbury Town 2. The Black Arabs 3. The Pirates 4. The Gas 5. The Eastville Stadium 6. 1996 7. Alan Ball 8. Ray and Gary Mabbutt 9. Vitalijs Astafjevs 10. Gerry Francis 11. They fielded an ineligible player 12. Steve Bailey 13. Geoff Bradfield 14. Lead Belly 15. Nigel Martyn.

Burnley

1. In what year did Burnley first play at Turf Moor?
2. Who was Burnley's first £1m signing in the winter of 2000?
3. In what year did Burnley last win the top English league?
4. Who is the main club mascot?
5. Which company were the first sponsor to appear on the Clarets' shirts?
6. In the 1986–7 season Burnley were only two positions and two points from dropping out of the league. Who went down instead?
7. In 2003–4 Arsenal broke a record Burnley had set back in 1920–1. What was it?
8. How many times have Burnley won the FA Cup?
9. Former Burnley central defender Ian Cox played international football for which country, despite being born in Croydon?
10. When did Burnley last get relegated from the top flight?
11. Who is Burnley's record goalscorer?
12. In which country was Burnley's keeper Nik Michopoulos born?
13. Which former England international was Burnley boss from 1997–8?
14. Who was the top scorer in the league for Burnley in 2000–1?
15. Who beat Burnley in the first round of the 2000–1 League Cup?

1. 1882 2. Ian Moore 3. 1960 4. Bertie Bee 5. Poco 6. Lincoln City 7. For the most consecutive unbeaten games in a top-flight season – Burnley had 30 8. Once 9. Trinidad & Tobago 10. 1976 11. George Beel (178 goals) 12. Greece 13. Chris Waddle 14. Andy Payton 15. Rushden & Diamonds.

Bury

1. What is the club's nickname?
2. What nationality is the 2008–9 team manager, Alan Knill?
3. The club was formed in 1885 after a meeting in which pub?
4. After the meeting a pitch was hired and the team still play in a stadium of the same name in the same area. What is it?
5. Bury have won the FA Cup twice. Name one of the years they achieved the honour.
6. Bury won both FA Cup finals at Crystal Palace. Name one of the teams they defeated.
7. Bury's run on the way to their second FA Cup win held two major achievements beyond picking up the trophy. Name one.
8. Which former Bury player went on to have a highly distinguished career with Wales and Everton in the 1980s?
9. Why did David Adekola become infamous with Bury fans in the Noughties?
10. Name these two successes of Bury's recent youth policy: one went on to win an FA Cup medal with Portsmouth. The other played for Turkey in Euro 2008.
11. Which famous Zimbabwean player donned the club's jersey?
12. Which former Manchester United and Northern Ireland legend played for the Shakers?
13. True or false: Luther Blissett started his career at Bury?
14. Which pair shared the honour of being top scorers in the league for Bury in 2000–1?
15. From which club did Bury sign Ian Lawson in September, 2001?

1. The Shakers 2. Welsh 3. The Swan and Cemetery (which still exists today) 4. Gigg Lane 5. 1900 and 1903 6. Southampton (4–0) and Derby County (6–0) 7. They didn't concede a single goal and had the biggest win ever in a final (6–0) 8. Neville Southall 9. He allegedly tricked the club into believing that he was a former Nigerian international player with top-flight experience. His performances didn't reflect his claims 10. David Nugent and Colin Kazim-Richards 11. Bruce Grobbelaar 12. Sammy McIlroy 13. False. He moved there towards the end of his career 14. Colin Cramb and Jon Newby 15. Stockport County.

Cardiff City

1. Which country's Under-21s side did manager Dave Jones play for?
2. In what year did Cardiff win the English FA Cup?
3. Who scored a 10-minute hat-trick for Cardiff against Carlisle in 1971?
4. In 2007, who was the youngest player to make his debut for Cardiff?
5. Who did the Bluebirds beat in their 2008 FA Cup semi-final?
6. How much did Cardiff pay Stoke for Graham Kavanagh?
7. How many international goals did Nathan Blake score?
8. What were City known as when founded in 1899?
9. Where do City play their home matches?
10. Who did Cardiff beat in the 2003 Second Division play-off final?
11. In what year were the club re-named Cardiff City?
12. Who were the last team to knock City out of the European Cup Winners' Cup?
13. True or false: Robert Earnshaw scored over 100 goals in all competitions for Cardiff?
14. How much did Sunderland pay Cardiff for Michael Chopra in 2007?
15. Up to 2008-9, how many times had Cardiff beaten Swansea in the FA Cup?

1. England 2. 1927 3. Alan Warboys 4. Aaron Ramsey 5. Barnsley 6. £1m 7. Four 8. Riverside 9. Ninian Park 10. QPR 11. 1908 12. Standard Liege 13. True 14. £5m 15. Never.

Carlisle United

1. Which on-loan goalkeeper scored an injury-time goal in the final match of the 1998–99 season to save the club from relegation?
2. Which club was he on loan from?
3. Who did Carlisle replace when they were elected to the Football League in 1928?
4. Carlisle were formed when Shaddongate United merged with which other team in 1902?
5. Which future Liverpool manager was in charge of the club from 1949 to 1951?
6. Carlisle paid a club record £140,000 for Joe Garner in August 2007 but who did he sign from?
7. The club's best run in the FA Cup came during the 1974–5 season, but who did they lose to in the quarter-finals?
8. What was the score in that quarter-final match?
9. Which former Carlisle player scored England's only goal in their record 7–1 defeat away to Hungary?
10. He also has the distinction of being the first player to do what, at a cost of £18,000, in January 1949?
11. Where do Carlisle play their home games?
12. Which survivor of the Munich Air Disaster managed Carlisle from October 1986 to November 1987?
13. Bob Stokoe has managed the club on three separate occasions – 1968–70, 1980–83 and when else?
14. Which former Liverpool and Newcastle player signed for Carlisle in 1979 and left the club in 1982?
15. Who has made the most appearances for the club, playing in 466 games between 1963 and 1979?

1. Jimmy Glass scored in the fourth minute of injury-time to give Carlisle a 2-1 victory 2. He was signed on an emergency loan from Swindon Town 3. Durham City 4. Carlisle Red Rose 5. Bill Shankly 6. Blackburn Rovers 7. Fulham 8. Les Barrett scored the only goal of the game as Fulham won 1-0. They went on to lose 2-0 to West Ham in the final 9. Ivor Broadis 10. As player-manager of Carlisle he transferred himself to Sunderland, who paid £18,000 for his services 11. Brunton Park 12. Harry Gregg 13. 1985-86 14. Peter Beardsley 15. Alan Ross.

Charlton Athletic

1. As of 2007–8, what year featured Charlton's only FA Cup win?
2. Who did Charlton beat 1–0 on their return to The Valley in 1992?
3. How many league wins did Iain Dowie mastermind as manager in his 12 games in charge?
4. Who did Charlton beat on penalties to win the 1998 Division I play-off final?
5. How much did Chelsea pay Charlton for Scott Parker?
6. What is Charlton's nickname?
7. How much did Charlton pay Wimbledon for Jason Euell, breaking the club record?
8. Which club did assistant manager Phil Parkinson get sacked from in 2006?
9. Who managed Charlton from 1982 to 1991?
10. Against which club did Jason Euell score his first Premier League goal for Charlton?
11. Who shared the managership of Charlton with Alan Curbishley from 1991 to 1995?
12. Charlton Athletic's meeting with Fulham in September, 2001 was the first between the teams in the top league since which season?
13. On which two grounds did Charlton play their home games between 1985 and 1992?
14. Who was the top scorer in the league for Charlton in 2002–3?
15. Which two players scored the three own-goals for Charlton in their away win at Sunderland on 1 February, 2003?

1. 1947 2. Portsmouth 3. Two 4. Sunderland 5. £10m 6. The Addicks 7. £4,750,000 8. Hull City 9. Lennie Lawrence 10. Derby County 11. Steve Gritt 12. 1951–2 13. Selhurst Park and Upton Park 14. Jason Euell 15. Stephen Wright and Michael Proctor.

Chelsea

1. Which player took just 42 seconds to score the fastest-ever FA Cup Final goal in 1997?
2. On Boxing Day of which year did Chelsea become the first English team to name an entirely foreign starting line-up?
3. What is the name of Chelsea's infamous hooligan 'firm'?
4. Against which team did Chelsea record their biggest-ever, top-flight victory?
5. Ron 'Chopper' Harris played a record 795 games for Chelsea, but how many goals did he score?
6. Kerry Dixon started out as an apprentice with which club?
7. A portrait of what adorned the club's first-ever crest?
8. How many points did Chelsea collect during their record-breaking 2004–5 season?
9. What was significant about Chelsea's match with Swansea Town on 25 August, 1928?
10. What was the nickname of former goalkeeper, Peter Bonetti?
11. Who, in 2003, was voted Chelsea's best-ever player?
12. When did Chelsea first win the FA Cup?
13. When did Chelsea first win a European competition?
14. Jose Mourinho cut his managerial teeth working as a translator for which English manager?
15. Who was manager of Chelsea at the beginning of the 2008–9 season?

1. Roberto Di Matteo 2. 1999 3. The Headhunters 4. Leeds United (7–1, 1935) 5. 14 6. Tottenham Hotspur 7. A Chelsea Pensioner 8. 95 9. They were, along with Arsenal, the first club to wear numbered shirts 10. The Cat 11. Gianfranco Zola 12. 1970 13. 1971, the European Cup Winners' Cup 14. Sir Bobby Robson, at Barcelona 15. Luis Felipe Scolari.

Cheltenham Town

1. Which player joined Cheltenham from West Ham for a club-record fee of £50,000 in January, 2003?
2. What is Cheltenham's nickname?
3. Who became the club's youngest player to play in the Football League when he came on as a substitute against Carlisle on 17 September, 2005?
4. Who, during three spells with the club, scored a record 240 goals?
5. During the 1974–5 season he broke the club record for the number of goals in a single season. How many did he score?
6. On 2 November 1935 Cheltenham beat Chippenham Rovers by a club-record scoreline in the FA Cup. What was it?
7. Which former Barbados captain played 11 games on loan at Cheltenham in 2001?
8. Which club did Kayode Odejayi join in 2007 for £200,000?
9. Who did Cheltenham beat in the 2005–6 League Two play-off final?
10. Who scored the only goal in that play-off final?
11. In which year did Cheltenham win the FA Trophy for the first time?
12. Who was in charge when Cheltenham were first promoted to the Football League in 1999?
13. Which club was he in charge of before Cheltenham and which club did he join after he left in 2002?
14. Where do Cheltenham play their home games?
15. Which Hungary international spent a month on loan with Cheltenham from Wolverhampton in 2007?

1. Grant McCann 2. The Robins 3. Sosthene Yao who was 18 years and 40 days 4. Dave Lewis 5. 53 in all competitions 6. 12-0 7. Gregory Goodridge 8. Bristol City 9. They beat Grimsby 1-0 10. Steve Guinan won it for Cheltenham with a goal in the 63rd minute 11. 1998 12. Steve Cotterill 13. He started his managerial career with Sligo Rovers in Ireland and left to join the Robins in 1997 and he left Cheltenham to manage Stoke City 14. Whaddon Road 15. Dénes Rósa.

Chester City

1. In what year did Chester join the football league?
2. Chester won their first-ever league championship in 2004. Which one was it?
3. By what name is the stadium where Chester play their home games most commonly known?
4. At which ground did the club play until 1990?
5. Which two teams amalgamated to create Chester FC?
6. Against which side, in 1933, did Chester's biggest FA Cup victory come?
7. In 1936, against York City, the team recorded their biggest-ever league victory. What was the score?
8. True or false: all of Chester City's stadium and club premises are in Wales?
9. When did Wales and Everton legend Kevin Ratcliffe manage Chester?
10. Which of his old rivals took over the role in 2004–5?
11. Give either of the side's two main nicknames.
12. Which longstanding rivals have their ground just 12 miles from Chester?
13. At the start of the 2008–9 season, which club had the better record between Chester and their aforementioned rivals in head-to-head matches?
14. Which player had made most appearances for the club prior to the 2008–9 season?
15. Which Englishman set the record for the most goals for the club in 1998?

1. 1931 2. The Conference 3. The Deva Stadium 4. Sealand Road 5. Chester Rovers and Old King's Scholars FC 6. Fulham (5-0) 7. 12-0 8. False. The club offices are situated in England 9. 1995 to 1999 10. Ian Rush 11. The Seals/The Blues 12. Wrexham 13. At the start of 2008-9, Wrexham were edging it (30-26) 14. Ray Gill, 1951-1962. 406 appearances 15. Stuart Rimmer, 135 goals.

Chesterfield

1. Who started the 2001–2 season as Chesterfield manager?
2. Who was the top scorer in the 2000–1 season?
3. From which club did Chesterfield sign Glynn Hurst in 2001?
4. Chesterfield is in which English county?
5. In which year did Chesterfield win the Division Three play–off final?
6. In what year did the club go on an amazing run to the FA Cup semi–finals?
7. Who were the last club from outside the top two divisions to achieve such a feat?
8. Chesterfield spent most of their recent history playing at The Recreation Ground, but how is it more commonly known?
9. Who was fired as team manager in 2007?
10. What is the team's nickname?
11. Playing between the 1940s and 1960s, which player accumulated the most games for the club?
12. Who set the longstanding club record number of goals in 1974?
13. Which former England goalkeeper played over 20 times for the club in the 1950s?
14. Who scored the equaliser for Chesterfield in their 3–3 draw with Boro in the 1997 FA Cup semi–final?
15. True or false: after hanging up his boots in 2002, Jamie Hewitt's 574 games made him the player with the second–most appearances ever for the club?

1. Nicky Law 2. Luke Beckett 3. Stockport County 4. Derbyshire 5. 1995 6. 1997 7. Plymouth Argyle, in 1984 8. Saltergate - after the road on which it is located 9. Roy McFarland 10. The Spireites 11. Dave Blakey, 1948-1967, with 617 appearances 12. Ernie Moss, 1968-1974, with 162 goals 13. Gordon Banks 14. Local boy, Jamie Hewitt 15. True. Dave Blakey (1948-67) is first with 617 appearances.

Colchester United

1. In what year were Colchester United founded?
2. Which rival league club is the closest geographically to Colchester United?
3. Which club did United sign Kevin Lisbie from in 2007?
4. True or False: Jamie Cureton made over 50 appearances for United?
5. How many points did United accumulate while finishing bottom of the Championship in 2007–8?
6. How much did Colchester receive from Newcastle United for Lomano LuaLua?
7. Said to be the club's finest hour, who did the U's beat in the 1971 FA Cup fifth round?
8. Who did Colchester play in their last game at Layer Road?
9. In what year did the U's win the FA Trophy?
10. How many caps did manager Geraint Williams win for Wales?
11. Who did Colchester beat in the Third Division play-off final in 1998?
12. Mark Yeates signed for the U's from which Premier League side?
13. How old was Teddy Sheringham when he played his first match for the U's?
14. Who was the top scorer in the league for Colchester in 2000–1?
15. From which club did Colchester sign Kevin Rapley in August, 2001?

1. 1937 2. Ipswich 3. Charlton 4. True 5. 38 6. £2.25m 7. Leeds United 8. Stoke 9. 1992 10. 13 11. Torquay 12. Tottenham Hotspur 13. 41 14. Mick Stockwell 15. Notts County.

Coventry City

1. What were City originally called?
2. Who did Coventry beat in the 1987 FA Cup Final?
3. Striker Dion Dublin made his first Football League appearance for which club?
4. Which team beat City in their only appearance in the UEFA Cup second round?
5. Who finished top scorer in the 2007–8 season?
6. How much did Coventry sell striker Robbie Keane to Inter Milan for in 2000?
7. Who scored the last Coventry goal at Highfield Road?
8. In which year did Jimmy Hill leave as manager?
9. Who scored both goals for Coventry in their 4–2 defeat by Manchester United in April, 2001?
10. Who started the 2000–1 season as Coventry manager?
11. In which year did he become manager of Coventry City?
12. Who scored a hat-trick for Coventry City in their 6–1 win at Crewe in February, 2002?
13. Which trio shared the honour of being top scorers in the league for Coventry in 2000–1?
14. Which Welshman made his Division One debut appearance in 2001–2 for Coventry?
15. Which Coventry player made his full international debut for the Republic of Ireland against Greece in 2000?

1. Singers FC 2. Tottenham Hotspur 3. Cambridge United 4. Bayern Munich 5. Michael Mifsud 6. £13m 7. Andrew Whing 8. 1967 9. John Hartson 10. Gordon Strachan 11. 1996 12. Lee Hughes 13. Craig Bellamy, John Hartson and Mustapha Hadji 14. Lee Fowler 15. Barry Quinn.

Crewe Alexandra

1. Who replaced Peter Morris as the club's manager in June 1983?
2. How many years did he spend as the sole manager of the club?
3. Who were the opponents for Dario Gradi's 1,000th match in charge of the club?
4. What was the score in that game?
5. Who played 436 games for the club between 1966 and 1978?
6. Which former Crewe player went on to play in Italy and captain England?
7. Which club signed him from Crewe in 1988?
8. After drawing 2–2 with Tottenham in the FA Cup fourth round in the 1959–60 season, what was the score in the replay at White Hart Lane?
9. Who scored five goals in a match against Colchester United on 24 April 1994?
10. Who joined Crewe for a club-record fee of £650,000 in August 1998?
11. Which club did he sign from?
12. Crewe sold Seth Johnson to Derby for a club-record £3m in June 1999. Which other player left the club for the same fee in January 2005?
13. Who paid Norwich £7.25m for his services in January 2006?
14. Where do Crewe play their home games?
15. What is the club's nickname?

1. Dario Gradi 2. 24, he became technical director in 2007 3. Norwich City on 20 November 2001 4. The match at Carrow Road finished 2–2 5. Tommy Lowry 6. David Platt 7. He moved to Aston Villa for £200,000 8. Tottenham won the game 13–2, a club-record loss for Crewe 9. Tony Naylor 10. Rodney Jack 11. Torquay United 12. Dean Ashton 13. West Ham 14. Gresty Road 15. The Railwaymen.

Crystal Palace

1. In what year were Palace founded?
2. Who did The Eagles lose to in the 1990 FA Cup Final replay?
3. Against which team did Palace win their 2004 play-off final?
4. Which former England manager had his first managerial role at Selhurst Park in 1976?
5. What is the highest Crystal Palace have finished up the league ladder?
6. Which team knocked Palace out of the 2008 play-offs?
7. How many goals did Ian Wright score for Palace?
8. Who scored an 11-minute hat-trick against Grimsby in 1996?
9. Which current league club are geographically Palace's closest rivals?
10. What was the score in the last 'Selhurst Park derby' between Wimbledon and Crystal Palace?
11. How much did Everton pay Palace for Andy Johnson in 2006?
12. Which Italian international had a brief spell as manager of the club in 1998?
13. Who was the top scorer for the club in the 2000–1 season?
14. From which Japanese club did Palace sign Toni Popovic in 2001?
15. Who started the 2000–1 season as Palace manager?

1. 1905 2. Manchester United 3. West Ham 4. Terry Venables 5. Third in 1991 6. Bristol City 7. 117 8. Dougie Freedman 9. Millwall 10. 1-0 to Wimbledon 11. £8.6m 12. Attilio Lombardo 13. Clinton Morrison 14. Sanfrecce Hiroshima 15. Aki Riihilahti

Dagenham & Redbridge

1. Which two Dag & Red players hit the crossbar in Sky TV's 'Crossbar Challenge'?
2. What is the team's nickname?
3. Where did they play their home games in 2006–7?
4. Which four clubs' histories ended with the formation of Dagenham & Redbridge?
5. The club played their first-ever match in the Football League on 11 August, 2007. It was a 1–0 defeat to which side?
6. Who scored the only goal for The Daggers in their first-ever away victory in the Football League against Mansfield Town in 2007?
7. Which national side, other than England, is club captain Anwar Uddin eligible to play for?
8. Who was top scorer when The Daggers won the Isthmian Premier in 1999–2000?
9. Who was top scorer for three consecutive season between 2003 and 2006?
10. In the 2006–7 season the club sold two players for a new club record fee. They were sold for £125,000 each. Name them.
11. The Daggers won the conference after beating Aldershot Town 2–1. Who scored their goals that day?
12. What was unusual about the club's shirt sponsors, West & Coe, that year?
13. In 2004, The Daggers were humiliated on a match televised live on Sky after losing by a record margin, 9–0. Who beat them?
14. Who ended the 2007 season as manager?
15. Which player represented Barbados in 2008?

1. Dave Rainford and Ed Thompson 2. The Daggers 3. Victoria Road 4. Ilford, Leytonstone, Walthamstow Avenue and Dagenham 5. Stockport County 6. Shane Huke 7. Bangladesh 8. Paul Cobb 9. Chris Moore 10. Craig Mackail-Smith and Shane Blackett 11. Paul Benson and Dave Rainford 12. They are funeral directors 13. Hereford United - it equalled the record highest losing scoreline in the Conference 14. John Still 15. Jon Nurse.

Darlington

1. Which club did Tommy Taylor manage before taking over at Darlington in October, 2001?
2. Which two players were sent off in the 7–1 defeat at Scunthorpe in November, 2001?
3. Who was Darlington's top scorer in the league in 2000–1?
4. Who began the 2000–1 season as Darlington manager?
5. What is the side's unusual nickname and where does it come from?
6. Supply any two of the names given to the club's new ground since its opening in 2003.
7. Darlington was founded at Darlington Grammar School in 1883, but when did the club turn professional?
8. In 1957–8 the club had its best-ever FA Cup run. How far did it get?
9. Who managed Darlington to successive Conference and Fourth Division championships in 1989–90 and 1990–1?
10. Which side beat Darlington in the 1996 play-offs?
11. In 1999–2000 Darlington became the first team to lose an FA Cup tie and still qualify for the next round. How?
12. In 2002, Darlington had failed bids to buy two 'colourful' (arguably 'troubled') former superstars. Who were they?
13. Who was voted the club's 'greatest-ever player' by fans in 2003?
14. How many goals did Darlington's 'greatest-ever player' score in his two seasons at the club?
15. At the beginning of the 2008–9 season, which player held the record for the most appearances in the club's history?

1. Leyton Orient 2. Mark Ford and Barry Conlon 3. Mark Sheeran 4. Gary Bennett 5. The Quakers because of the religious movement that had a historic influence on the town 6. Balfour Webnet Darlington Arena, George Reynolds Arena, the New Stadium, the Williamson Motors Arena and the 96.6 TFM Darlington Arena 7. It turned professional in 1908 and joined the North Eastern League 8. The last 16 9. Brian Little 10. Plymouth Argyle 11. Manchester United were involved in the World Club Championship and did not enter the FA Cup. The Quakers won a 'lucky losers' draw and were given United's place in the next round. (They lost their third-round tie 2-1 to Aston Villa) 12. Paul Gascoigne and Faustino Asprilla 13. Marco Gabbiadini 14. 50 15. Ron Greener, 1955-67, 439 appearances.

Derby County

1. From which club did Derby sign Andy Todd?
2. In which year was the club founded?
3. When chairman Robert Maxwell put a freeze on transfers in 1990, how many subsequent games did Derby go without winning?
4. Who scored the winning goal in a 1–0 victory over Manchester United at the end of the 2000–1 season to keep Derby in the Premiership?
5. Which player broke the record for youngest player to appear for Wales in March 2006?
6. Which team did Derby beat 6–3 in their first-ever league game?
7. Which club did manager Brian Clough brand 'cheating bastards' after allegations of bribing match officials during the European Cup semi-final?
8. Up to 2007–8, what was the highest transfer fee ever received by Derby County?
9. In which year did Derby County first win the FA Cup?
10. Who, at the start of 2008–9, remained Derby's most-capped international?
11. Where did Derby County call 'home' from 1884 to 1895?
12. How many Premiership games did Derby play before the bookmaker Paddy Power paid out on all bets that they would be relegated in the 2007–8 season?
13. In which year did Brian Clough lead Derby to victory in the First Division for the first time in their history?
14. Which player scored a hat-trick in a 4–1 win over Real Madrid at the Baseball Ground in 1975?
15. Which French winger returned to the Premier League with Derby County in January 2008?

1. Blackburn Rovers 2. 1884 3. 20 4. Malcolm Christie 5. Lewin Nyatanga 6. Bolton Wanderers 7. Juventus 8. £7m from Leeds United for Seth Johnson 9. 1946 – their only win in the competition to date 10. Deon Burton, with 42 caps for Jamaica 11. The Racecourse Ground 12. Five, a record at the time 13. 1972 14. Charlie George 15. Lauren Robert.

Doncaster Rovers

1. Who did Doncaster pay a club-record £300,000 for in May 2008?
2. Which player scored a record 42 goals during the 1923–4 season?
3. When did Doncaster play their first competitive match at the Keepmoat Stadium?
4. Who were their opponents and what was the score?
5. Who was the first player to score at the Keepmoat Stadium?
6. Which two Premier League teams did Doncaster knock out of the 2005–6 League Cup on their way to the quarter-finals?
7. Who knocked Doncaster out of the 2005–6 League Cup at the quarter-final stages?
8. In which season did Doncaster set the record for the number of games lost in a season, 34, when they were relegated to the Football Conference?
9. Who did Doncaster beat to win the Football League Trophy in the 2006–7 season?
10. Defender Len Graham is the club's most-capped international player, but which country did he represent?
11. What is the furthest Doncaster have gone in the FA Cup?
12. Who scored the winning goal in Doncaster's play-off victory over Dagenham & Redbridge in 2003?
13. Which current Premier League manager was born in Doncaster and was rejected by the club after a trial for the youth team?
14. Aged 52 years and 11 months who is the oldest player to play for Doncaster to date?
15. What record did Doncaster set at the end of the 1946–7 season?

1. Matthew Mills from Manchester City 2. Clarrie Jordan 3. New Year's Day 2007 4. Doncaster beat Huddersfield 3–0 5. Mark McCammon had the honour of scoring the first goal with a volley after just nine minutes 6. Manchester City and Aston Villa 7. They went out to Arsenal on penalties after the game had finished 2–2 8. 1997–8, they won just four games all season 9. Bristol Rovers 10. Graham won 14 caps playing for Northern Ireland between 1951 and 1958 11. They have reached the fifth round on four occasions – 1951–2, 1953–4, 1954–5, 1955–6 12. Francis Tierney 13. Kevin Keegan 14. John Ryan. The Rovers chairman made a cameo appearance in the final minute of his side's 4–2 win at Hereford on the last day of the Conference season in 2003 15. They won 33 of their 42 league fixtures.

Everton

1. In which year was Everton Football Club founded?
2. What was Everton's original name?
3. To the theme tune of which TV show have the Everton players traditionally taken to the pitch since the 1960s?
4. William Ralph 'Dixie' Dean scored a record 473 goals for Everton, including 60 in the 1927–8 season. What was his average goals-per-game record?
5. Up to 2007–8, Everton had received the highest number of red cards in the Premiership. Which Everton player shares the dubious honour of having received the most Premier League red cards (along with Patrick Vieira)?
6. Against which club did Wayne Rooney score on his debut, minutes after coming on as a 16-year-old substitute in 2002?
7. How many goals did Gary Lineker score in his first season at Goodison?
8. At the start of the 2008–9 season, which former player held the record for appearances in an Everton shirt?
9. What is the Everton motto and what does it mean?
10. Against which club did David Moyes' Everton secure victory in his first game in charge?
11. Who scored the first-ever goal at Goodison Park in 1892?
12. Which player scored his first goal for Liverpool in a Merseyside derby in 2000, having recently moved from Everton?
13. What was unusual about Everton's kit in the 1933 FA Cup Final?
14. Up to 2007–8, four of the ten youngest Premier League scorers ever notched their first goals for Everton. Name two.
15. What colours did the club play in when they first moved to Goodison Park?

1. 1878 2. St Domingo's FC 3. *Z-Cars* 4. 0.94 5. Duncan Ferguson (8) 6. Arsenal 7. 40 8. Neville Southall 9. 'Nil Satis Nisi Optimum', meaning 'Only the best is good enough' 10. Fulham. Everton won 2-1 at Goodison Park in March, 2002 11. Fred Geary 12. Nick Barmby 13. The shirts were numbered 1-11; the first time this had been seen 14. James Vaughan, Wayne Rooney, Michael Ball and Danny Cadamarteri 15. Salmon shirts with blue shorts.

Exeter City

1. Which Nationwide Conference side knocked City out of the 2001–2 FA Cup?
2. The club's home pitch has remained the same for most of its history. Which other club has a stadium with a very similar name?
3. City registered record league victories in 1926 and 1935. Both were 8–0 wins. Name either of their defeated opponents on those days.
4. Less impressively, City lost 9–0 in both 1948 and 1958. Name either of their victorious opponents in those games.
5. In 2005, Exeter registered their biggest-ever away crowd. Who were they playing and what was the score?
6. Who was the team's top scorer in the league in 2000–1?
7. True or false: Exeter City's first competitive match was a home win against the Royal Artillery?
8. Which South American national side is thought to have played its first-ever game against City during their 1914 South American tour?
9. Who scored City's winning goal in the play-off final of 2007–8?
10. Who started as manager for the 2000–1 season?
11. In 2004, a Brazilian masters side including Careca and Dunga beat Exeter 1–0 at home. What was the special occasion?
12. In recent years the club's fans held a moving tribute to one of their former managers by chanting his name during a game just four days after his death. Name the former manager in question.
13. Who was the club's top goalscorer in 2007–8 with 18 goals?
14. The last time City played main rivals Plymouth Argyle was in 2002. What was the score?
15. For which three-year period was Alan Ball in charge of the club?

1. Dagenham & Redbridge 2. Newcastle United 3. Coventry City and Aldershot 4. Notts County (1948) and Northampton Town (1958) 5. Manchester United in the FA Cup. It was 0–0 6. Steve Flack 7. True 8. Brazil. City lost 2–0 on an otherwise winning tour 9. Rob Edwards 10. Noel Blake 11. It was the club's centenary 12. Alan Ball 13. Richard Logan 14. Exeter City lost 3–0 15. 1991–94.

Fulham

1. Which Fulham hero was the first player to be paid £100 per week?
2. Which player, who later played for and managed the England team, began his career at Fulham?
3. After Fulham were relegated in 1968, how many years did it take the club to return to the top flight?
4. How many times have Fulham won the FA Cup?
5. Which Fulham player was the only American to have scored goals at more than one World Cup at the start of the 2008–9 season?
6. In which year did Fulham celebrate their 125th anniversary?
7. What is Fulham's slightly unfortunate nickname?
8. Which team did Jean Tigana manage after leaving Fulham?
9. Which football legend described Johnny Haynes as 'the greatest passer of the ball I've ever seen'?
10. In which year did the 'dream team' of Kevin Keegan and Ray Wilkins arrive at Craven Cottage?
11. George Best arrived at Fulham in 1976. How long did the crowd have to wait for his first goal?
12. At which rival ground did Fulham spend two years while renovating Craven Cottage to Premier League standards?
13. In which year did Fulham first wear an all-white kit?
14. How much did Fulham receive from Manchester United for Louis Saha?
15. In 1961, Haynes led England to an emphatic victory over Scotland. What was the final score?

1. Johnny Haynes 2. Bobby Robson 3. 33 4. None 5. Brian McBride (1998 and 2002) 6. 2004 7. The Cottagers 8. Besiktas 9. Pele 10. 1997 11. He scored after just 71 seconds of his debut 12. Loftus Road (QPR) 13. 1903 14. £13m 15. 9–3.

Gillingham

1. What animal is featured in The Gills' team badge?
2. The club was actually founded in 1893, but what was the team called back then?
3. True or false: at the start of the 2008–9 season Gillingham were the only Kent-based club in the Football League?
4. To which weapon-storing side did Gillingham (then playing under their original name) lose in their first-ever match?
5. Which manager led The Gills out of the old Fourth Division in 1964?
6. True or false: the club's championship win in 1964 was the only one in their history?
7. Who beat The Gills in the Division Three 1986–7 play-offs?
8. Which future Republic of Ireland forward is said to have been bought from non-league Crockenhill in exchange for tracksuits?
9. Which former Gillingham player lifted the FA Cup twice and has three Premiership winners' medals?
10. The Gills stopped the hearts of *Grandstand* vidiprinter viewers throughout the country after registering 8–1 and 10–0 victories in consecutive weeks. Who did they beat?
11. Which manager was controversially sacked just a few months later?
12. How much did London-based businessman, Paul Scally, pay for the club in 1995?
13. Which manager took The Gills into League One in 1999-2000?
14. What was the name of the stadium where Gillingham played their first home match in 2008–9, the same pitch they had played on since the club's creation?
15. Whose logo was the first to appear on Gillingham shirts during a shirt sponsorship deal which lasted from 1984 to 1987?

1. A horse 2. New Brompton 3. True 4. Woolwich Arsenal's reserve side (5–0) 5. Freddie Cox 6. True 7. Swindon Town 8. Tony Cascarino 9. Steve Bruce 10. Southend United (8–1) and Chesterfield (10–0) 11. Keith Peacock 12. £1 (the club had gone into administration) 13. Peter Taylor 14. Priestfield Stadium 15. Zanussi.

Grimsby Town

1. What is the club's nickname?
2. In which town is their longstanding home stadium, Blundell Park, situated?
3. True or false: having played in the top flight and reached FA Cup semi-finals, Grimsby are the most successful team in Lincolnshire?
4. Which former Grimsby manager won a number of domestic and European honours with another club?
5. Which former manager guided Southampton to the 1976 FA Cup?
6. The club lost in the FA Cup semi-finals in 1936 and 1939. Which two teams beat them?
7. Which American Secretary of State famously watched the side play Gillingham in 1976?
8. In 1997–8 The Mariners won the AutoWindscreens Shield Final at Wembley Stadium. Who scored the winning 'golden goal'?
9. In the same year, Grimsby knocked the holders out of the League Cup. Who were they?
10. With whom do the club share a rivalry, dubbed the 'Cod War' after the infamous 'Cod Wars' of the 1970s?
11. Which Mariner was capped once for England and has small roads named after him in Grimsby and Cleethorpes?
12. Who was the winner of Grimsby's BBC Cult Heroes poll in 2004?
13. In which decade did future England manager, Graham Taylor, play for The Mariners?
14. Who did fans vote Player of the Year in 2007–8?
15. Which of the club's stalwarts won the Young Player of the Year awards in 1987, 1990 and 1992?

1. The Mariners 2. Cleethorpes 3. True 4. Bill Shankly 5. Lawrie McMenemy 6. Wolverhampton Wanderers and Arsenal 7. Henry Kissinger 8. Wayne Burnett 9. Leicester City 10. Hull City 11. Jackie Bestall (1926-38, 427 games) 12. Clive Mendonca (Player from 1991 to 1997, 187 games) 13. The 1960s 14. Phil Barnes 15. John McDermott.

Hartlepool United

1. Which manager began his managerial career with Hartlepool in 1965?
2. Which shirt number did Hartlepool retire following the death of Michael Maidens in 2007?
3. In what year was the club formed?
4. Which ground did the club move into the year they were formed?
5. Who made a club-record 447 appearances between 1948 and 1964?
6. Who became the youngest player to represent the club when he came on as a substitute on 25 August, 2003?
7. Who was his debut against?
8. The son of which former Manchester United manager took charge of Hartlepool in 1983?
9. Who scored a club-record 98 league goals for the club between 1949 and 1964?
10. Who did Hartlepool record a club-record 10–1 victory against in April 1959?
11. Who took over the club in December 1989 and won promotion to the Third Division?
12. What happened to the club's mascot, Angus the Monkey, in 2002?
13. Who did Danny Wilson manage before being appointed Hartlepool manager in June 2006?
14. Who played at Victoria Park during the 1986–7 season after being locked out of their ground?
15. Who began the 2001–2 season as Hartlepool manager?

1. Brian Clough 2. 25 3. 1908 4. Victoria Park 5. Wattie Moore 6. David Foley, who was aged 16 years and 44 days when he made his debut 7. Port Vale, the game ended 2–0 in Hartlepool's favour 8. Mick Docherty, son of Tommy Docherty, was manager for just six months 9. Ken Johnson 10. Barrow 11. Cyril Knowles 12. He was elected mayor of Hartlepool even though his candidacy was just a publicity stunt 13. MK Dons 14. Middlesbrough 15. Chris Turner.

Hereford United

1. What is the club's motto?
2. Who became the club's manager in 1995 and then club chairman in 1998?
3. Who did Hereford beat in the 2005–6 Football Conference play-off final?
4. By what scoreline did Hereford win that match?
5. Who scored the winning goal in extra-time?
6. Where have Hereford always played their home league games?
7. As a Southern League team in 1974, who did Hereford famously knock out of the FA Cup?
8. Hereford United was formed in 1924 after the merger of which two local teams?
9. Which former Welsh international joined Hereford in 1966 and became the club's player-manager a year later?
10. Where did the club sign him from?
11. Who replaced Colin Addison as manager in 1974 and again in 1991?
12. Who made a club-record 549 appearances for the club between 1946 and 1964?
13. Which player scored a club-record 184 goals for Hereford between 1945 and 1958?
14. Which former Hereford player was capped 34 times by Poland?
15. Which former Finland international played 13 league games on loan at Hereford during the 1996–7 season?

1. Our greatest glory lies not in never having fallen, but in rising when we fall 2. Graham Turner 3. Halifax Town 4. The game finished 3–2 after extra-time 5. Ryan Green 6. Edgar Street 7. Newcastle United 8. St Martins and RAOC (Rotherwas) 9. John Charles 10. Cardiff City 11. John Sillett 12. John Layton Snr 13. Charlie Thompson 14. Adam Musial 15. Mika Kottila.

Huddersfield Town

1. What were Huddersfield the first team to achieve in 1926?
2. Who did Huddersfield beat to win the 1922 FA Cup Final?
3. What was special about this FA Cup Final?
4. Gianfranco Labarthe Tome made just three substitute appearances for Huddersfield in 2003, but what nationality is he?
5. Who replaced Peter Jackson as manager in 1999, before being sacked the following season?
6. Peter Jackson returned for a second spell in charge in 2003. Who did he replace?
7. What was unique about Huddersfield's match with Charlton on 21 December, 1957?
8. Who was in charge for that defeat?
9. Who did Huddersfield sell to Manchester City for £55,000 in 1960?
10. This transfer enabled Huddersfield to purchase what at their Leeds Road ground?
11. When did Huddersfield play their first game at what was then named the Alfred McAlpine Stadium (now called the Galpharm Stadium)?
12. Who were their opponents that day and what was the score?
13. The club paid a record £1.2m for which player in July 1996?
14. Who did he sign from?
15. In February 2000 he left to join which club for £2.75m?

1. They were the first English team to win three consecutive league titles in the top division, then called the First Division 2. Preston North End 3. It was the last before Wembley Stadium opened its doors 4. Tome is Peruvian 5. Steve Bruce 6. Mick Wadsworth 7. Huddersfield became the first team to score six goals in a match and still end up the losing side. They lost the match 7-6 8. Bill Shankly 9. Denis Law 10. Floodlights 11. 20 August, 1994 12. They lost 1-0 to Wycombe 13. Marcus Stewart 14. Bristol Rovers 15. Ipswich Town.

Hull City

1. On which ground was Hull City's first professional match played?
2. Who was the first player Hull paid £1m for?
3. Former City players Theodore Whitmore and Ian Goodison played international football for which country?
4. Who is the only Tigers manager to win back-to-back promotions?
5. Who scored the goal against Bristol City in the 2007–8 Play-off Final which took Hull City into the Premiership for the first time?
6. How many goals did former England striker Mark Hately score for the Tigers?
7. Who beat Hull in their one and only appearance in the FA Cup semi-finals, in 1930?
8. What is the record attendance for a Hull City home game (this was set in 1949)?
9. Who had a remarkable six-goal haul during the 1996 FA Cup first-round replay against Whitby Town?
10. Who finished top scorer during the 'Great Escape' season of 1998–9?
11. What is the name of the current mascot?
12. Which company was the first sponsor to appear on a Hull City shirt?
13. Remarkably, only one team has ever beaten Hull City in the play-offs, who was it?
14. How old was Dean Windass when he scored his first Tigers goal?
15. What does the KC in the KC Stadium stand for?

1. The Boulevard 2. Caleb Folan 3. Jamaica 4. Peter Taylor 5. Dean Windass 6. Three 7. Arsenal 8. 55,019 9. Duane Darby 10. David Brown 11. Roary 12. Hygena 13. Leyton Orient 14. 22 15. Kingston Communications.

Ipswich Town

1. Which World Cup-winning manager was in charge of Town from 1955 to 1963?
2. In what year did Ipswich win the English league title?
3. Who did Jon Walters score his first Town hat-trick against?
4. How much did Alan Lee cost Ipswich in 2006?
5. In what year did George Burley win Premier League Manager of the Year with Town?
6. What year were Ipswich Town founded?
7. Who did The Tractor Boys lose their 1985 League Cup semi-final to?
8. Which side did Town beat in the 2001 Division One play-off final?
9. Who knocked Ipswich out of the play-offs in both 2004 and 2005?
10. With which side did Bobby Robson start his managerial career?
11. For which two clubs other than Ipswich has Jim Magilton made over 100 league appearances?
12. Against which team did Darren Bent make his Premier League debut in 2001–2?
13. Who was Ipswich's top scorer in the 2000–1 season?
14. Against which team did Marcus Bent make his Premier League debut in 2000–1?
15. In which year did Ipswich win the FA Cup?

1. Alf Ramsey 2. 1962 3. Bristol City 4. £100,000 5. 2001 6. 1878 7. Norwich 8. Barnsley 9. West Ham 10. Fulham 11. Oxford United and Southampton 12. Bolton Wanderers 13. Marcus Stewart 14. Middlesbrough 15. 1978.

Leeds United

1. Leeds have been champions of England on three occasions. When was the first time they won the title?
2. When was the last time the club were crowned champions of England's top division?
3. What was unique about this achievement?
4. Who succeeded Don Revie as the club's manager in 1974?
5. Who did Revie go on to manage when he left Leeds?
6. Leeds were runners-up in the 1975 European Cup Final, but who did they lose to?
7. What was the score in that final?
8. Who did Leeds beat to win the Inter City Fairs Cup for the second time in 1971?
9. Which English team did they beat in the semi-final?
10. Who denied Leeds a return to the top flight by beating them in the 2005–6 Championship play-off final?
11. Where did the club finish the following season?
12. During the club's first 15 years they sported blue-and-white stripes as their home kit, based on which other Yorkshire team's colours?
13. In which year did Leeds first play in an all-white strip?
14. Why did Don Revie want Leeds to play in all-white?
15. Leeds signed Eric Cantona from which French club in 1991?

1. 1968–69 2. 1991–92 3. Leeds were the last club to win the First Division before it became the Premier League 4. Brian Clough 5. He became manager of the English national side 6. Bayern Munich 7. Bayern won 2–0 8. The final with Juventus ended 3–3 after two-legs, but having scored two away goals in the first leg Leeds won the trophy 9. Liverpool 10. Watford 11. They finished bottom having being docked 10 points after going into administration 12. Huddersfield 13. 1961 14. Because he wanted to emulate the great Real Madrid side of the time who played in all-white 15. Nimes.

Leicester City

1. Who did Peter Shilton score his only career goal against, while playing for City in October 1967?
2. How much did Liverpool pay for striker Emile Heskey from Leicester in 2000?
3. Where did City play their home games before moving on to the Walkers Stadium?
4. What were Leicester known as when they were founded in 1884?
5. Which former Leicester player scored the winning penalty against them in a shoot-out with Blackburn Rovers in the 1992 Division 1 play-off final?
6. Who scored the first competitive goal at the Walkers Stadium?
7. How many senior goals did Gary Lineker score for Leicester?
8. Who scored the goal which beat Crystal Palace in the 1996 Division 1 play-off final?
9. Who holds the record for most league appearances for the club?
10. Leicester's highest league position came in 1928–9 when they finished second; who won the First Division?
11. Who beat Leicester 6–1 in their promotion season of 2002–3?
12. Who scored in five of Leicester's final nine games to clinch promotion to the Premiership in 2002–3?
13. What is the nickname of the club?
14. At the start of the 2008–9 season who had been Leicester's longest-serving manager since Jock Wallace left the club in 1982?
15. In which year did he become manager of the club?

1. Southampton 2. £11m 3. Filbert Street 4. Leicester Fosse 5. Mike Newell 6. Brian Deane 7. 95 8. Steve Claridge 9. Adam Black, 528 10. The Wednesday/Sheffield Wednesday 11. Ipswich Town 12. Trevor Benjamin 13. The Foxes 14. Martin O'Neill 15. 1995.

Leyton Orient

1. What is Leyton Orient's nickname?
2. Where do Leyton Orient play their home league games?
3. How much did former chairman Tony Wood OBE sell the club for in 1995?
4. When did Leyton Orient play their only season in England's top flight?
5. Which famous goalkeeper made his final nine appearances of a 30-year career at Leyton Orient?
6. Who were the opponents as he made his 1,000th league appearance on 22 December, 1996?
7. Which former West Ham and Newcastle manager started his playing career with Leyton Orient?
8. Which England international left Leyton Orient to join Reading for £25,000 in 2001?
9. Leyton Orient have beaten four teams by a club-record scoreline of 8–0, but who were the last team they beat by that margin?
10. Who did Leyton Orient pay a club record fee of £175,000 for in 1989?
11. Which Leyton Orient player scored the fastest goal in a play-off final after just 28 seconds in May 2001?
12. Who were their opponents that day and what was the final score?
13. Who was top scorer in the league for Orient in 2000–1?
14. Who began the 2000–1 season as manager of the club?
15. From which club did Orient acquire Jeff Minton in July, 2001?

1. The O's 2. The Matchroom Stadium, also known as Brisbane Road 3. £5 4. 1962-3 5. Peter Shilton 6. Brighton 7. Glenn Roeder 8. Nicky Shorey 9. Doncaster Rovers on 28 December, 1997 10. The club bought Paul Beesley from Wigan 11. Chris Tate 12. Blackpool defeated Leyton Orient 4-2 13. Carl Griffiths 14. Tommy Taylor 15. Rotherham United.

Lincoln City

1. Why are Lincoln called 'The Imps'?
2. Which ground did the club move to in 1895?
3. The Imps won the old Division Four championship in 1975–6 under whose stewardship?
4. In the same year the club broke the record for most points in a season when two instead of three points were awarded for a win. How many did they get?
5. Which league did The Imps win in 1987–8?
6. Prior to the 2008–9 season, what had been the club's highest position ever in the league, recorded in the 1901–2 season?
7. True or false: Lincoln set a record five consecutive years of play-off failures between 2002 and 2007?
8. Which famous movie theme is normally played when The Imps score at home?
9. Why was this chosen?
10. Who is the Stacey-West Stand named after?
11. The club has a long-standing league attendance record set in 1949. Against which club was it recorded?
12. Prior to the 2008–9 season, which player in the club's history had most appearances for the team in all competitions?
13. Allan Hall has the record for most goals scored in a season. How many did he bag?
14. When the club sold Jack Hobbs in 2005 they received their largest ever pay-off – over £750,000. Who was he sold to?
15. Who did The Imps defeat 7–1 at home in 2006–7?

1. After the legend of the Lincoln Imp 2. Sincil Bank 3. Graham Taylor 4. 74 points 5. The Conference 6. They reached fifth in Division 2 (now known as the Championship) 7. True 8. The *Dambusters'* theme 9. Because 'The Dambusters' were based just outside Lincoln at nearby RAF Scampton 10. After two lifelong supporters - Bill Stacey and Jim West - who died in the 1985 Bradford Fire 11. Grimsby 12. Grant Brown 13. 41 (1951–2) 14. Liverpool 15. Rochdale.

Liverpool

1. Who was Liverpool manager immediately prior to Bill Shankly?
2. Who scored Liverpool's first Premiership goal?
3. How many league titles as manager and player did 'King Kenny' win with the Reds?
4. Against which team did Robbie Fowler score his first league goal?
5. Who scored Liverpool's winner in 'that' first 4–3 game against Kevin Keegan's Newcastle United in April 1996?
6. Which team did Kevin Keegan leave Liverpool to join?
7. What year was Liverpool's first European Cup success?
8. Who had Fernando Torres' squad number prior to the talented Spaniard joining the club?
9. Who provided the opposition for the record attendance at Anfield?
10. Which player has scored the most hat-tricks for the Reds?
11. In 2001–2, Liverpool recorded their highest-ever Premiership finish. Where did they finish?
12. How many European Cups had Liverpool won up to and including 2007–8?
13. Name the Liverpool scorers for the 'miracle of Istanbul'.
14. When was Liverpool's year of formation?
15. Who was Liverpool's first shirt sponsor?

1. Phil Taylor 2. Mark Walters versus Sheffield United at Anfield on Wednesday 19 August, 1992 3. Eight First Division Championships: 1978–9, 1979–80, 1981–2, 1982–3, 1983–4, 1985–6 (player/manager), 1987–8 (player/manager) and 1989–90 (player/manager) 4. Oldham 5. Stan Collymore 6. Hamburg 7. 1977 8. Robbie Fowler (no.9) 9. 61,905 v Wolves, 1951–2 FA Cup fifth round 10. Gordon Hodgson (17) 11. Second, 2001–2 12. Five 13. Steven Gerard, Xabi Alonso and Vladimir Smicer 14. 1892 15. Hitachi.

Luton Town

1. Who signed Luton defender Chris Perry at the start of the 2008–9 season?
2. What penalty did Luton receive at the start of the 2008–9 season after having been found guilty of misconduct?
3. In what county, near London, are Luton-based?
4. What nickname do the team have?
5. In the 1980s which comedian was Luton's most famous fan?
6. 1886–7 marked the club out as pioneers. In what way were Luton's players special?
7. Who defeated Luton Town 2–1 in the 1959 FA Cup Final?
8. Who created a scoring record, by notching 10 goals in a single match, in 1936?
9. Where do Luton play their home games?
10. Against which side did Luton suffer a pitch invasion featuring much hooliganism in an FA Cup match on 13 March, 1985?
11. What unusual measure did Luton take to solve the hooligan problem?
12. In which year did Luton beat Arsenal to win the League Cup, their only major piece of silverware, and who was manager?
13. When 2–1 up in the final Arsenal missed a penalty. Which player missed it?
14. Which player scored Luton's first and last goals on the day?
15. In which year did Luton win League One?

1. Southampton 2. A 10-point deduction and a £50,000 fine for financial irregularities plus a further 20-point deduction for breaking rules on insolvency 3. Bedfordshire 4. The Hatters 5. Eric Morecambe 6. Several Luton players received money from the gate, making them the first professional players in the South of England. At the time professionalism was restricted to the North 7. Nottingham Forest 8. Joe Payne v Bristol Rovers, still an English record 9. Kenilworth Road 10. Millwall 11. They banned away fans from all home games 12. 1988, Ray Harford 13. Nigel Winterburn 14. Brian Stein 15. 2005.

Macclesfield Town

1. In what decade was the club formed?
2. Macclesfield made history by scoring the final goal of the last millennium. Who had the honour?
3. Who guided the club to the GM Vauxhall Conference Championship in 1994–5?
4. Which national side did he go on to coach?
5. How many games did Paul Ince take to register his first win for the club as manager?
6. The team then went on a nine-match unbeaten run. Who ended the run?
7. Which national side used the club's stadium, Moss Rose, as a training base during Euro 96?
8. Which competition did the club win in 1996?
9. Which Canadian midfielder was included in the 2008–9 squad?
10. In which city was defender James Jennings born?
11. Which Nigerian international played for The Silkmen between 1999 and 2004?
12. Which player made a record number of Macclesfield League appearances (263) between 1997 and 2003?
13. The most goals scored by a Macclesfield player in a single season is 83. Who set the record in 1933–34?
14. Which club did Efe Sodje go to after leaving Macclesfield?
15. Against which side did Paul Ince play his only game for the club?

1. 1870s (1874) 2. Chris Priest 3. Sammy McIlroy 4. Northern Ireland 5. Twenty 6. Chelsea, in the FA Cup 7. Germany – the eventual winners of the competition 8. The FA Trophy 9. Terry Dunfield 10. Manchester 11. George Abbey 12. Darren Tinson 13. Albert Valentine 14. Luton Town 15. Notts County.

Manchester City

1. Which City legend was the youngest member of England's 1966 World Cup-winning team?
2. Ardwick AFC became Manchester City in which year?
3. What was the nickname of former player and manager Stuart Pearce?
4. In which year did City first win the FA Cup?
5. What do the three stripes on the City badge represent?
6. Who was City's all-time record goalscorer going into the 2008–9 season?
7. Where did City play their home matches before moving to Maine Road in 1923?
8. Which player played the final fifteen minutes of the 1956 FA Cup final with a broken neck?
9. City legend Shaun Goater began his professional career at which club?
10. How many goals did Georgi Kinkladze score in 106 appearances for Manchester City?
11. In which year was the club founded?
12. Which father-and-son combo have both played for City in the 21st century?
13. Who actually 'owns' the City of Manchester stadium?
14. How much did Chelsea pay City for Shaun Wright-Philips in July 2005?
15. City's first European silverware came with victory in which competition in 1970?

1. Alan Ball 2. 1894 3. 'Psycho' 4. 1904 5. The three rivers of Manchester: the Medlock, the Irwell and the Irk 6. Eric Brook (177) 7. Hyde Road 8. Bert Trautmann 9. Manchester United 10. 20 11. 1880 12. Peter and Casper Schmeichel 13. The city council. The club have rented it on a 250-year lease 14. £21m 15. The European Cup-Winners' Cup.

Manchester United

1. In which season did United first win the Double?
2. In which year was Denis Law named European Footballer of the Year?
3. Which team inflicted United's first-ever home defeat in Europe?
4. United's biggest victory over Arsenal came with a 6–1 win at Old Trafford in 2001. Which player scored a hat-trick?
5. Against which team did European Cup hero Ole Gunnar Solskjaer score his first and last goals for the club?
6. Which player recently broke Bobby Charlton's appearance record of 758 games?
7. Who became the first player since George Best to score 20 league goals in a season when he got 24 in 1987–8?
8. Who, in 1982, broke Pele's record as the youngest player to play in the World Cup?
9. Who, at the start of 2008–9, remained United's longest-serving club captain?
10. Which United winger currently holds the record for most assists in the history of the Premier League?
11. Up to the end of the 2007–8 season, which player had the highest goals-to-games ratio of any Manchester United player in history?
12. Which former Red Devil became the first Englishman to reach 100 Champions League appearances?
13. When the club was formed as Newton Heath L&YR FC in 1878, what colour were their shirts?
14. Who acts as agent for Gary Neville?
15. Sir Bobby Charlton is related to which legendary Newcastle United player?

1. 1993–4 2. 1964 3. Fenerbahce 4. Dwight Yorke 5. Blackburn Rovers 6. Ryan Giggs 7. Brian McClair 8. Norman Whiteside 9. Bryan Robson (1982–94) 10. Ryan Giggs (96 by the end of the 2007–8 season) 11. Ruud van Nistelrooy. He scored 150 goals in 219 appearances, giving him a ratio of 0.685 goals per game 12. David Beckham 13. Green and gold 14. His father, Neville Neville 15. Jackie Milburn. Jackie was the cousin of Charlton's mother, Cissie Milburn.

Middlesbrough

1. In which year did Boro win their first-ever trophy?
2. Against which teams did Massimo Maccarone score last-minute winners for Boro, taking them to the UEFA Cup Final in 2006?
3. Who scored five in a club-record 9–0 win over Brighton in 1958?
4. Who arrived as head coach at Christmas 2000 to orchestrate Boro's escape from relegation after just two wins in 17 games?
5. Whose real name is Osvaldo Giroldo Junior?
6. Which player's nickname was 'The White Feather'?
7. Which winger left the club to join Kenny Dalglish's Premiership-winning Blackburn side in 1992?
8. Which political achievement can chairman Steve Gibson justly be proud of?
9. In which season were Boro finalists in both the League and FA Cups, yet were relegated from the top flight?
10. When did Boro move to the Riverside Stadium?
11. Who is Boro's record goalscorer?
12. Who did Middlesbrough beat 5–1 on 3 May, 2003?
13. Who was the most-capped Middlesbrough player ever at the beginning of the 2007–8 season?
14. Who was the top scorer in the league for Middlesbrough in 2002–3?
15. In which decade did Jack Charlton have a spell as Midlesbrough boss?

1. In 2004, they won the League Cup after a wait of 128 years 2. FC Basel and Steaua Bucharest 3. Brian Clough 4. Terry Venables 5. Juninho 6. Fabrizio Ravanelli 7. Stuart Ripley 8. He became Middlesbrough's youngest-ever Labour councillor at 21 when he was elected for the Park End ward 9. 1996–7 10. 1995 11. George Camsell (1925–46) scored 345 goals in 453 games 12. Tottenham Hotspur 13. Wilf Mannion 14. Massimo Maccarone 15. The 1970s.

Millwall

1. Why were Millwall allowed to kick off their games at 3.15pm, instead of the usual 3pm kick-off time, up until the early 1960s?
2. What was Millwall's nickname before they became known as The Lions?
3. Which European Cup-winning goalkeeper began his career at Millwall?
4. Which club signed him from Millwall for £50,000?
5. Which former Arsenal manager was in charge of Millwall from 1983 to 1986?
6. Who was his replacement at the Den?
7. Who did Millwall sign for £225,000 from Gillingham in 1987?
8. Who scored the first goal as Manchester United beat Millwall in the 2004 FA Cup Final?
9. Which Millwall player came on as an 89th-minute substitute to become the youngest player ever to play in an FA Cup Final?
10. What was unique about Millwall's participation in the 2004 FA Cup Final?
11. Who scored the goal that sent Millwall into the 2004 FA Cup Final?
12. Who was this player set to join before moving to Everton from Millwall for £1.5m before the start of the 2004–5 season?
13. Which Hungarian team knocked Millwall out of the 2004–5 UEFA Cup in the first round?
14. Which team were Millwall away to when their fans infamously clashed with home supporters in a 1985 FA Cup game?
15. Who was the top scorer in the league for Millwall's 2000–1 season?

1. To allow dock workers to arrive on time 2. The Dockers 3. Alex Stepney 4. Chelsea. He spent only three weeks at Chelsea, playing one game, before being sold to Manchester United for £55,000 5. George Graham 6. John Docherty 7. Tony Cascarino 8. Cristiano Ronaldo 9. Curtis Weston, aged 17 years and 119 days, beating a 125-year-old record 10. They were the first team outside the top flight to reach an FA Cup final since the formation of the Premier League in 1992 11. Tim Cahill scored the only goal as Millwall beat Sunderland 1–0 12. Crystal Palace. Palace chairman Simon Jordan pulled out of a move after refusing to pay Cahill's agent's fees 13. Ferencvaros 14. Luton Town 15. Neill Harris.

Milton Keynes Dons

1. Who was in charge of the club when they played their first game in the guise of MK Dons?
2. Who replaced him after a bad start to the 2004–5 season?
3. Which player made his debut for England Under-21s as an MK Don?
4. The player in question scored 60 goals for the club before signing for which team in August, 2007?
5. Which player was sent off on his MK Dons debut against Bury on the first day of the 2006–7 season?
6. Goalkeeper David Martin signed for which Premier League club from MK Dons in January 2006?
7. Where did MK Dons play their home games before their new stadium was built?
8. Who were MK Dons' opponents for their first-ever league game at stadium:mk?
9. Who was in charge for that first league game?
10. Which manager did Paul Ince replace?
11. Which League Two club did MK Dons beat to win the Football League Trophy in 2008?
12. Who scored the goals in the club's 2–0 win in that final?
13. Which team finished runners-up as MK Dons won the 2007–8 League Two title?
14. In what year was the club founded?
15. In order for their fans to be recognized by the Football Supporters' Federation, what did the club have to promise?

1. Stewart Murdoch 2. Danny Wilson 3. Izale McLeod 4. Charlton paid MK Dons £1.1m for McLeod 5. Adolfo Baines Pilart 6. Liverpool 7. The National Hockey Stadium 8. Bury. Dons lost the game 2-1 9. Paul Ince 10. Martin Allen, who left to join Leicester City 11. Grimsby Town 12. Keith Andrews, Sean O'Hanlon 13. Peterborough United 14. 2004 15. MK Dons promised to return the trophies and memorabilia of Wimbledon FC to the London Borough of Merton and to make no further claims to the history of that club.

Morecambe

1. What are the side's two main nicknames?
2. At which hotel was the club set up, in 1920?
3. After which chairman is the current stadium named?
4. Who did Morecambe beat in the Lancashire Senior Cup Final in 1968?
5. Morecambe were promoted to the Football League for the first time in their history after winning the 2007 Conference play-off final against which side?
6. Who scored Morecambe's goals that day?
7. Who managed the side?
8. True or false: Morecambe's first game in the Football League ended in a 2–0 victory over Barnet?
9. In August 2007, the club played and earned a shock win in their very first League Cup fixture. Who did they beat, 2–1?
10. Name one of the scorers.
11. Which Championship side were also defeated in Morecambe's' second-ever League Cup fixture?
12. Which club stalwart managed the side from 1994 to 2006?
13. Which 2007 squad member played international football for Northern Ireland's Under-17s before opting for the Republic of Ireland, with whom he won the Youth Olympic Tournament in Spain (2001)?
14. In which city was captain Jim Bentley born?
15. Which club did goalkeeper Steven Drench play for before moving to Morecambe?

1. The Shrimps, The Erics 2. West View Hotel 3. JB Christie (Christie Park) 4. Burnley 5. Exeter City (2-1) 6. Garry Thompson and Danny Carlton 7. Sammy McIlroy 8. False. It was 0-0 9. Preston North End 10. Jim Bentley and David Artell 11. Wolverhampton Wanderers (3-1) 12. Jim Harvey 13. Henry McStay 14. Liverpool 15. Blackburn Rovers.

Newcastle United

1. A bronze statue of which player stands outside St James' Park today?
2. For which player did the club receive a record transfer fee of £13.667m in 2004?
3. In which year did the club win its first-ever FA Cup?
4. What is the capacity of St James' Park?
5. Which team beat Ruud Gullit's Newcastle side 4–1 in his first game in charge?
6. How many times had Newcastle won the FA Cup up to the end of the 2007–8 season?
7. How much did Kevin Keegan pay Bristol City for striker Andy Cole?
8. Against which team did Alan Shearer break Jackie Milburn's record of 200 club goals?
9. When the club was first formed, what was its name?
10. What were the club's original colours?
11. Who scored a hat-trick for Newcastle during a 3–2 win at St James' Park in 1997?
12. In which year did Paul Gascoigne win the PFA Young Player of the Year award while playing at Newcastle?
13. How many different spells did crowd favourite Peter Beardsley have with Newcastle?
14. From which club did Newcastle sign Malcolm Macdonald?
15. In which year did Newcastle United first adopt St James' Park as its home ground?

1. Jackie Milburn 2. Jonathan Woodgate 3. 1910 4. 52,387 5. Liverpool 6. Six (1910, 1924, 1932, 1951, 1952 and 1955) 7. £1.75m 8. Portsmouth 9. Stanley AFC 10. Red shirts, white shorts 11. Faustino Asprilla 12. 1988 13. Three 14. Luton Town 15. 1892

Northampton Town

1. Which comedian is the son of former Northampton player and manager Graham Carr?
2. In which season did Northampton become champions of the then Third Division?
3. What was the score when Northampton played Manchester United in the fifth round of the FA Cup during the 1969–70 season?
4. How many goals did the great George Best score in that FA Cup fifth-round tie?
5. What was the name of the unfortunate player charged with marking Best?
6. Which youth team duo were selected for the Cyprus Under-19 squad in 2008?
7. What year was the club formed?
8. What feat have Northampton achieved that no other Football League club has managed?
9. The original County Ground was destroyed by fire in which year?
10. Which future star was sold by Northampton to Liverpool for £65,000 in 1975?
11. What was unusual about the 1989 match against Hereford?
12. What was the date of the final match at the County Ground?
13. Who scored the winning goal in the 1996–7 Division 3 play-off final at Wembley?
14. Who replaced Martin Wilkinson as manager in October 2003?
15. Who were Northampton playing when their match was abandoned due to high wind in March 2004?

1. Alan Carr 2. 1962–3 3. Manchester United beat Northampton 8–2 4. Six 5. Roy Fairfax 6. Odysseas Economides and Alexandros Konstantinou 7. 1897 8. They are the only club to have been promoted from the fourth tier of the Football League to the top tier and then relegated all the way back down in successive seasons 9. 1929 10. Phil Neal 11. Northampton ended the match with only seven players on the pitch 12. 12 October, 1994 13. John Frain 14. Colin Calderwood 15. Huddersfield Town.

Norwich City

1. In which season did City achieve their highest top-flight finish of third?
2. How much did Norwich sell Chris Sutton to Blackburn for in 1994?
3. Which side did Glenn Roeder manage prior to the Canaries?
4. In which comedy film did the Norwich manager go on to be the England boss?
5. Mark Bowen played international football for which country?
6. By what score did the Canaries win to become the first English team to beat Bayern Munich in the Olympic Stadium (in the UEFA Cup)?
7. Who did Norwich beat in the 1985 League Cup Final?
8. How much did West Ham pay the Canaries for the services of Dean Ashton in 2006?
9. Who was the only team to knock Norwich out of Europe prior to 2008–9?
10. In what year did Norwich first win the League Cup?
11. Against which club did Robert Green make his Division One debut for Norwich in 1999?
12. From which club did Norwich buy Mark Rivers in 2001?
13. Who had two spells as Norwich boss (1992–94 and 1996–98)?
14. In which year of the 1990s did the Canaries reach the semi-finals of the FA Cup?
15. Who was the top scorer in the league for Norwich in the 2000–1 season?

1. 1992–3 2. £5m 3. Newcastle 4. *Mike Bassett: England Manager* 5. Wales 6. 2–1 7. Sunderland 8. £7.25m 9. Inter Milan 10. 1962 11. Ipswich Town 12. Crewe 13. Mike Walker 14. 1992 15. Iwan Roberts.

Nottingham Forest

1. Where did the club first play their league games before moving to the City Ground in 1898?
2. Who scored the only goal for Forest when they won the European Cup for the first time in 1979?
3. A year later the club retained the European Cup by beating which team?
4. How many times have Forest won the FA Cup?
5. What was former Forest manager Billy Walker the first English footballer to do on April 12 1924?
6. Who scored the winning goal for Tottenham when they beat Forest in the 1991 FA Cup Final?
7. Brian Clough took over as the club's manager in 1975 and stayed at the club for 18 years, but who did he replace?
8. How many major trophies did Clough win while in charge at the County Ground?
9. Who in November, 2001 became the youngest Nottingham Forest player to appear in a league match?
10. Who was the top scorer in the league for Forest in 2000–1?
11. Who took over from David Platt as Forest manager in July, 2001?
12. Which Forest player scored but was then sent off in the home fixture against Coventry in December, 2001?
13. Who scored a hat-trick for Nottingham Forest at Millwall in their October 2001 league encounter?
14. When was the club founded?
15. Who started the 2008–9 season as manager?

1. The Forest Recreation Ground 2. Trevor Francis headed in on the stroke of half-time to give Forest a 1–0 win over Malmo 3. Hamburg 4. Twice. They beat Derby County 3–1 in 1898 and in 1959 they triumphed over Luton Town, winning 2–1 5. Walker became the first Englishman to score a goal at Wembley, netting in England's 1–1 with Scotland 6. It was an own goal from Forest defender Des Walker in extra-time that sealed Spurs' 2–1 win 7. Allan Brown, who was sacked in January 1975 after just over a year in charge 8. Seven: one league title, two European Cups and four League Cups 9. Craig Westcarr 10. Chris Bart-Williams 11. Paul Hart 12. Nicky Summerbee 13. Stern John 14. 1865 15. Colin Calderwood.

Notts County

1. Which animals are represented on the team badge?
2. When was the last time Meadow Lane hosted a top-flight clash?
3. True or false: the club was set up in the same year as the Football Association?
4. In what year did the team first reach the FA Cup Final?
5. Where was that final played?
6. The Magpies won their only FA Cup in 1894, against whom?
7. Where did they win that FA Cup Final?
8. Who scored the first hat-trick in FA Cup Final history that day?
9. Which European Cup-winning side is said to have derived its playing kit from County's?
10. True or false: Nottingham Forest have used County's ground for home games during at least two seasons?
11. Which Chelsea star did Notts County stun the football world by signing in the late 1940s?
12. Which former Celtic player is credited with transforming The Magpies from a struggling fourth-division side into a top-flight outfit in less than a decade?
13. Against whom did Neil Warnock's side register a famous 1-0 victory in 1991 to book a place in the quarter-final of the FA Cup?
14. In Mick Walker's first season in charge County sealed a memorable 2-1 victory over Forest on February 12. Who scored the late winner?
15. What has the day become known as to County fans?

1. Magpies 2. 1991-2 3. False. It pre-dated the FA, having been created in 1862 4. 1891. They were defeated 3-1 by Blackburn 5. The Oval 6. Bolton Wanderers (4-1) 7. Goodison Park 8. Jimmy Logan 9. Juventus - Englishman John Savage is thought to have acquired their kits from contacts in Nottingham 10. True. Once due to flooding and once due to fire at their own stadium 11. Tommy Lawton 12. Jimmy Sirrel 13. Manchester City 14. Charlie Palmer 15. 'Sir Charlie Palmer Day'.

Oldham Athletic

1. What was the score when Oldham played Nottingham Forest in the 1990 League Cup Final?
2. Aston Villa paid £1.7m for which Oldham player in February 1992?
3. Oldham broke their transfer record when they signed Ian Olney from which club in June 1992 for £750,000?
4. Who replaced Graeme Sharp as manager in 1997 but stayed at the club for just one season?
5. Oldham have reached the FA Cup semi-finals on three occasions, losing to Aston Villa in 1913 and to which other club in 1990 and 1994?
6. Who did Oldham beat 4–3 on the final day of the 1992–3 Premier League season to avoid relegation?
7. Which player scored the fourth goal to put Oldham 4–1 up?
8. What nationality is he?
9. Who scored a club-record 33 goals in one season during the 1936–7 campaign?
10. Which player set a new appearance record for Oldham after playing 525 games for the club between 1966 and 1980?
11. What club record did Oldham break on Boxing Day 1962?
12. Who were the opponents on that day and what was the score?
13. What were Oldham called when they were founded in 1895?
14. Who scored the only goal as Oldham beat Everton 1–0 in the 2007–8 FA Cup third round?
15. Who spent 12 years as Oldham manager from 1970 to 1982?

1. Nottingham Forest won 1-0 2. Earl Barrett 3. Aston Villa 4. Neil Warnock 5. Manchester United. Both times United went on to win the trophy 6. Southampton 7. Gunnar Halle 8. Norwegian 9. Tommy Davies 10. Ian Wood 11. They recorded the club's biggest-ever league win 12. They beat Southport 11-0 13. Pine Villa FC 14. Gary McDonald 15. Jimmy Frizzell

Peterborough United

1. Who scored a club- and Football League-record 52 goals in Peterborough's first season in the Football League?
2. Tottenham paid Peterborough £700,000 for which player in December 1999?
3. Which winger also made the switch to Tottenham at the same time?
4. Which famous England goalkeeper started his career at Peterborough before he was sold to Birmingham City?
5. Who replaced Barry Fry as manager when he left in 2005?
6. Who replaced Barry Fry as chairman in September 2006?
7. Who did Peterborough beat 9–1 in September 1998 to set a new club-record league win?
8. Who did Peterborough pay a club-record £350,000 for in July 1996?
9. In which year were Peterborough formed?
10. Who beat Peterborough to end their best-ever FA Cup run during the 1964–5 season, knocking them out at the quarter-final stage?
11. Which team denied Peterborough a place in the 1966 League Cup Final, beating them 4–2 in the semi-final?
12. What is Peterborough's nickname?
13. Who finished his playing career at Peterborough in 1998 and went on to manage Watford?
14. Wigan paid Peterborough £275,000 for the services of which player in 2003?
15. From which club did United acquire Jimmy Bullard in May, 2001?

1. Terry Bly 2. Simon Davies 3. Matthew Etherington 4. David Seaman 5. Mark Wright 6. Darragh MacAnthony 7. Barnet 8. Martyn O'Connor from Walsall 9. 1934 10. Chelsea. The match at Stamford Bridge finished 5–1 11. West Bromwich Albion 12. The Posh 13. Aidy Boothroyd 14. Jimmy Bullard 15. West Ham United.

Plymouth Argyle

1. Who did Argyle lose to in the FA Cup semi-final in 1984?
2. In which year did Plymouth turn professional?
3. What ship is featured on the Plymouth badge?
4. Who were the first sponsors of Plymouth?
5. How many points did Argyle amass in the 2001–2 season to break the club record?
6. How many seasons have Plymouth spent in the English top flight?
7. In which year did Bruce Grobbelaar play for the Pilgrims?
8. Where do Argyle play their home matches?
9. What is the club mascot called?
10. Who was Ian Holloway's first signing as Pilgrims manager?
11. In the 2007–8 season, who were Plymouth's closest Championship rivals geographically?
12. Who are the only other league club to have a green home shirt?
13. True or false: Peter Shilton played over 50 league games for Plymouth?
14. Against which team did Nick Chadwick score after 11 seconds in 2005?
15. Who began the 2008–9 season as Argyle manager?

1. Watford 2. 1903 3. *The Mayflower* 4. Beacon Electrical 5. 102 6. None 7. 1997–8 8. Home Park 9. Pilgrim Pete 10. Sylvan Ebanks-Blake 11. Bristol City 12. Yeovil 13. False – 34 14. Crystal Palace 15. Paul Sturrock.

Port Vale

1. Besides The Vale, what other nickname do the club go by?
2. Who was club chairman at the start of the 2008–9 season?
3. In what town and county are the team based?
4. True or false: Port Vale is one of the few English league teams not to be named after a geographical location?
5. Who replaced Martin Foyle in the role of caretaker manager in 2007?
6. Where did the club play before moving to Vale Park in 1950?
7. In which season did Vale fans stand for the last time on the Lorne Street stand?
8. Who became the club's major shareholder in 2006?
9. He also provided a theme song called 'It's Only Us' for a blockbuster console game on condition that Port Vale were included in the game. Which game was it?
10. Who scored the winning goal at Vale Park to complete a 2–1 aggregate Division 3 play-off final victory over Bristol Rovers in the late 1980s?
11. Manager John Rudge oversaw a number of FA Cup giant-killings. In 1988, while in Division 3, they beat Terry Venables' Tottenham side. Name one of the scorers for Vale.
12. Port Vale won the FA Giantkillers Award in 1995–6 for beating Crystal Palace, Everton, Southampton and forcing a reply with Leeds. But who ended the run with two late goals for Leeds United?
13. In 1997–8, Vale earned two amazing FA Cup draws with one of England's top sides. They were, however, eventually beaten by which team in a penalty shoot-out?
14. Port Vale set a longstanding record for the club's best league win (9–1) in September 1932. Who did they beat?
15. To within five, how many games did Neville Southall play for Port Vale in 1983?

1. The Valiants 2. Bill Bratt 3. Burslem, Staffordshire – one of the six towns that make up the city of Stoke-on-Trent 4. True; however, the name Port Vale is said to exist on maps predating the formation of the club in 1876 5. Dean Glover 6. The Old Recreation Ground in Hanley, which stood on what later became a multi-storey car park for the Potteries Shopping Centre 7. 1997–98, after which it was demolished 8. Robbie Williams 9. FIFA 2000. They are located in the Rest of World section! 10. Robbie Earle 11. Ray Walker and Phil Sproson 12. Gary McAllister. The Valiants had been one up with 12 minutes to go 13. Arsenal 14. Chesterfield 15. He played nine games.

Portsmouth

1. Who, in April 1991, became the first player to be sent off for two different teams at Fratton Park?
2. Who became the first Portsmouth player since Jimmy Dickinson in 1956 to represent England when he took the field against Brazil in 1984?
3. Who did Pompey beat 1-0 to clinch promotion to the Premier League in April 2003?
4. In their opening season in the Southern League in 1899, Pompey finished runners-up to which team?
5. Why can Pompey claim to be the team that has held the FA Cup for the longest period?
6. Why was the early Portsmouth team nicknamed the 'Shrimps'?
7. What was unusual about Andy Gray's 'hat-trick' for Crystal Palace against Pompey in April 1986?
8. Which director of Portsmouth Football Club presented TV's *How 2* series?
9. What was unusual about Pompey's match with Newcastle at St James' Park in 1931?
10. Why was legendary midfielder Jimmy Dickinson known as 'Gentleman Jim'?
11. Which literary figure was involved in Pompey's formation?
12. Who inflicted Pompey's record 0-10 defeat in October 1928?
13. In which year did Pompey acquire their famous red socks?
14. Which World Cup winner managed Pompey during the 1980s?
15. Which Pompey favourite is the most 'highly decorated' African footballer in history?

1. Carlton Palmer, for Portsmouth and West Bromwich Albion 2. Mark Hateley 3. Burnley 4. Tottenham Hotspur 5. They won the cup in 1939 and didn't return the cup until after the end of the war in 1945 6. They wore a pink kit 7. Only two of the goals were for his own side; Palace won 2-1 8. Fred Dinenage 9. It is believed to be the only game in which there were no corners 10. He never once received a caution in his entire career 11. Sir Arthur Conan Doyle 12. Leicester City 13. 1947 14. Alan Ball 15. Nwankwo Kanu.

Preston North End

1. North End won the first two league championships holding the title from 1888 to 1890. How many times have they won it since?
2. How many games did David Beckham play on loan at Preston in 1995?
3. What did Preston legend Tom Finney do an apprenticeship in before signing professional papers for North End?
4. True or false: Bill Shankly played over 250 competitive matches for the Lilywhites?
5. Which BBC football pundit played for Preston between 1974 and 1977?
6. How much did Portsmouth pay North End for David Nugent in 2007?
7. Which country does former Preston striker Ricardo Fuller play for?
8. Which England World Cup winner managed Preston in the years 1977 to 1981?
9. When did Preston last play in the top flight?
10. Three of the four stands at Deepdale are named after former players: Tom Finney, Bill Shankly and who?
11. Work on the stand was completed in October, 2001. Which team were the visitors for its first game in Division One?
12. Who was the top scorer in the league for Preston in the 2000–1 season?
13. Who took over from David Moyes as the Lilywhites' manager during the 2001–2 season?
14. From which club did Preston sign Jon Macken?
15. In which country was the on-loan player Sadio Sow born?

1. None 2. Five 3. Plumbing 4. True 5. Mark Lawrenson 6. £6m 7. Jamaica 8. Nobby Stiles 9. 1961 10. Alan Kelly 11. Manchester City 12. Jonathan Macken 13. Craig Brown 14. Manchester United 15. Senegal.

Queens Park Rangers

1. At which ground did QPR win 4–1 on New Year's Day 1992, live on ITV?
2. Who beat Rangers in the 1982 FA Cup Final?
3. Iain Dowie was caretaker manager of the Hoops for two games in 1998. How many of them did he win?
4. In what year were QPR formed?
5. True or false: Loftus Road holds under 25,000 fans?
6. Which former Wimbledon 'hard man' made nine appearances for Rangers in 1999?
7. Who signed Kevin Gallen when he left Rangers in 2000?
8. How many England caps did maverick midfielder Stan Bowles win?
9. How much did Newcastle pay QPR for the services of Les Ferdinand?
10. Which manager led QPR to their best-ever league finish?
11. Who did the Hoops beat in the 1967 League Cup Final?
12. How old was Ray Wilkins on his final first-team appearance for Rangers?
13. From which club did Rangers sign Trevor Sinclair in 1993?
14. Which striker scored 44 goals in the 1967–8 season?
15. How many points behind League Champions Liverpool did Rangers finish in the 1975–6 season?

1. Old Trafford 2. Tottenham 3. One 4. 1886 5. True 6. Vinnie Jones 7. Huddersfield Town 8. Five 9. £6m 10. Dave Sexton 11. West Brom 12. 39 13. Blackpool 14. Rodney Marsh 15. One.

Reading

1. Where did Reading play their home games before moving to the Madejski in 1998?
2. On 25 March 2006, Reading reached the top flight for the first time in their history with a 1–1 draw against which side?
3. Which iconic star made four pre-season appearances for Reading but never played a league game?
4. Which goalkeeper went a record 1,103 minutes without conceding a goal?
5. Reading's record 10–2 win in 1946 came against which club?
6. From which club did Reading sign Linvoy Primus?
7. Who was the first Reading player to play in the World Cup?
8. In which year was the club formed?
9. Which player holds the record for most appearances for Reading?
10. In 1999, which player did Reading fans vote for as their 'Player of the Millennium'?
11. For which country did former goalkeeper Shaka Hislop play international football?
12. Against which country did Reading defender Nicky Shorey make his England debut?
13. Which player was the first England international to play in 10 games without finishing on the losing side?
14. Which player began his career at Reading and went on to win the FA Cup with Wimbledon in 1988?
15. What is Reading's nickname?

1. Elm Park 2. Leicester City 3. George Best 4. Steve Death 5. Crystal Palace 6. Barnet 7. Bobby Convey (USA) 8. 1871 9. Martin Hicks (603) 10. Robin Friday 11. Trinidad & Tobago 12. Brazil 13. Johnny Holt 14. Lawrie Sanchez 15. The Royals.

Rochdale

1. Who took over as Rochdale manager in December, 2000–1?
2. In which decade were Rochdale runners-up in the League Cup?
3. Who began the 2001–2 season as manager?
4. From which club did Rochdale acquire Michael Oliver in July, 2000?
5. Who was Rochdale's top scorer in the 2000–1 league season?
6. In what year were The Dale founded?
7. The Dale amazingly reached the League Cup Final in 1962 despite being in the league's bottom division. Who ended their dream in the final?
8. Why did Rochdale change their kit in the 2007–8 season?
9. Name the Northern Irish defender named in the 2008–9 squad.
10. Which player retired in 1973, having set a record for the most league goals for the club?
11. What is the least number of wins the club has ever had in a season?
12. Name the ground that will host The Dale's home games in 2008–9.
13. Name two 'keepers in the 2008–9 squad.
14. To the nearest 500, what is the capacity of Rochdale's ground?
15. Give either the Latin or the English version of the club motto.

1. John Hollins 2. The 1960s 3. Steve Parkin 4. Darlington 5. Paul Connor 6. 1907 7. Norwich City 8. To mark the club's centenary 9. Rory McArdle 10. Reg Jenkins, 1964–73, 129 goals 11. Two, in 1973–4 12. Spotland 13. James Spencer and Sam Russell 14. 10,249 15. 'Crede Signo', which means 'Believe in the Sign'.

Rotherham United

1. Why will The Millers play their home games at the Don Valley Stadium in Sheffield during the 2008–9 season?
2. What is the highest division the club had played in prior to the 2008–9 season?
3. In which year did The Millers win the old Division Three title?
4. Which former player guided Rotherham into the Championship?
5. During the financial turmoil of 2006, which club loaned Rotherham Stephen Quinn and Jonathan Forte and paid their wages?
6. What action did West Ham's team take while in Millmoor in 2003 that raised a few eyebrows?
7. Who started as manager for the 2008–9 season?
8. Graham Coughlan started the 2008–9 season as club captain, but with which side did he win the Division Three and Division Two championships?
9. With which Irish side did he begin his career, signing in 1994?
10. Shaun Goater joined The Millers from which side, where he made no appearances?
11. Goater played 36 times for Bermuda. How many goals did he get for his country?
12. True or false: Shaun's full title is Leonardo Shaun Goater MBE?
13. Which goalkeeper, who moved to Wigan, held the record for most appearances when he left the club in 2005?
14. Which team did Mark Robins join when he left Manchester United?
15. Who scored more goals for the club – Mark Robins or Shaun Goater?

1. Due to a dispute with the landlords at their former home, Millmoor 2. The Football League Championship 3. 1981 4. Ronnie Moore 5. Sheffield United 6. They refused to change in the dressing rooms at Millmoor 7. Mark Robins 8. Plymouth Argyle 9. Bray Wanderers 10. Manchester United – he of course came back to haunt them, particularly Gary Neville! 11. 32 goals 12. True! 13. Michael Pollitt (301) 14. Norwich 15. Goater – he did play for nearly twice as long.

Scunthorpe United

1. In which year did Scunthorpe join the Football League?
2. Who scored the winning goal for United in the 1999 Division Three play-off final?
3. Which former England cricketer played for The Iron?
4. Which former England player and manager started his professional career with United?
5. Where do Scunthorpe play their home matches?
6. How much did Scunthorpe sell Ray Clemence to Liverpool for in 1966?
7. A club record, how much did Stoke pay for the services of Martin Paterson in 2007?
8. What kind of animal is the Scunthorpe mascot?
9. Which club did Billy Sharp sign for in 2007?
10. The last two games at the Old Showground finished with the same score. What was it?
11. Where did The Iron sign Jamie Forrester from in 1997?
12. Who scored the first league goal at Scunthorpe's new stadium?
13. True or false: Peter Beagrie played over 150 games for The Iron?
14. Brian Laws left United to join which Yorkshire club?
15. How much did The Iron pay for Steve Torpey?

1. 1950 2. Alex Calvo-Garcia 3. Ian Botham 4. Kevin Keegan 5. Glanford Park 6. £18,000 7. £425,000 8. Rabbit 9. Sheffield United 10. 1-1 11. Grimsby Town 12. Dave Cowling 13. True 14. Sheffield Wednesday 15. £200,000

Sheffield United

1. What sport was originally played at Bramall Lane?
2. In what year did Dave Bassett leave Sheffield United?
3. When was United's only season in the bottom tier of English football?
4. Who finished as the Blades' top scorer in the 2007–8 season?
5. How much did Everton pay the Blades for Phil Jagielka?
6. Who won the Championship when United were promoted as runners up in 2005–6?
7. How many England caps did Brian Deane win while playing for United?
8. Who did Neil Warnock manage directly before United?
9. How many points did United accumulate in the 2006–7 Premier League season?
10. When was the last time United did the league double over Wednesday?
11. What colour did United originally play in?
12. How many times have Sheffield United won the English league?
13. Who became the Blades' manager in December 1999?
14. Which on-loan player scored twice for United in their 4–3 win at home to Portsmouth in February, 2002?
15. Who was the top scorer in the league for United in the 2000–1 season?

1. Cricket 2. 1995 3. 1981-82 4. James Beattie 5. £4m 6. Reading 7. Three 8. Bury 9. 38 10. 2005-6 11. White 12. Once 13. Neil Warnock 14. Paul Furlong 15. David Kelly.

Sheffield Wednesday

1. What is the name of Wednesday's mascot?
2. Who hold the all-time record for most league goals for Wednesday with 199?
3. Who did the Owls buy Paolo Di Canio from for £4.7m in 1997?
4. How old was goalkeeper Peter Fox when he made his Owls debut in 1973?
5. Who did Wednesday lose both the FA Cup and League Cup Finals to in the 1992–3 season?
6. Who was the manager when Wednesday lifted the 1991 League Cup?
7. In what year were Wednesday founded?
8. Who did the Owls beat in the 2005 League One play-off final?
9. Up to 2007–8, how many times had the Owls won the FA Cup?
10. How much did Wednesday pay Marseille for Chris Waddle?
11. Who was the top scorer in the league for Sheffield Wednesday in 2000–1?
12. Who managed Wednesday from 1983 to 1988?
13. From which club did Wednesday buy Trond-Egil Soltvedt?
14. Who started the 2000–1 season as Sheffield Wednesday manager?
15. The maximum capacity of Hillsborough is under 39,000 – true or false?

1. Ozzie Owl 2. Andy Wilson 3. Celtic 4. 15 5. Arsenal 6. Ron Atkinson 7. 1867 8. Hartlepool United 9. Three 10. £1.25m 11. Gerald Sibon 12. Howard Wilkinson 13. Southampton 14. Peter Shreeves 15. False.

Shrewsbury Town

1. Shrewsbury were formed in May of which year?
2. The club grew from a team called Castle Blues. Why is it believed that this team re-formed as Shrewsbury Town?
3. Before moving to the pitch at New Meadow, where did the team play their home games for 97 years?
4. Who ended The Shrews' 1979 FA Cup run in a sixth-round replay?
5. Who was in charge of the 1978–9 team that won the Third Division Championship?
6. Which team ended the side's dream of a semi-final place in the 1981 FA Cup?
7. Who scored the quickest Town hat-trick (4mins 32secs) against Bradford City in 1990?
8. What was the score in Shrewsbury's final match at Gay Meadow in which they hosted Grimsby Town?
9. In which well-known movie does rocker Derek Smalls sport a retro Shrewsbury shirt?
10. Who was 'Coracle Man'?
11. What landmark did the club narrowly miss out on by failing to beat Blackburn Rovers in the League Cup, thereby stopping them from progressing to the next round and a home tie against Tottenham?
12. Which future West Brom manager made two appearances for Shrewsbury in 1995?
13. Jimmy Quinn made 15 Conference appearances for the side and scored four goals. How old was he in his last game?
14. True or false: David Moyes made 100 appearances for The Shrews?
15. Which former Town player reached the European Cup Winners' Cup in 1976, with Wrexham?

1. 1886 2. Several of their games had been marred by on- and off-field violence and change was required 3. Gay Meadow 4. Wolverhampton Wanderers 5. Graham Turner 6. Leicester City 7. Gary Shaw 8. 2-2 9. *This Is Spinal Tap* 10. Fred Davies who was a local coracle-maker. During home games he would take his coracle to the River Severn, which runs alongside Gay Meadow. There, Davies would collect stray footballs that were kicked into the river and return them. He has passed away but his legend lives on 11. Spurs were the only team in the League that The Shrews had not played at Gay Meadow 12. Gary Megson 13. 44 14. False. He fell just short with 96 appearances 15. Mickey Thomas.

Southampton

1. How old was Theo Walcott when he made his Saints debut?
2. At the start of the 2008–9 season, who stood as the Saints' all-time top scorer?
3. Who scored the last competitive goal at the Dell?
4. Who was top scorer for the Saints in 2007–8?
5. Which team were the first (and last) club to play the Saints at the Dell?
6. How much did Southampton receive for defender Dean Richards in 2001?
7. In what year were Southampton formed?
8. Prior to the 2008–9 season, who had won the most international caps as a Southampton player?
9. Who was the top scorer in the 2002–3 season?
10. In which year of the 20th century did Southampton win the FA Cup?
11. Which former England international succeeded Ian Branfoot as manager of Southampton in 1994?
12. Which club did Glenn Hoddle take over as manager of, in 2001, after leaving Southampton?
13. Who created a Premier League record of 112 matches without being substituted up to 18 January, 2003?
14. Who did Southampton beat 2–1 in the FA Cup semi-final in 2002–3?
15. Who has made the most league appearances for Southampton – 713 between 1956 and 1974?

1. 16 years and 143 days 2. Mick Channon, 185 goals 3. Matt LeTissier 4. Stern John 5. Brighton 6. £8m 7. 1885 8. Peter Shilton 9. James Beattie 10. 1976 11. Alan Ball 12. Tottenham Hotspur 13. Wayne Bridge 14. Watford 15. Terry Paine.

Southend United

1. Which former England international made just two appearances for Southend before he was released in 2006?
2. Which club did Southend sign Eddie Firmani from and later sell back to?
3. Which Liverpool player joined Southend in 1994 and later had a spell as player-manager?
4. Former Southend striker Tesfaye Bramble has been capped by which country?
5. Which World Cup winner was in charge of Southend from 1984 to 1986?
6. Who made a club record 506 appearances for the club between 1972 and 1984?
7. Who between 1954 and 1960 became the club's all-time leading goalscorer with 135 goals?
8. In which year were Southend elected to the Football League?
9. Where do Southend play their home games?
10. Who did Southend beat in the 2004–5 League Two play-off final?
11. What was the score and who scored for Southend?
12. Who beat Southend in the Football League Trophy Final in the same year?
13. Who did Steve Tilson replace as manager in 2003?
14. Who beat Southend 3–1 on the final day of the 2006–7 Championship season to send them down to League One?
15. Which striker was bought from Southend by Nottingham Forest for £3.57m in 1993?

1. Michael Ricketts 2. Charlton Athletic 3. Ronnie Whelan 4. Montserrat 5. Bobby Moore 6. Alan Moody 7. Roy Hollis 8. 1920 9. Roots Hall 10. Lincoln City 11. Southend won 2–0 with both goals coming in extra-time from Freddy Eastwood and Duncan Jupp 12. Wrexham won 2–0 13. Steve Wignall 14. Luton Town 15. Stan Collymore.

Stockport County

1. By what name were Stockport County known when they first formed in 1883?
2. As well as County, by what other nickname are the club known?
3. In which season did Stockport finish as runners-up in the Football League Trophy to Port Vale?
4. What was the score in that final?
5. Stockport received a club record fee of £1.6m from which club for which player in February 1998?
6. Stockport paid a club record fee of £800,000 for which striker in July 1998?
7. Where did he sign from?
8. Who became the youngest player to play for the club when he made an appearance against Wrexham on 30 April 2005?
9. What nationality was former Stockport player Jarkko Wiss?
10. Who replaced Danny Bergara as the club's manager in 1995?
11. Which former England international replaced Andy Kilner as County's manager during the 2001–2 season?
12. From which club did County sign Petri Helin in July, 2001?
13. Against which team did Jon Daly make his league debut for County in October, 1999?
14. Who beat County in the second round of the 2001–2 League Cup?
15. Who was the club's top scorer in the league in 2000–1?

1. Heaton Norris Rovers 2. The Hatters 3. 1992-3 4. Stockport lost 2-1 5. Middlesbrough paid that fee for striker Alun Armstrong 6. Ian Moore 7. Nottingham Forest 8. Paul Turnbull 9. Finnish 10. Dave Jones 11. Carlton Palmer 12. Luton Town 13. Walsall 14. Nottingham Forest 15. Aaron Wilbraham.

Stoke City

1. Who scored City's last goal of the 2007–8 promotion season?
2. What year were Stoke founded?
3. In his playing days, what was Tony Pulis' preferred position?
4. Which top-class continental team did the Potters face in their centenary match?
5. How many goals did Geoff Hurst score for City?
6. Which Stoke legend was the first footballer to be knighted?
7. From which club did the Potters sign central defender Leon Cort?
8. How much did Nottingham Forest pay City for Peter Shilton?
9. Who did Stoke play in their last game at the Victoria Ground?
10. City are the second-oldest football league club in England. Who are the oldest?
11. Which mascot was introduced first: Pottermiss or Pottermus?
12. Who did Stoke beat in the 1972 League Cup Final to win their first major trophy?
13. What was the result of the last derby with Port Vale at the Victoria Ground?
14. Who took over as Potters manager from Brian Little?
15. With which team did former Stoke hero Stanley Matthews win the FA Cup?

1. Richard Cresswell 2. 1863 3. Central defence 4. Real Madrid 5. 30 6. Stanley Matthews 7. Crystal Palace 8. £250,000 9. West Brom 10. Notts County 11. Pottermus 12. Chelsea 13. Stoke won 2-0 14. Gary Megson 15. Blackpool.

Sunderland

1. What is the association with 'Black Cats' which gave Sunderland their nickname?
2. Sunderland left Roker Park in 1997 after how many years at the ground?
3. What was the club's name when it was formed in 1879?
4. Who played 313 of the club's 336 games between the 1970–1 and 1977–8 seasons?
5. How many goals did Kevin Phillips score in 1998–9 to win the European Golden Shoe award?
6. Which player scored 63 goals in 68 games in just 18 months at Sunderland?
7. Who was appointed caretaker manager in March 2006 after the club parted company with Mick McCarthy?
8. How many times were Sunderland league champions before the Second World War?
9. Who was the first player to score at the Stadium of Light?
10. Sunderland manager Roy Keane began his career at which club?
11. What was unusual about Sunderland's promotion to the top flight in 1990?
12. Who holds the record for the most appearances for Sunderland?
13. On what island was striker Kenwyne Jones born?
14. Which former player had the nickname 'The Clown Prince of Football'?
15. From which club did Sunderland sign Craig Gordon for £9m, a record transfer for a goalkeeper, in 2007?

1. Workmen in 1805 renamed a gun battery the 'Black Cat' battery after hearing a mysterious cat's wail 2. 99 3. Sunderland and District Teachers' Association 4. Bobby Kerr 5. 30 6. Brian Clough 7. Kevin Ball 8. Six: 1892, 1893, 1895, 1902, 1913 and 1936 9. Niall Quinn, against Manchester City in 1997 10. Cobh Ramblers 11. They lost the play-off final to Swindon. However, Swindon's victory was revoked after they were found guilty of financial irregularities 12. Jimmy Montgomery (623) 13. Trinidad 14. Len Shackleton 15. Hearts.

Swansea City

1. How many goals did manager Roberto Martinez score during his playing days at Swansea?
2. Who scored City's last goal at the Vetch Field in April 2005?
3. Which England midfielder played 11 games on loan with the Swans in the 1995–6 season?
4. With which rugby club do City share the Liberty Stadium?
5. Who did Swansea lose to in their first post-war FA Cup semi-final in 1964?
6. Which team's mascot did Cyril the Swan famously remove the head of and kick into the North Bank?
7. In which year did John Toshack leave the Swans for Sporting Lisbon?
8. How much did Swansea pay Wrexham for Lee Trundle?
9. How many appearances did Gerry Francis make for City?
10. Who did Swansea hammer 12–0 in the European Cup Winners' Cup in 1982?
11. How many first-team matches did local legend John Charles play for the Swans?
12. How many points did Swansea collect in the 2007–8 season?
13. Who was Swansea's first post-war overseas manager?
14. What was the club called when founded in 1912?
15. Who did City beat in the 2006 Football League Trophy Final?

1. Four 2. Adrian Forbes 3. Frank Lampard 4. Ospreys 5. Preston North End 6. Millwall's Zampa the Lion 7. 1984 8. Nothing 9. Three 10. Sliema Wanderers of Malta 11. None, despite the fact he has a plaque in the stadium 12. 92 13. Jan Molby 14. Swansea Town 15. Carlisle United.

Swindon Town

1. Swindon won the League Cup in 1969, beating which team?
2. What was the score in that cup final?
3. Who scored two goals in extra-time to win the trophy for Swindon?
4. In which season did Swindon first reach the semi-finals of the FA Cup?
5. Who scored a hat-trick as Swindon beat Roma 5–2 in the Anglo Italian League Cup in 1969?
6. Who replaced Lou Macari as the club's manager in 1989?
7. Where do Swindon play their home games?
8. Who made a record 882 appearances for Swindon between 1960 and 1980?
9. What did Swindon achieve at the end of the 1985–6 season that only York City had managed to do before?
10. Swindon ended the 1992–3 season with the largest amount of what items in Premier League history?
11. What is Swindon's nickname?
12. Which former Scottish international started his managerial career with Swindon in 1971?
13. Who managed the club from August to December, 2001?
14. Which two Swindon players were sent off in the 0–0 home draw with AFC Bournemouth on Boxing Day, 2001?
15. From which Australian club was Danny Invincible signed?

1. Arsenal 2. Swindon won 3–1 after extra-time 3. Don Rogers 4. 1909–10 5. Arthur Horsfield 6. Ossie Ardiles 7. The County Ground 8. John Trollope 9. They recorded over 100 points in one season, finishing with 102 points 10. Goals conceded – 100 in total 11. The Robins 12. Dave Mackay 13. Roy Evans 14. Andy Gurney and Giuliano Grazioli 15. Marconi Stallions.

Tottenham Hotspur

1. Which former Spurs player is believed to have been the first British-born black army officer as well as the first black officer to lead white British troops into battle?
2. How many goals did Clive Allen score in 1986–7?
3. Who set a new record for the fastest Premiership goal in 2000 when he scored after 10 seconds away at Bradford?
4. In which year did Spurs become the first team in the 20th century to win the league and cup 'double'?
5. How much had Robbie Keane generated in transfer fees by the time he swapped his Spurs shirt for the red of Liverpool in July, 2008?
6. Three of Spurs' 1961 'Double Side' came from Scotland. Name two.
7. Who is the only player to be given a testimonial by both Spurs and fierce rivals Arsenal?
8. Which Spurs player became the first-ever Premier League substitute when he came on against Coventry in August 1992?
9. Who did Spurs beat in the final of the 1963 European Cup Winners' Cup to become the first British team to win a major European trophy?
10. How many goals did Gary Lineker score in his 139 appearances for Tottenham?
11. Who holds the record for most first-team appearances for Spurs?
12. Which player completed an amazing run of 247 consecutive games for Spurs in the 1950s?
13. Against which team did Bobby Smith score 17 goals in 16 games – the most goals scored by any Tottenham player against any one opponent?
14. Who scored the winner for ten-man Tottenham in the final minute of the 1999 League Cup Final?
15. How many cautions did the double-winning Spurs side of 1960–1 collect?

1. Walter Tull 2. 49 3. Ledley King 4. 1961 5. £58m 6. Dave Mackay, Bill Brown and John White 7. Pat Jennings 8. Erik Thorstvedt 9. Atletico Madrid, 5-1 10. 80 11. Steve Perryman, 854 appearances 12. Goalkeeper Ted Ditchburn 13. West Bromwich Albion 14. Allan Nielsen 15. One.

Tranmere Rovers

1. Tranmere were formed by the merger of two clubs from which other sport?
2. Where do Tranmere play their home games?
3. Who replaced Brian Little as manager in May 2005?
4. Who beat Tranmere in the 1999–2000 League Cup Final?
5. Who scored Tranmere's goal in that final?
6. Who scored 40 goals for Tranmere during the 1991–2 season?
7. In which year did the same player take over as the club's manager?
8. Which Spanish club did Tranmere sign him from?
9. Up to the start of 2008–9, Tranmere had reached the FA Cup quarter-finals on three occasions. When did they first reach this stage?
10. Who left the club to join West Brom in 2002 for a fee of £2.5m?
11. The club broke their transfer record to sign which player from Aston Villa for a fee of £250,000 in 1995?
12. Who became the youngster player to represent Tranmere when he played against Swindon in 2000?
13. What record did Eric Nixon break when he played against Crewe on 21 September, 2002?
14. Who did Tranmere beat 1–0 to win the Division Three play-off final in 1991?
15. Which club did Pat Nevin join after leaving Tranmere in 1997?

1. Cricket 2. Prenton Park 3. Ronnie Moore 4. Leicester City won 2–1 5. David Kelly scored after 77 minutes 6. John Aldridge 7. 1996 8. Real Sociedad 9. 1999–00 10. Jason Koumas 11. Shaun Teale 12. Iain Hume at 16 years, 167 days 13. He became the oldest player to play for the club at 39 years, 352 days 14. Bolton Wanderers 15. Kilmarnock.

Walsall

1. What is the name of the stadium where Walsall played their home games in the 2008–9 season?
2. In which year did Walsall move into that stadium?
3. Which player started his career at Walsall and went on to win the League Championship under Don Revie at Leeds United?
4. Who did Walsall sign for a second time and for a club record fee of £175,000 in June 1979?
5. Against which top-flight team did Walsall lose to in the 1983–4 League Cup semi-final?
6. What was the score after two legs?
7. Which Danish manager replaced Chris Nicholl at the helm in June 1997?
8. Coventry City paid £1m for which Walsall player in January 2008?
9. Goalkeeper Clayton Ince is an international keeper for which country?
10. Who finished as Walsall's top goalscorer in the 1997–8 season with 24 goals?
11. Which former Arsenal player joined the club in 2003 and had a brief spell as manager?
12. Who did Walsall sign from Feirense for a fee of £150,000 in July, 2000?
13. Where did Walsall play their home games before moving to their current home?
14. From which French club did Walsall acquire Frederic Biancalani in August, 2001?
15. Who was top scorer for Walsall in the FA Cup in the 2000–1 season?

1. The Bescott Stadium 2. 1990 3. Allan Clarke 4. Alan Buckley 5. Liverpool 6. Liverpool won 4-2. The first leg was drawn 2-2 and Liverpool won the second 2-0 7. Jan Sorenson 8. Scott Dann 9. Trinidad & Tobago 10. Roger Boli 11. Paul Merson 12. Jorge Leitao 13. Fellows Park 14. Nancy 15. Andy Tillson.

Watford

1. Which rugby club share Vicarage Road with Watford?
2. Who beat Watford in the 1984 FA Cup Final?
3. Who was the Hornets' all-time top goalscorer going into the 2008–9 season?
4. How many goals did John Barnes score for Watford?
5. Who did Graeme Taylor start his managerial career with?
6. Which side beat Watford to the league title in 1982–3?
7. Which Watford nickname could be described as most 'precious'?
8. Which England goalkeeper started his career with the Hornets in 1989?
9. In which year did Watford play their first game in England's top division?
10. Who did Watford play in their first-ever, top-tier match?
11. Who was Watford's first overseas manager?
12. In which season did he take over as manager?
13. Who was top scorer for Watford in the 2000–1 season?
14. In which season did Tommy Smith make his first league appearance for Watford?
15. Which singer is a life president of the Hornets?

1. Saracens 2. Everton 3. Luther Blissett, 158 4. 65 5. Lincoln City 6. Liverpool 7. The Golden Boys 8. David James 9. 1982 10. Everton 11. Gianluca Vialli 12. 2001–2 13. Tommy Mooney 14. 1997–8 15. Sir Elton John.

West Bromwich Albion

1. In which year were West Brom crowned First Division champions?
2. Who were the first shirt sponsors of the Baggies?
3. Which club gave Tony Mowbray his first full-time managerial job?
4. What was special about the media coverage of the Baggies' FA Cup win in 1968?
5. Who were Albion's opponents in the first game at the Hawthorns?
6. How many goals did Jeff Astle score for West Brom?
7. Who finished top scorer in 2007–8?
8. Which team finished ahead of Albion when they were promoted to the Premiership in 2003–4?
9. With which team is the Black Country derby contested?
10. What type of bird is Baggie Bird meant to be?
11. Who was top scorer for the team in 2000–1?
12. From which Portuguese club did West Brom sign Jordao in August, 2000?
13. Apart from the 'Baggies', what are West Brom's other main nicknames?
14. For which country did Larus Sigurdsson play?
15. West Brom were a founder member of the Football League – true or false?

1. 1920 2. BSR Housewares 3. Hibernian 4. It was the first UK game to be televised live in colour 5. Derby County 6. 174 7. Kevin Phillips 8. Norwich 9. Wolverhampton Wanderers 10. Throstle – a type of song thrush 11. Lee Hughes 12. Sporting Braga 13. The Albion or the Throstles 14. Iceland 15. True.

West Ham United

1. Who was the Hammers' only member of the 1998 England World Cup squad?
2. Which goalkeeper scored an own goal to help West Ham on their way to the 2006 FA Cup Final?
3. In three FA Cup-winning finals (1964, 1975 and 1980), only one player of the thirty used wasn't English. Who was he?
4. What was West Ham and England's World Cup-winning skipper Bobby Moore's first wage upon turning professional?
5. Why did David Unsworth ask to leave the club in 1998?
6. What was the original name of West Ham United?
7. When did the Hammers first win the FA Cup?
8. West Ham's Geoff Hurst famously hit a hat-trick in the 1966 World Cup Final. Which fellow Hammer completed the scoring for England?
9. By what score did West Ham beat Bury at home in October 1983?
10. Which former captain was nicknamed 'The Terminator'?
11. Which ex-Hammer became manager of Wales in the 1990s?
12. Which player has scored the most goals for West Ham in a season?
13. Which player has won most 'Fans' Player of the Season' awards for West Ham?
14. Who scored the winning goal in the 2004 Championship play-off final?
15. Products of the famed West Ham Academy, which two players went on to win the Champions League Final in 2008 with Manchester United?

1. Rio Ferdinand 2. Jussi Jaaskelainen 3. Ray Stewart in 1980 (Scottish) 4. £12 (the maximum allowed at the time) 5. His wife didn't take to London life 6. Thames Ironworks 7. 1964 8. Martin Peters 9. 10-0 (their record victory to date) 10 Julian Dicks 11. Bobby Gould 12. Vic Watson scored 42 league goals during the 1929-30 season. He netted 50 times in all competitions that season, also a West Ham record. 13. Trevor Brooking (five) 14. Bobby Zamora 15. Rio Ferdinand and Michael Carrick.

Wigan Athletic

1. What is Wigan's highest league position to date?
2. With which Rugby League club do Wigan Athletic share their home, the JJB Stadium?
3. By what score did Wigan beat Carlisle in the FA Cup during the 1934–5 season to set a new record for the biggest victory by a non-league club over a league club?
4. Wigan payed a record £5.5m for which player in July 2006?
5. Which player holds the record for first-team league appearances for Wigan?
6. Micky Quinn began his career with Wigan, making 69 appearances. How many goals did he score?
7. In which year did Dave Whelan purchase the club?
8. Which member of England's 1966 World Cup-winning side was briefly caretaker manager of Wigan?
9. At which club did former manager Paul Jewell start his playing career?
10. Who was Wigan's top goalscorer in the 2005–6 season?
11. How many different teams had belonged to Wigan before Wigan Athletic was formed in 1932?
12. Who did Wigan beat over two legs of the 2006 League Cup semi-final?
13. Who did Wigan beat 3–1 to secure promotion to the Premier League in 2005?
14. Who was sold to Tottenham in August 2006, having demanded a transfer minutes after the last game of the 2005–6 season?
15. For how many games was Colin Greenall in charge of Wigan in 2001?

1. 10th in the Premiership in 2006 2. Wigan Warriors 3. 6–1 4. Emile Heskey 5. Kevin Langley, 317 6. 19 7. 1995 8. Sir Bobby Charlton 9. Liverpool 10. Jason Roberts (14) 11. Four: County, United, Town and Borough 12. Arsenal 13. Reading 14. Pascal Chimbonda 15. Six.

Wolverhampton Wanderers

1. In which year did Wolves move to Molineux?
2. Who did Wolves lose to in the first ever UEFA Cup Final?
3. Which club did Mick McCarthy manage before joining Wolves?
4. Where did Wolves striker Sylvan Ebanks-Blake start his career?
5. Which striker scored 250 goals for Wanderers between 1986 and 1999?
6. Who was Wolves' top scorer in 2002-3?
7. Which club paid Wolves £2m for Neil Emblen in 2002-3?
8. Who beat Wolves on penalties after a 4-4 draw in the second round of the Worthington Cup in 2002-3?
9. Who scored a hat-trick for Wolves in their 3-0 win at Bradford City in October, 2001?
10. What was the score, and who were the opponents, when Wolves won the final play-off to get into the Premiership in 2002-3?
11. Who was voted Player of the Year for 2007-8, then missed the whole of the following season after suffering a knee injury?
12. Which club did Steve Bull play for after leaving Wolves?
13. For which Italian club did former midfield general Paul Ince play for two seasons in the 1990s?
14. From which club did Wolves get Shaun Newton for the 2000-1 season?
15. How many FA Cups have Wolves won?

1. 1889 2. Tottenham Hotspur 3. Sunderland 4. Manchester United 5. Steve Bull 6. Kenny Miller 7. Crystal Palace 8. Rotherham United 9. Kenny Miller 10. Wolves 3 Sheffield United 0 11. Goalkeeper Matt Murray 12. Hereford United 13. Internazionale 14. Charlton Athletic 15. Four - 1893, 1908, 1949, 1960.

Wycombe Wanderers

1. True or false: the club was founded by a group of furniture-makers?
2. 1990 was a big year. The club changed grounds and took on which future star manager?
3. This manager won the conference, two FA Trophies and took the side to Division Two. Which club lured him away?
4. Lawrie Sanchez then took the club on a famous FA Cup run in 2000–1. Which round did they get to?
5. The cup run was ended by Liverpool who beat them 2–1 at Villa Park. Who scored Wycombe's only goal?
6. True or false: before managing The Chairboys Tony Adams had previously spent two years playing at the club?
7. Name two London-based sides that were beaten by The Chairboys in their 2006–7 League Cup run.
8. Who was announced as Wycombe's new manager on 29 May, 2008?
9. With which team did former manager Paul Lambert collect a winners' medal in the 1997 UEFA Champions League?
10. From which country does Wycombe player Sergio Raul Torres hail?
11. Who was the top scorer for Wycombe in the 2000–1 season?
12. Which country did Mark Rogers represent at international level?
13. How many times did Wanderers win the Isthmian League?
14. What was the aggregate score in the Chelsea–Wycombe League Cup semi-final in 2006–7?
15. What was the score after the first leg at Adams Park?

1. True, hence the nickname The Chairboys 2. Martin O'Neill 3. Norwich City 4. Semi-final 5. Keith Ryan 6. False 7. Fulham and Charlton Athletic 8. Peter Taylor 9. Borussia Dortmund 10. Argentina 11. Andy Rimmell 12. Canada 13. Eight 14. 5–1 15. 1–1.

Yeovil Town

1. Where do Yeovil play their home games?
2. What is the club's nickname?
3. In which year did Yeovil win promotion to the Football League?
4. Which manager was in charge when they were promoted from the Conference to League Two?
5. Who replaced him when he left to take charge of Bristol City?
6. Which national side did Gary Johnson manage from 1999 to 2001?
7. Who denied Yeovil a place in the Championship after winning the 2006–7 play-off final?
8. Who did Yeovil beat in the semi-final despite losing the first leg 2–0?
9. What was the score in the second leg?
10. Which former England cricketer joined Yeovil on a non-contract basis in 1985?
11. Who made a club-record 691 appearances for Yeovil between 1958 and 1972?
12. Which player started his career at Yeovil before going on to play for Aston Villa and Sheffield Wednesday in the Premier League?
13. Which two Yeovil players left the club to join Nottingham Forest for a combined fee of £1.2m in July, 2007?
14. At the end of the 2005–6 season Yeovil achieved their highest league finish. What was it?
15. Yeovil broke their attendance record on 25 April, 2008 when 9,527 fans turned up to watch them play which team?

1. Huish Park 2. The Glovers 3. 2002 4. Gary Johnson 5. Steve Thompson, but he was later demoted to first-team coach 6. Latvia 7. Yeovil were beaten 2–0 by Blackpool 8. Nottingham Forest 9. Yeovil won 5–2 after extra-time to take the tie 5–4 10. Sir Ian Botham 11. Len Harris 12. Guy Whittingham 13. Chris Cohen and Arron Davies 14. Fifth in League One 15. Leeds United

Scottish League Clubs

Aberdeen

1. Aberdeen won the European Cup Winners' Cup in 1983. Who did they defeat in the final and what was the score?
2. Who scored for Aberdeen in that 1983 final?
3. What was unique about the Dons winning the European Super Cup later that year, against European Cup winners Hamburg?
4. Prior to 2008–9, Aberdeen were the last club outside the Old Firm to win the league title. In what year did they achieve this?
5. In 1970 Aberdeen became the first team to be knocked out of Europe on penalties – who beat them?
6. How many times, prior to 2008–9, had the Dons won the Scottish League/SPL?
7. What is the name of the ground that Aberdeen have played at since its inception?
8. In 1990 Aberdeen won the Scottish Cup, beating Celtic in the final. What was unique about the occasion?
9. Who is the Dons' most successful manager of all time?
10. Who was club captain during that most successful period, culminating in lifting the European Cup Winners' Cup and being chosen as captain of Scotland, too?
11. From which English club did Aberdeen acquire Derek Whyte in 1997?
12. Who was the Dons' top scorer in the Premier League in 2006–7?
13. Which Moroccan scored a hat-trick for the Dons in their 4–1 win at Dundee in September, 2001?
14. From which Norwegian club did Aberdeen acquire Thomas Solberg?
15. From which club did the Dons acquire Leon Mike in February, 2002?

1. Real Madrid (2-1) 2. Eric Black and John Hewitt 3. It made them the only Scottish team ever to win two European trophies 4. 1984–85 5. Honved 6. Four (1955, 1980, 1984, 1985) 7. Pittodrie. It was the first all-seated and all-covered stadium in the United Kingdom, and was also the first football stadium to feature a dugout 8. It was the first time a Scottish Cup Final had been decided by a penalty shoot-out (9-8 in favour of the Dons) 9. Alex Ferguson (manager 1978 to 1986). The Dons were League Champions three times (1980, 1984, 1985); runners-up three times (1978, 1981, 1982); Scottish Cup winners four times (1982, 1983, 1984, 1986); Scottish League Cup winners once 1986; European Cup Winners' Cup winners once, 1983; European Super Cup winners once, 1983 10. Willie Miller 11. Middlesbrough 12. Darren Mackie 13. Hicham Zerouali 14. KK Viking Stavanger 15. Manchester City.

Celtic

1. Celtic were the first-ever British winners of the European Cup. In which year?
2. Who did they play in the final?
3. Going into the 2008–9 season, Celtic had lost in two major European competition finals. To whom did they lose those matches?
4. To date, the most league goals scored by a Celtic player in a single season was 53. Who was the player?
5. Which player has played most matches for the club?
6. Going into the 2008–9 season, who was Celtic's most expensive signing?
7. In 1998, when Celtic won the Scottish League title to prevent Rangers from winning 10 league titles in a row, who was Celtic's manager?
8. Which former Celtic legend was the first player to score 100 league goals in both the English and Scottish leagues?
9. Going into 2008–9, only three Celtic managers had managed the club to three consecutive league championships. Name them.
10. Which player has scored the most goals ever for the club?
11. Only three clubs have been in the top division in Scotland since it was expanded in 1904. Celtic are one. Who are the other two?
12. Who did Celtic beat 4–0 at home in 2005, but still went out to in a Champions League qualifier?
13. From which English club did Celtic buy Neil Lennon in December, 2000?
14. For which two Scottish clubs, before Celtic, did Paul Lambert play league football?
15. From which French club did Celtic acquire Bobo Balde?

1. 1967 2. Inter Milan (2–1) 3. Feyenoord Rotterdam (European Cup Final 1970, 2–1 after extra-time); Porto (UEFA Cup Final 3–2 after extra-time in 2003) 4. Henrik Larsson 5. Billy McNeil, 790 from 1957 to 1975 6. Scott Brown (£4.4m in 2007) 7. Wim Jansen 8. Kenny Dalglish 9. Willie Maley (winners 1905–1910), Jock Stein (winners 1966–1974), Gordon Strachan (winners 2006–2008) 10. Jimmy McGrory (468 in total) 11. Rangers and Aberdeen 12. Artmedia Bratislava who won 5–4 on aggregate 13. Leicester City 14. St Mirren and Motherwell 15. Toulouse.

Dundee United

1. What is the name of Dundee United's stadium?
2. Prior to 2008–9, United had won the Scottish League championship once. In what year?
3. Which manager, the club's most successful of all time, oversaw that success?
4. The following year, in the European Cup, United were defeated in the semi-finals. By whom?
5. In 1986–7 United reached the final of the UEFA Cup. Who defeated them in the final?
6. Who scored for United in the defeat?
7. Prior to 2008–9, United had won the Scottish Cup once. In which year?
8. Which United player scored an own goal in the 6–1 home defeat by Rangers in September, 2001?
9. From which club did United sign Hasney Aljofree in June, 2000?
10. From which club did United acquire Jamie Fullarton in November, 2000?
11. Who began the 2000–1 season as manager of United?
12. Name either of Dundee United's fans' two main nicknames.
13. When founded in 1909 what was the team's name?
14. True or false: Dundee United were set up by the city's Irish community, having been inspired by Hibernian and Celtic?
15. Who was Dundee United's replacement for Jim McLean in 1994, a man who was the league's first continental manager?

1. Tannadice 2. 1982–3 3. Jim McLean 4. AS Roma, who were later found guilty of attempting to bribe the referee, and as a result were banned from European competition for a year, and fined accordingly. United won 2–0 at home but were beaten 0–3 in Rome, following a controversial penalty decision 5. IFK Gothenburg 2–1 on aggregate: 1–0 defeat in Gothenburg followed by a 1–1 draw at Tannadice 6. John Clark 7. 1994. A Craig Brewster goal defeated Rangers 1–0 8. Jamie Buchan 9. Bolton Wanderers 10. Crystal Palace 11. Alex Smith 12. The Terrors or The Arabs 13. Dundee Hibernian 14. True 15. Ivan Golac

Falkirk

1. What is the club's nickname?
2. In 1922 the club paid a world-record transfer fee of £5,000 to buy which player from West Ham?
3. What is the name of Falkirk's ground, in use for the 2008-9 season?
4. What are Falkirk's traditional home colours?
5. The youngest person in Scottish football history, and it is argued in top-flight football history, ever to captain a club at senior level was at Falkirk. He later went on to represent Liverpool, where his achievements included winning one European Cup and three league titles. Who was he?
6. Up until the beginning of the 2008-9 season, which player had made the most appearances for the club?
7. At the beginning of the 2008-9 season, which player had scored the most senior goals in the club's history?
8. In what year was the club founded?
9. Who finished the 2007-8 season as manager?
10. In which decade did Bob Shankly manage the side?
11. In which year did Ian McCall manage the side?
12. Which club did Alex Ferguson leave Falkirk for?
13. Which manager granted Alex Ferguson his request to move?
14. How many goals did Mo Johnston score for Falkirk in his 41 games for the club?
15. From which club did Falkirk sign Johnston?

1. The Bairns 2. Syd Puddefoot 3. Falkirk Park – Brockville Park, their home until 2004, was sold to Morrisons supermarket chain 4. Navy blue tops with white shorts 5. Gary Gillespie, in 1977, aged 17 6. Tom Ferguson, 450, 1919-20 to 1931-2 7. Kenneth Dawson, 150 goals (204 including wartime goals) (1934-5 to 1950-1) 8. 1876 9. John Hughes 10. The 1950s (1950 to 1957) 11. 2002-3 12. Ayr United 13. John Prentice 14. Six 15. Hearts.

Hamilton Academical

1. What is the club's nickname?
2. What is the name of their home ground?
3. In 1971 Hamilton became the first football club in the United Kingdom to recruit players from behind the Iron Curtain when they signed three players from which former communist country amid great publicity?
4. In 1936–7 which player scored a club-record 35 league goals in a season?
5. What are the club's traditional home colours?
6. The club shared a ground with which two other clubs during the period 1994 to 2001?
7. Colin Miller, the club's player-manager in 1998–9, won 61 international caps for which country?
8. In 1965, the club suffered a record defeat to which Scottish club?
9. In which year did the club move to New Douglas Park?
10. The club lost in the Scottish Cup Final in both 1911 and 1935. Which two sides beat them?
11. What nationality is Accies player Simon Mensing?
12. In which three seasons, prior to 2008–9, had Hamilton Academical won Division One?
13. Against whom did the club set their record home attendance of 28,690 in 1937?
14. The club recorded their unfortunate record defeat in 1965. What was the score?
15. At the start of the 2008–9 season, which Hamilton player, with 29 caps, had the most international appearances?

1. The Accies 2. New Douglas Park 3. Poland 4. David Wilson 5. Red and white horizontal stripes 6. Albion Rovers and Partick Thistle 7. Canada 8. Hibernian 9. 2001 10. Celtic in 1911 and Rangers in 1935 11. German 12. 1985–6, 1987–8, 2007–8 13. Hearts 14. 1–11 against Hibernian 15. Colin Miller (Canada).

Heart of Midlothian

1. In what city do Heart of Midlothian play?
2. What is the name of Hearts' ground?
3. What colour is Hearts' traditional home jersey?
4. In 2007 Hearts received what was then a British record fee for a goalkeeper. Who was the player and where did he go?
5. As of the start of the 2008–9 season, how many times had Hearts won the Scottish League Championship?
6. In 1985–6 Hearts were agonisingly pipped to the Scottish League title on the last day of the season on goal difference. By whom?
7. Who scored the other team's winning goals that day?
8. Hearts were also beaten in the Scottish Cup final that year. Who by?
9. Who is Hearts' most successful manager, in terms of trophies won?
10. At the beginning of the 2008–9 season, which player had scored most league goals for Hearts?
11. And which player had made the most appearances for the club, up to the beginning of the 2008–9 season?
12. From which club did Hearts sign Antti Niemi?
13. Name the four men who coached the club in 2006–7.
14. From which Northern Irish club did Hearts buy Andy Kirk in 1999?
15. From which club did Hearts acquire Stephane Mahe on a free transfer in August, 2001?

1. Edinburgh 2. Tynecastle 3. Maroon 4. Craig Gordon, sold for £9m to Sunderland 5. Four – 1894-5 1896-7, 1957-8 1959-60 6. Celtic. Hearts needed only to avoid defeat on the final day but lost 2-0 to Dundee 7. Albert Kidd, in the 83rd and 89th minutes. Those were the only goals he scored that season 8. Aberdeen 9. Tommy Walker – two league trophies, a Scottish FA Cup, and four Scottish League Cups (1951 to 1966) 10. John Robertson 214 (1983 to 1998) 11. Gary Mackay, 640 (1980 to 1997) 12. Rangers 13. Valdas Ivanauskas, Eduard Molofeev, Eugenijus Riabovas and Anatoly Karobochka 14. Glentoran 15. Celtic.

Hibernian

1. Name Hibernian's home ground.
2. What was unusual about Hibs' first appearance in Europe?
3. Going into the 2008–9 season, which Hibs player had made the most league appearances for the club?
4. During the 1950s, who set the club record for most league goals scored in a season ?
5. Who set the club's all–time scoring record for league goals?
6. Going into the 2008–9 season, how many times had Hibs won the Scottish League Championship?
7. Going into the 2008–9 season, how many times had Hibs won the Scottish League Cup?
8. Going into the 2008–9 season, how many times had Hibs won the Scottish Cup?
9. Since they were formed, Hibs' home kit has consisted of the same two colours. What are they?
10. In 2008, who was the owner of Hibs, a man who is credited with preventing a merger of Hibs with their arch–rivals Hearts in 1990?
11. From which club did Hibs sign Frederic Arpinon in 2001?
12. Why are Hibs known as The Cabbage?
13. In 2007, who did Hibs defeat to win their first trophy in 16 years?
14. When did the club level the famous Easter Road slope?
15. Which film by Danny Boyle contains a number of references to Hibs?

1. Easter Road 2. They played in the European Cup in 1955 despite having only finished fifth in their league 3. Arthur Duncan (446) 4. Joe Baker, 42 (1959-60) 5. Gordon Smith (364) 6. Four – 1902-3, 1947-8, 1950-1, 1951-2 7. Three – 1972-3, 1991-2, 2006-7 8. Two – 1887, 1902 9. Green and white 10. Sir Tom Farmer 11. Troyes 12. It is rhyming slang, short for 'Cabbage and Ribs' (Hibs) 13. Hibs beat Kilmarnock 5-1 in the CIS Cup 14. At the end of the 1999-2000 season 15. *Trainspotting*.

Inverness CT

1. What is the name of Caley's home ground?
2. The club was formed in 1994, following the merger of which two clubs?
3. The famous 3–1 Scottish Cup victory over Celtic in February, 2000, which spawned the even more famous newspaper headline 'Super Caley Go Ballistic Celtic Are Atrocious', precipitated the sacking of which head coach of Celtic?
4. Who managed the side in 2007–8?
5. Who defeated Caley 3–2 in the November 2003 Scottish Cup semi-final?
6. Why did Caley play their 2004 home games at Aberdeen's ground?
7. Who was the player-manager in charge for the 2005–6 season?
8. In December, 2007 Caley came from two goals down to beat Celtic 3–2. Who scored?
9. Who scored the club's 1,000th goal?
10. In May 2008, Caley broke the record for the largest SPL win (6–1). Who was on the receiving end?
11. What nationality was Sergei Baltacha who managed the side in 1994–5?
12. Former manager John Robertson was a playing legend with which famous club?
13. What nationality is Caley defender Richard Hastings?
14. Which country has Marius Constantin Niculae represented at national level?
15. In which year did Caley win the Scottish Third Division?

1. Tulloch Caledonian Stadium (sponsored by Tulloch Construction Company) 2. Caledonian FC and Inverness Thistle FC, both members of the Scottish Highland League 3. John Barnes 4. Craig Brewster 5. Dunfermline 6. Because the recently promoted side did not have a stadium up to Premier League standards 7. Craig Brewster 8. John Rankin, David Proctor and Don Cowie 9. Club captain Grant Munro 10. Gretna 11. Ukrainian 12. Hearts 13. Canadian 14. Romania 15. 1996–7.

Kilmarnock

1. What is the club's nickname?
2. At which stadium do the club play their home ties?
3. In what year did Kilmarnock win their first and, as of 2007–8, only Scottish League Championship?
4. Who was manager of the club at that time?
5. In what years have the club won the Scottish FA Cup?
6. Going into the 2008–9 season, which player had made the most appearances for the club?
7. Which player, at the start of 2008–9, had scored the most league goals for Kilmarnock?
8. In 2007 Kilmarnock received a £2m transfer fee for which player?
9. Kilmarnock are the oldest professional club in Scotland. In what year were they founded?
10. In 1966–7, Kilmarnock reached the semi-finals of the Fairs Cup (now the UEFA Cup), where they lost 4–2 to which English Club?
11. In which city was former 'keeper Gordon Marshall born?
12. From which club did Kilmarnock sign Sean Hessey in 1999?
13. Ian Durrant joined the club in 1998. In what year did he leave?
14. For which two seasons did Tommy Burns manage the side?
15. The club's longstanding record win (13–2) was set before 1900. Who did they beat?

1. Killie 2. Rugby Park 3. 1965 4. Willie Waddell 5. 1920, 1929, 1997 6. Alan Robertson, 484 (1972-1988) 7. Willy Culley, 149 (1911-23) 8. Steven Naismith when he signed for Rangers 9. 1869 10. Leeds United 11. Edinburgh 12. Huddersfield Town 13. 2002 14. 1992-3 and 1993-4 15. Saltcoats Victoria.

Motherwell

1. In which year did Motherwell win their only Scottish League Championship?
2. At the start of the 2008–9 season, which player had scored most league goals for Motherwell?
3. At the start of the 2008–9 season, for which player had Motherwell received their highest-ever transfer fee?
4. What is the name of Motherwell's stadium?
5. Which player holds the record for number of appearances for Motherwell?
6. In which years did Motherwell win the Scottish Cup?
7. From which club did Motherwell sign Eric Deloumeaux in November, 2001?
8. From which club did Motherwell sign Karl Ready in July, 2001?
9. Who scored a hat-trick for Motherwell in their 4–0 win over Hibernian in February, 2002?
10. From which club did Motherwell sign Greg Strong in July, 2000?
11. In which season did 'keeper Stephen Woods make his first appearance for the club?
12. Which Motherwell player was sent off in the February 2002, 3–0 away defeat at Rangers?
13. Which side put Motherwell out of the 2001–2 CIS Scottish League Cup?
14. Who scored twice for Motherwell in their 4–2 home win over Dundee in January, 2002?
15. Who was appointed as the club's manager on June 18, 2007?

1. 1931-2 2. Hughie Ferguson 284 goals in total (1916 to 1925) 3. 'Well legend Phil O'Donnell cost Celtic £1.75m in 1994. He later rejoined Motherwell but died after collapsing on the pitch in a game against Dundee United on 29 December, 2007 4. Fir Park, current capacity 13,742 5. Englishman Bob Ferrier, 626 (1917 to 1937) 6. 1952 and 1991 7. Le Havre 8. QPR 9. David Ferrere 10. Bolton Wanderers 11. 1994-5 12. Eric Deloumeaux 13. Airdrieonians 14. James McFadden 15. Mark McGhee.

Rangers

1. In what year did Rangers first win the European Cup Winners' Cup?
2. Who scored for Rangers that night?
3. Going into the 2008–9 season, Rangers had also contested three other major European finals. In what years?
4. Who is Rangers' all-time leading scorer?
5. In the 1960s, who set the record for most goals scored (all competitions) for Rangers in a single season?
6. In the 1930s, who set the record for most league goals scored for Rangers in a single season?
7. Which player has made the most appearances ever for Rangers?
8. The record transfer fee ever paid for a player by a Scottish league club was by Rangers. For whom?
9. Which Rangers manager has been most successful in terms of trophies won?
10. Who was manager when Rangers equalled Celtic's record nine-in-a-row League Championship wins in 1997?
11. True or False: in the year that Rangers won the Cup Winners' Cup, the second-round tie with Sporting Lisbon ended 6–6 on aggregate.
12. Going into the 2008–9 season, Rangers had won their national league championship a world record number of times. How many titles had they won?
13. Which player was discarded following an 'incident' on a plane?
14. From which club did Rangers sign Christian Nerlinger in June, 2001?
15. Which Rangers player scored a hat-trick in the 6–1 away win at Dundee United in September, 2001?

1. 1972, defeating Dynamo Moscow 3-2 2. Colin Stein, and Willie Johnston (2) 3. In 1960-1, they lost to Fiorentina 4-1 in the Cup Winners' Cup Final; they were defeated 1-0 by Bayern Munich in the 1966-7 Cup Winners' Cup Final; and in the 2008 UEFA Cup Final, 2-0, against Zenit St Petersburg 4. Ally McCoist, with 355 goals in 581 appearances, 1983 to 1998 5. Jim Forrest (57 goals, 1964-5) 6. Sam English (44 goals, 1931-2) 7. John Greig (755, 1960 to 1978) 8. Tore Andre Flo - bought for £12m from Chelsea in November 2000 9. Bill Struth (30 trophies in total during his reign from 1920 to 1954: 18 league championships, 10 Scottish Cups and two Scottish League Cups) 10. Walter Smith 11. True. The second leg was 3-2 to Sporting after 90 minutes and 4-3 to Sporting after extra-time. The referee incorrectly ordered a penalty shoot-out which Sporting won 3-0; UEFA later ruled that Rangers had won on away goals 12. 51 13. Fernando Ricksen, who was promptly loaned to Zenit St Petersburg 14. Borussia Dortmund 15. Tore Andre Flo.

St Mirren

1. What is the club's nickname?
2. Where do the club play their home games?
3. What are the traditional home colours of the club?
4. In what years, prior to 2008–9, did St Mirren win the Scottish Cup?
5. Going into the 2008–9 season, which player had made the most league appearances for the club?
6. At the beginning of the 2008–9 season, which player had scored the most League goals for the club?
7. The record for most League goals in a season, set in the 1920s, is currently held by whom?
8. Which famous manager, who has since won the European Cup, was sacked for the only time in his managerial career, by St Mirren in 1978?
9. True or false: St Mirren played in the European Cup in the 1980–1 season?
10. What is the name of the cup that St Mirren play for in an annual competition with their nearest rivals, Greenock Morton?
11. In what year was the club founded?
12. True or false: St Mirren were originally one of many clubs that were founded because cricket players wanted to change codes and take up football?
13. Against whom was the club's highest home attendance (47,438) recorded in August, 1949?
14. What nationality is former player, Jose Manuel Quitongo?
15. Which player left the club in 1985, having been there since 1981, to go on to become a very successful striker at West Ham United?

1. The Buddies, although they are also known as The Saints 2. St Mirren Park is the official name of the stadium, although it is more commonly known throughout football as Love Street 3. Black and white stripes 4. 1926, 1959, 1987 5. Tony Fitzpatrick, 351 (1973–9, 1981–9) 6. David McCrae, 221 (1923–4) 7. Dunky Walker, 45 (1921–2) 8. Sir Alex Ferguson (manager 1974 to 1978) 9. False 10. The Renfrewshire Cup 11. 1877 12. True 13. Celtic 14. Angolan 15. Frank McAvennie.

Selected Irish Teams

Bohemian

1. Who replaced Sean Connor as manager in December 2007?
2. In what year were Bohemians founded?
3. Where did Bohemians play their home games in 2007?
4. Bohemians is one of only two clubs to be members of the League of Ireland since its inception, Name the other.
5. Who was Bohemian's first player to sign professional terms?
6. How many times have Bohemians won the FAI Cup up to and including the 2007–8 season?
7. Who held the club record for appearances going into the 2008–9 season?
8. A Bohemians select side played Arsenal in March 1962 to mark which event?
9. Which trophy did Bohemians win for the first and only time in 1908?
10. Which former European Cup Winners' Cup champions were knocked out of Europe by Bohemians in 2000?
11. Bohemians are known as 'Bohs' and by which other nickname?
12. Who managed the club to league success in 2002?
13. In which year did Bohemians make their European debut?
14. What is the name of the stand that was opened in October 1999?
15. Bohemians record defeat was a 7–0 reverse against which team in 1955?

1. Pat Fenlon 2. 1890 3. Dalymount Park 4. Shelbourne 5. Tony O'Connell 6. Six 7. Tommy Kelly (575) 8. The turning on of the new floodlights 9. The Irish Cup 10. Aberdeen 11. The Gypsies 12. Stephen Kenny 13. 1970 14. The Jodi Stand 15. Shamrock Rovers.

Cliftonville

1. Where do Cliftonville play their home games?
2. Who did Eddie Patterson succeed as manager in 2005?
3. In what year was Cliftonville founded?
4. In which season did Cliftonville last win the league title?
5. Which company were Cliftonville's major sponsor for the 2007–8 season?
6. By which nickname are Cliftonville better known?
7. Following the completion of the 1900 Irish Cup tie between Cliftonville and Belfast Celtic the result was appealed and the match replayed. What was the basis for the appeal?
8. Cliftonville's team for the 2007–8 season contained two sets of brothers. Give the surname of one.
9. Who managed Cliftonville to their league success in 1997–8?
10. Who scored Cliftonville's winning goal in the 1979 Irish Cup Final?
11. Why were Cliftonville suspended from playing in the 1999 Irish Cup Final?
12. The first Irish Football League was made up of Cliftonville and seven other teams. Name three of them.
13. On how many occasions had Cliftonville won the County Antrim Shield up to the end of the 2007–8 season?
14. Michael Ingham moved from Cliftonville to which English club in 1999?
15. Against which team did Cliftonville win the end-of-season play-off to secure their top-flight status in 2004?

1. Solitude 2. Liam Beckett 3. 1879 4. 1997-8 5. MDS Pharma Services 6. The Reds 7. The goalposts were too short 8. Holland or Scannell 9. Marty Quinn 10. Tony Bell 11. They played an ineligible player in the semi-final 12. Clarence, Milford, Oldpark, Distillery, Glentoran, Ulster and Linfield 13. Seven 14. Sunderland 15. Armagh City.

Coleraine

1. By what nickname were Coleraine originally known?
2. Who replaced Marty Quinn as manager in 2008?
3. In what year did Coleraine win their only Irish League title?
4. Coleraine are the only Irish league club to have won two successive all-Ireland competitions, winning which cup in 1969 and 1970?
5. Who scored Coleraine's winning goal during the 2003 Irish Cup Final?
6. Which player moved from Coleraine to Lincoln City in 2004?
7. The final of which world-famous youth tournament is staged in Coleraine every year?
8. In what year were Coleraine founded?
9. Where do Coleraine play their home games?
10. Against which European giant did Coleraine make their European debut in 1965?
11. Which Northern Ireland and Celtic legend returned to Coleraine in 1961?
12. Which two local sides merged to form Coleraine FC?
13. Which former *Cold Feet* star is Coleraine's most famous celebrity fan?
14. Which two colours make up Coleraine's home kit?
15. Coleraine won its first trophy in the 1931–2 season, defeating which team in the final of the Gold Cup?

1. The Lilywhites 2. Davy Platt 3. 1974 4. The Blaxnit Cup 5. Jody Tolan 6. Gareth McAuley 7. The Milk Cup 8. 1927 9. The Showgrounds 10. Dynamo Kiev 11. Bertie Peacock 12. Coleraine Olympic and Coleraine Alexandra 13. James Nesbitt 14. Blue and White 15. Ballymena United.

Crusaders

1. At which ground do Crusaders play their home games?
2. Crusaders are known as 'the Crues' and by which other nickname?
3. What is the name of the man who managed the club during their most successful period in the early 1990s?
4. Which player was sold to Wrexham in 1993?
5. In what year were Crusaders founded?
6. Who is the only manager to be sacked during the entire history of Crusaders?
7. Name the player who won an Irish League winners' medal with Crusaders and an All Ireland Gaelic medal with Dublin in the same season.
8. Crusaders won back-to-back Irish cups in which years?
9. Which player finished as leading scorer during the 2007–8 season?
10. Which famous Northern Irish soccer commentator represented the Crues in the early 1970s?
11. Who managed Crusaders for their first senior match in 1949?
12. Crusaders were paired against which English giant in the European Cup of 1976?
13. Which team did Crusaders defeat in the Steel and Sons Cup Final in 2005?
14. Former Crusaders player and manager Aaron Callaghan was the manager of which FAI team for the 2007–8 season?
15. What two colours make up the Crusaders' home kit?

1. Seaview 2. The Hatchet Men 3. Roy Walker 4. Barry Hunter 5. 1898 6. Alan Dornan 7. Mick Deegan 8. 1967 and 1968 9. David Rainey 10. Jackie Fullerton 11. Jackie Vernon 12. Liverpool 13. Dundela 14. Longford Town 15. Red and black.

Derry City

1. Derry are better known by which nickname?
2. At which ground do Derry play their home games?
3. In what year were Derry founded?
4. In which year did Derry resign from the Irish League?
5. What is the name of Derry's most capped international player?
6. Which Scottish side did Derry defeat in the 2006–7 UEFA Cup?
7. Who moved from Derry to Celtic in the summer of 2008?
8. Which former Coleraine player managed Derry to league success in the 1996–7 season?
9. At the start of the 2008–9 season, which player held the record for appearances in a Derry shirt?
10. Who returned to the club as manager in 2008?
11. How many times had Derry won the FAI Cup up to the end of 2007–8?
12. From which English club did Derry adopt their home shirt?
13. Name Derry's all-time record goalscorer.
14. In which season did Derry complete the domestic treble?
15. As a result of the conflict in Ireland Derry were forced to play their 'home' games at which ground during 1971 and 1972?

1. The Candystripes 2. The Brandywell 3. 1928 4. 1972 5. Billy Gillespie (25 caps for ROI) 6. Gretna 7. Pat McCourt 8. Felix Healy 9. Peter Hutton 10. Stephen Kenny 11. Four 12. Sheffield United 13. Jimmy Kelly (363) 14. 1988–9 15. The Coleraine Showgrounds.

Glenavon

1. In what year were Glenavon formed?
2. Who was installed as Glenavon manager in June 2008?
3. Where do Glenavon play their home games?
4. What is the motto found under the club badge?
5. Glenavon reached the first round proper of the UEFA Cup in the 1995–6 season before being eliminated by which German club?
6. Gerard McMahon moved from Glenavon to which English Premier League club in 2002?
7. How many times had Glenavon won the Irish League title prior to 2008–9?
8. The one part of Glenavon's ground that remains as a terrace is known by which name?
9. Who moved to Glenavon for an Irish League record fee of £32,000 in 1990?
10. Who scored Glenavon's winning goal in the 1997 Irish Cup Final?
11. Which team did Glenavon defeat in the 2004–5 play-off to reach the Premier League?
12. Which former Glenavon player scored the winning goal for Northern Ireland in their first-ever World Cup final-stages match?
13. Who replaced Billy Hamilton as Glenavon manager in 1998?
14. Who was Glenavon's leading goalscorer during their first league-winning season, 1951–2?
15. Who was in charge when Glenavon last lifted the Irish Cup during the 1996–7 season?

1. 1889 2. Stephen McBride 3. Mourneview Park 4. Be Just and Fear Not 5. Werder Bremen 6. Tottenham Hotspur 7. Three 8. The Hospital End Terrace 9. Raymond McCoy 10. Tony Grant 11. Crusaders 12. Wilbur Cush 13. Roy Walker 14. Jimmy Jones 15. Nigel Best.

Glentoran

1. Glentoran won which European trophy in 1914?
2. Who replaced Roy Coyle as manager in February 2006?
3. Which Premier league player scored the winning goal in the 1996 Irish Cup Final for Glentoran?
4. Which two Glentoran players were included in the Northern Ireland squad for the 1982 World Cup in Spain?
5. Glentoran became the first team to be eliminated by which method during their 1967 European Cup encounter with Benfica?
6. Which former Northern Ireland manager began his career with Glentoran in 1948?
7. At the start of 2008–9, who was the club's record goalscorer?
8. What is the English translation of the Glentoran motto?
9. Glentoran competed in a tournament in the United States in the late 1960s under which name?
10. In what year were Glentoran founded?
11. Glentoran are known as 'The Glens' and by which other nickname?
12. How many league titles had Glentoran won up to the end of the 2007–8 season?
13. Who were unveiled as the club's major sponsor for the 2008–9 season?
14. Glentoran play their home games at which ground?
15. From which club did Gary Hamilton join in 2005?

1. The Vienna Cup 2. Paul Millar 3. Glen Little 4. Jonny Jameson and Jim Cleary 5. The away goal rule 6. Billy Bingham 7. Trevor Thompson (375 goals) 8. The game above all 9. The Detroit Cougars 10. 1882 11. The Cock and Hens 12. 22 13. Fonacab 14. The Oval 15. Portadown.

Linfield

1. In which year were Linfield founded?
2. Due to a ban imposed by UEFA from 1988 to 1990, Linfield were prevented from playing at home in European competition. At whose ground did they play?
3. How many times had Linfield won the Irish Cup up to 2007–8?
4. Which team did Linfield defeat in the final of the inaugural Setanta Cup in 2005?
5. Who joined Linfield for an Irish League record fee of £55,000 in January 1998?
6. Against which team did goalkeeper Alan Manus score in 2003?
7. Michael Gault made his senior international debut against which country in March 2008?
8. Linfield legend Tommy Dickson was better known to fans by what nickname?
9. What three-word inscription is found under the original Linfield badge?
10. To which French club did George O'Boyle move from Linfield in 1988?
11. What is the name of the most successful manager in Irish league history who bossed Linfield from 1975 to 1990?
12. At which ground did Linfield play their home games in 2006?
13. Against which team did Glenn Ferguson score his 500th career goal?
14. Which player is known to Linfield fans as 'Pistol Pete'?
15. Linfield's most successful European campaign saw them reach the quarter-final of the European Cup in 1967 before being knocked out by which club?

1. 1886 2. Wrexham 3. 39 times 4. Shelbourne 5. Glenn Ferguson 6. Omagh Town 7. Georgia 8. The Duke of Windsor 9. Audaces Fortuna Juvat (Fortune Favours the Bold) 10. Bordeaux 11. Roy Coyle 12. Windsor Park 13. Crusaders 14. Peter Thompson 15. CSKA Sofia.

Lisburn Distillery

1. At which ground do Distillery play their home games?
2. By which nickname are Distillery known?
3. In what year were Distillery founded?
4. From 1971 to 1980 Distillery played their home games in north Belfast, sharing with Crusaders and which other team?
5. Which English Premier League manager played for Distillery during the 1970–1 season?
6. Name the English legend who came out of retirement to play for Distillery against Benfica in the European Cup.
7. Andrew Waterworth moved to which Scottish club for £20,000 in January 2008?
8. Distillery's stadium hosts football matches and which other type of sport?
9. Which player holds the club record for appearances?
10. Which company was the major sponsor of the club for the 2007–8 season?
11. How many times have Distillery lifted the Irish Cup?
12. In which year were Distillery last relegated from the top flight of Irish League football?
13. Who is Distillery's all-time record goalscorer?
14. Why did Distillery have to leave their Grosvenor Park home in 1971?
15. Which Spanish side did Distillery host in the 1971 European Cup Winners' Cup?

1. New Grosvenor 2. The Whites 3. 1879 4. Brantwood 5. Martin O'Neill 6. Sir Tom Finney 7. Hamilton Academical 8. Greyhound Racing 9. Bertie McMinn (524) 10. Lagan Valley Steel 11. Twelve 12. 1995 13. Sam McAdam (229) 14. It was firebombed during the Troubles 15. FC Barcelona.

St Patrick's Athletic

1. In what year were St Pat's founded?
2. Which former Republic of Ireland international moved from St Pat's to Manchester Utd in 1982?
3. What is the English meaning of the St Pat's motto 'ni neart go cur le cheile'?
4. In which year were St Pat's admitted to the senior ranks of the League of Ireland?
5. Which former Republic of Ireland manager managed St Pat's between 1986 and 1996?
6. What was the name of the unregistered player who cost St Pat's 15 points during the 2001–2 season?
7. St Pat's were the first Irish team to progress past the first round of which European competition?
8. Where do St Pat's play their home games?
9. How many league titles had St Pat's won up to the end of the 2007–8 season?
10. Which former England goalkeeper made his one and only appearance for St Pat's in October 1977?
11. At the start of the 2008–9 season, who held the St Pat's record for the most goals in a single season?
12. St Pat's record league win was an 8–0 home win against who in December 1967?
13. Who replaced Eamon Collins as manager in 2004?
14. Where did St Pat's play their home games during the redevelopment of their ground between 1989 and 1993?
15. Which former St Pat's player scored 13 goals during his first season in the English Premier League?

1. 1929 2. Paul McGrath 3. No strength without unity 4. 1951 5. Brian Kerr 6. Charles Livingstone Mbabazi 7. The Intertoto Cup 8. Richmond Park 9. Seven 10. Gordon Banks 11. Shay Gibbons 12. Limerick 13. John McDonnell 14. Harolds Cross 15. Kevin Doyle.

European Clubs

AC Milan

1. True or false: after winning the Champions League in 2006–7 AC Milan became the team to win the tournament the most times?
2. The AC in Milan stands for Football Association. But what Italian words do A and C represent?
3. By what nickname are the side commonly known?
4. Which controversial character owns AC Milan?
5. Who coached AC Milan to the 2006–7 Champions League title?
6. AC Milan was founded in 1899, but not as a football club. What type of sports club was it?
7. In what year did Milan win their first Serie A title?
8. True or false: Inter Milan grew out of AC Milan after an internal feud?
9. Which coach is credited with guiding Milan to success after success in the golden era of the late 1980s and early 1990s?
10. What is unusual about the club's name, even when spoken in Italian?
11. Which three Dutchmen were considered the stars of the early–1990s team?
12. Under what circumstances might Paolo Maldini's retired number 3 shirt be restored (other than by him playing on)?
13. One other shirt has been retired by Milan. Whose?
14. How many times did Milan win Serie A between 1990 and 2000?
15. In the 1989 European Cup Final Milan beat their rivals 4–0, with two goals apiece for Gullit and Van Basten. Who did they beat?

1. False. Real Madrid had won it more times 2. Associazione Calcio 3. The *Rossoneri* (Red-Blacks) 4. Silvio Berlusconi 5. Carlo Ancelotti 6. It was a cricket club set up by English ex-pats 7. 1901 8. True 9. Arrigo Sacchi 10. Milan is spelt the English way. It is Milano in Italian. It was done in honour of its English founder 11. Marco van Basten, Ruud Gullit and Frank Rijkaard 12. It might be restored for either of Maldini's sons 13. Franco Baresi's (No. 6) 14. Five 15. Steaua Bucharest.

Ajax

1. Ajax are based in which city?
2. Ajax are one of five teams to have gained the UEFA Badge of Honour for winning the European Cup three times consecutively or on five separate occasions. Who are the other four?
3. True or false: Ajax lost in the first Intertoto Cup Final?
4. Prior to 2008–9, Ajax were one of only three clubs to have won all three European trophies at least once. Who are the other two?
5. What is the team's 'heavenly' nickname?
6. Ajax play their home games at which modern stadium?
7. Which head coach has been credited with introducing the concept of 'Total Football' to the club?
8. Ajax's big derby is against Feyenoord. Which city are they from?
9. True or false: Ajax fans are known as 'Joden' (Jews)?
10. True or false: Ajax was managed only by Englishmen for the first 30 years of its professional existence?
11. In which three consecutive years did Ajax win the European Cup?
12. In what year did Ajax win the first Intertoto Cup?
13. Ajax beat Italian sides in 1971–2 and 1972–3. From what country were their opponents in the 1970–1 final?
14. Who did Ajax beat in the 1991–92 UEFA Cup Final?
15. True or false: captain Johann Cruyff scored both goals in the 1971–2 European Cup Final?

1. Amsterdam. The club's full title is Amsterdamsche Football Club Ajax 2. Liverpool, AC Milan, Bayern Munich, Real Madrid 3. False. They won it 4. Juventus and Bayern Munich 5. Godenzonen (Sons of the Gods) 6. The Amsterdam ArenA 7. Former Ajax player, Rinus Michels 8. Rotterdam 9. True. This was a pre-World War II tradition 10. False. For the first five years, there was an Irishman in charge. For the subsequent 25 years Englishmen were in charge 11. 1971, 1972, 1973 12. 1962 13. Greece (Panathinaikos) 14. Torino 15. True.

Barcelona

1. In what year was Barcelona FC founded?
2. True or false: in 2008–9, Camp Nou (or the Nou Camp) had a capacity of over 100,000?
3. Who was the chairman of Barcelona at the beginning of the 2008–9 season?
4. The club's motto is 'Més que un club'. What does it mean?
5. Prior to 2008–9, Barca were one of three clubs never to have been relegated from La Liga. Who were the other two?
6. True or false: Barca pipped main rivals Real to the first-ever La Liga title in 1929–30?
7. During the Civil War, Barcelona competed in the Republican Mediterranean League. Where did it finish in the league?
8. Who led Barca to their solitary league title of the 1980s?
9. Which famous Dane left Johann Cruyff's 'dream team' in the 1990s to join arch-rivals Real Madrid?
10. How many consecutive titles did Johann Cruyff lead Barca to as manager?
11. Which former player, a fiery Bulgarian, picked up the 1994 European Player of the Year award?
12. Name the four Brazilian 'Rs' who between them won the World Player of the Year award six times as Barca players from 1994 to 2005?
13. Which former Irish international and Barca player went on to become a successful television presenter in Spain?
14. Why was Barca's stadium closed to the public for six months in 1925?
15. How is the encounter between Barca and Real Madrid commonly known in Spain?

1. 1899 2. False. It holds 98,772 3. Joan Laporta 4. More than a club 5. Real Madrid and Athletic Bilbao 6. True 7. First 8. Terry Venables 9. Michael Laudrup 10. Four (1990–4) 11. Hristo Stoichkov 12. Romario, Ronaldo, Rivaldo, and Ronaldinho 13. Michael Robinson 14. As punishment for fans jeering the Spanish national anthem 15. El Clásico.

Bayern Munich

1. How are Bayern Munich known in German?
2. How many Champions League titles had Munich won at the start of the 2008–9 season?
3. Name one of the club's three main nicknames.
4. What is the name of the club's stadium?
5. True or false: the club's chairman in 2008 once coached in France?
6. Who managed the 2007 side?
7. Who do the Bavarians play their big derby against?
8. In what year was the club founded?
9. Against which British club did Munich win the 1967 Cup Winners' Cup in injury-time?
10. Branko Zebec coached a disciplined style of play which led the club to which famous landmark in the 1960s?
11. Which Spanish side were hammered by Munich in the 1974 European Cup Final?
12. Against which British side did Munich retain the European Cup?
13. In 1976, Munich won the European Cup for the third consecutive year. How many other teams had already achieved that landmark?
14. Against whom were Bayern cruelly denied a Champions League victory after conceding two goals in injury-time?
15. Which of the Laudrup brothers played for Bayern in the 1990s?

1. FC Bayern München (popularly FC Hollywood) 2. Four 3. Der FCB (The FCB), Die Bayern (The Bavarians), Die Roten (The Reds) 4. The Allianz Arena 5. True. Franz Beckenbauer coached Marseille 6. Jürgen Klinsmann 7. TSV 1860 Munich 8. 1900, by members of a Munich gymnastics club 9. (Glasgow) Rangers 10. The club achieved the first league and cup double in Bundesliga history, using only 13 players throughout the season 11. Atlético Madrid 12. Leeds United 13. Two. Real Madrid and Ajax 14. Manchester United 15. Brian Laudrup.

Benfica

1. In which city do Benfica play?
2. What is the club's full title in Portuguese?
3. In what year was the club founded?
4. What is the name of Benfica's famous stadium, which was adopted by Sunderland in 1997?
5. Benfica are one of an elite group of three clubs who have never been relegated from the league. Who are the other two?
6. From which bird do the club get their nickname?
7. Between 1960 and 1970, Benfica reached five European Cup finals. How many did they win?
8. Against which two teams were Benfica surprise European Cup victors in 1961 and 1962?
9. Benfica have retired just one squad number. Which one?
10. What nationality was the coach of Benfica's European Cup-winning side in the 1960s?
11. True or false: Benfica is the biggest club in the world in terms of 'associate members'?
12. Who was Benfica's manager at the start of the 2008–9 season?
13. Which former Benfica player was the first player to be presented with the Golden Boot Award?
14. How many goals did he score in the 1962 European Cup Final?
15. In which year was he the top scorer at the World Cup?

1. Lisbon 2. Sport Lisboa e Benfica 3. 1904 4. Estádio da Luz or the Stadium of Light 5. FC Porto and Sporting CP 6. The eagle (As Águias – the Eagles) 7. Two 8. Barcelona (1961) and Real Madrid (1962) 9. Number 29, which belonged to Hungarian player Miklós Fehér, who died of cardiac arrhythmia in January 2004 after falling unconscious during a match in the Portuguese Liga 10. Hungarian, Bela Guttmann (1959 to 1962) 11. In November 2006, the *Guinness Book of Records* declared the club the largest with 160,398 associates 12. Quique Sánchez Flores 13. Eusebio, in 1968 14. Two, against Real Madrid 15. 1966, with nine goals.

FC Porto

1. In what year was FC Porto founded?
2. Up until 2008–9, how many times had Porto won the European Cup?
3. When did Porto win its first UEFA Cup?
4. Prior to 2008–9, Porto set a Portuguese record by winning the league title how many times in a row?
5. How many league titles had they won in total, prior to 2008–9?
6. Which Portuguese team, or teams, have won the league more times than Porto?
7. What is the name of Porto's new ground?
8. The old ground up until 2003 was called...?
9. True or false: Porto was founded by a wine merchant?
10. What is Porto's nickname?
11. Which Englishman had a successful stint as Porto manager between 1994 and 1996?
12. Who did Porto beat 3–0 to win the Champions League in 2003–4?
13. Prior to 2008–9, who was the club's all-time top scorer?
14. Prior to 2008–9, who was the club's most-capped player?
15. Name two of the three other sports that the club is famous for.

1. In Porto, 1893 2. Twice 3. 2003 4. Five times 5. 23 6. Only Benfica with 31 league titles 7. Estádio do Dragão 8. Estádio das Antas 9. True. António Nicolau de Almeida' fell in love with the game on a trip to England 10. Dragões (Dragons) 11. Bobby Robson 12. AS Monaco 13. Fernando Gomes with 288 14. Joao Pinto with 407 15. Rink hockey (played on roller skates), handball, and basketball.

Fiorentina

1. In which region of Italy is Florence?
2. Fiorentina have won only one European honour. Which one?
3. Who did they beat in the final?
4. They narrowly lost out in the 1957 European Cup Final. Who beat them?
5. Which footballing legend got the first goal on the night?
6. Name the stadium where the club will play their first game of the 2008–9 season.
7. Why do Fiorentina bear the nickname, the 'Viola'?
8. In which decade did the club win their first Scudetto title?
9. Luca Toni was the eighth World Cup winner from Fiorentina in 2006. All but one have been Italian. Who was the non-Italian?
10. Who scored the winner for Fiorentina against Atalanta in the 1995–6 Copa Italia?
11. True or false: the club adopted the purple kit by mistake after a dye problem when washing their old red-and-white kits?
12. Name either of the club's Swedish managers.
13. Which Fiorentina star scored for Romania in the first round of the Euro 2008 tournament?
14. What was Gabriel Batistuta's nickname?
15. True or false: Batistuta never won Serie A?

1. Tuscany 2. UEFA Cup Winners' Cup 3. Rangers 4. Real Madrid 5. Di Stefano 6. Stadio Artemio Franchi 7. After the purple kit they wear 8. 1950s 9. Daniel Passarella (Argentina 1978) 10. Gabriel Batistuta 11. True 12. Nils Liedholm (1971–73) and Sven-Göran Eriksson (1987–89) 13. Adrian Mutu 14. Batigol 15. False. He finally won it when he moved to Roma.

Galatasaray

1. Name either of Galatasaray's main nicknames.
2. Name their ground.
3. In what city is the club based?
4. True or false: prior to the 2008–9 season only Fenerbahce had won more Turkish titles than Galatasaray?
5. Galatasaray won the 1999–2000 UEFA Cup Final. Which English team did they beat on penalties in the final?
6. Only one English player managed to score a penalty against Galatasaray that night. Who?
7. Galatasaray won the European Super Cup the same year. Which Spanish side did they beat?
8. Who are the club's two main Istanbul-based rivals?
9. Which top-level American goalkeeper played for Galatasaray in the 1990s?
10. Which World Cup-winning Brazilian used to keep goal for the club?
11. Which Romanian starred in the club's team during the glory years of the late 1980s and also managed the team in 2004–5?
12. How did Graeme Souness almost spark a riot in Istanbul in 1996?
13. What nickname did it earn Souness?
14. True or false: Souness never won the league with Galatasaray?
15. Who was manager at the begining of the 2008–9 season?

1. Aslanlar (The Lions), Cimbom Avrupa Fatihi (Conqueror of Europe) 2. The Ali Sami Yen Stadium 3. Istanbul 4. False. Galatasaray have won more 5. Arsenal 6. 'Romford' Ray Parlour 7. Real Madrid 8. Besiktas and Fenerbahce 9. Brad Friedel 10. Claudio Taffarel 11. Gheorghe Hagi 12. He placed a large Galatasaray flag in the centre of the pitch of archrivals Fenerbahce after Galatasaray had beaten them in the Turkish Cup Final 13. Ulubatli Souness - after Turkish hero Ulubatli Hasan, who was killed as he planted the Ottoman flag at the Siege of Constantinople 14. True 15. Michael Skibbe.

Inter Milan

1. What is the team's full name?
2. After winning in 2007–8, Inter had won Serie A 16 times. Which two teams have won it more than that?
3. True or false: Inter are the only one of the big three clubs in Italy not to have won the European Cup/Champions League?
4. What is Inter's ground called?
5. How many Portuguese managers have the club had?
6. Which Englishman managed the club on two separate occasions?
7. In which two consecutive years did Inter win the European Cup?
8. When Ronaldo and Vieri were bought, both broke the club's transfer record. Who was more expensive?
9. True or false: the restaurants owned by Christian Vieri and Fabio Cannavaro in Milan were vandalized after defeats by AC Milan?
10. Inter beat Real 3–1 in the final of the 1963–4 European Cup. Name one of their scorers.
11. Which Italian club were beaten by Inter in the 1997–8 UEFA Cup Final?
12. Inter won the Copa Italia in both 2004–5 and 2005–6. Which team did they beat in both finals?
13. Who beat Inter in the European Cup Final of 1967?
14. Which European star scored two goals in the final to end Inter's hopes of European Cup glory in 1971–2?
15. True or false: on both of the occasions that Inter won the European Cup, they went on to win the Intercontinental Cup?

1. Football Club Internazionale Milano 2. Juventus and AC Milan 3. False 4. Stadio Giuseppe Meazza 5. One. Jose Mourinho 6. Roy Hodgson 7. 1963–4 and 1964–5 8. Christian Vieri (£31m). Ronaldo was a snip at £19.5m 9. True 10. Mazzola and Milani 11. Lazio 12. Roma 13. Glasgow Celtic 14. Johan Cruyff 15. True.

Juventus

1. Name either of the club's feminine nicknames.
2. What is Juve's stadium called?
3. Which former Chelsea manager started the 2008–9 season in charge of Juve?
4. What does Juve mean in Italian?
5. True or false: Juventus have never been relegated to Serie B?
6. After beating Argentinos Juniors in the Intercontinental Cup Final in 1985, Juventus became the only club to reach which major footballing landmark?
7. Where did Juventus beat Liverpool in the 1985 European Cup Final?
8. Who scored for Juventus in the 1985 European Cup Final?
9. In 1984, Juventus beat FC Porto in the final of the Cup Winners' Cup, but which English team were their victims in the semis?
10. In 2001, Juve broke their current transfer fee by paying 72 million Euros for which player?
11. In which decade did the stars Raimundo Orsi, Luigi Bertolini and Giovanni Ferrari help Juve to five consecutive Serie A titles?
12. On which car manufacturer's fortune is the club built?
13. Which Welsh forward did the club sign in 1957–8?
14. In the same season the club were awarded a Golden Star for Sports Excellence to wear on their kit. What had they done to deserve it?
15. Which Italian goalkeeping legend managed the side from 1988 to 1990?

1. La Vecchia Signora (The Old Lady) or La Fidanzata d'Italia (The girlfriend of Italy) 2. Stadio Olimpico 3. Claudio Ranieri 4. Youth 5. False. They were relegated in 2006–7 for match-fixing 6. They became the only team in the world to have won all official major international cups and championships 7. Heysel Stadium, Brussels 8. Michel Platini 9. Manchester United 10. Zinedine Zidane 11. The 1930s 12. Fiat 13. John Charles 14. They were the first Italian side to win ten league titles 15. Dino Zoff

Lyon

1. True or false: Lyon did not win a French League title before 2000?
2. Up to and including 2007–8, how many league titles had Lyon won in a row?
3. How many times had Lyon reached the semi-finals of the Champions League, prior to 2008–9?
4. What was the club's original name?
5. In what year was the club founded?
6. Which controversial manager coached Lyon to their first French League title in 2002?
7. Which manager took Lyon to league titles in 2003, 2004 and 2005?
8. Which former Liverpool manager continued the club's success in 2005–6?
9. What are the fanatical supporters of Lyon known as?
10. Against who do Lyon play their biggest local derby?
11. Lyon has two consecutive retired numbers. What are they?
12. Between 1981 and 1983 Lyon unusually had a non-French manager. Where was he from?
13. Which French great managed both Lyon and Fulham?
14. Which former Republic of Ireland captain had a tough time playing at Lyon?
15. As a player, former Lyon manager, Jean Tigana was one part of the French national side's 'Magic Diamond'. Name two of the other three?

1. True 2. Seven 3. None 4. Lyon Olympique Universitaire 5. 1899 6. Jacques Santini, who was disliked for his defensive approach to the game 7. Paul Le Guen 8. Gerard Houllier 9. The 'Bad Gones' 10. Saint-Étienne 11. 16, which belonged to French goalkeeper Luc Borrelli who was killed in a road accident in February 1999; 17, which belonged to Cameroon midfielder Marc-Vivien Foé who died while playing for Cameroon in the 2003 FIFA Confederations Cup at Stade de Gerland, Lyon 12. Serbia (Vladica Kovacevic) 13. Jean Tigana 14. Mick McCarthy 15. Michel Platini, Luis Fernandez and Alain Giresse.

Marseille

1. What is the full title of Marseille football club?
2. In which year was the club founded?
3. True or false: Marseille are the only French team to have won the Champions League?
4. What is the most number of consecutive years that the club has won the French league?
5. What is the name of Marseille's stadium, which seats just over 60,000?
6. What does the club's motto, Droit Au But, mean?
7. Which successful former Belgian star started the 2008–9 season as Marseille manager?
8. Who captained the 1992–3 side to European Cup glory?
9. Which former Uruguayan national wowed the Marseille crowds during the 1980s and early 1990s?
10. True or false: Fabien Barthez became the youngest goalkeeper to win the European Cup when Marseille lifted the trophy in 1992–3?
11. Why did Marseille fail to play even one game in defence of their European Cup title?
12. In what year did the side return to France's Division 1?
13. Which famous German World Cup winner has managed the side?
14. Which Republic of Ireland international had a spell upfront for Marseille?
15. Which two regulars in Bobby Robson's England team played for Marseille in the 1980s?

1. Olympique de Marseille 2. 1899 3. True (1993) 4. Four (1989-1992) 5. Stade Vélodrome 6. Straight to the Goal 7. Eric Gerets 8. Didier Deschamps 9. Enzo Francescoli 10. True (Deschamps was also the youngest captain) 11. They were demoted in the French league and thrown out of the tournament due to 'financial irregularities' and a match-fixing scandal 12. 1996 13. Franz Beckenbauer 14. Tony Cascarino 15. Trevor Steven and Chris Waddle.

Olympiakos

1. When was the club founded (clue – it is written on the club logo)?
2. In which city is the club based?
3. Olympiakos is a sports club for 17 different sports, but which sport was it originally started for?
4. What colours are the club's usual home kit?
5. Which decade was the club's most successful in terms of Greek Super League titles?
6. In what other two decades did they win five or more Greek league titles?
7. True or false: the club have never won a major European trophy?
8. When did Olympiakos win their first league title?
9. Who was the manager at the beginning of the 2008–9 season?
10. A line-up of five brothers in attack brought the club notoriety and success in the 1930s. What was the family name?
11. Where do the team play?
12. What is the club's best performance in the Champions League?
13. For how many years after their debut did Olympiakos fail to win an away game in the Champions League?
14. Who were the first team they beat away from home in the Champions League?
15. Which former World Player of the Year plied his trade for Olympiakos?

1. 1925 2. Piraeus, Athens 3. Football 4. Red and white 5. The Noughties (they won eight up to 2008) 6. 1930s and 1950s 7. True 8. 1930–1 9. Ernesto Valverde 10. Andrianopoulos 11. The Karaiskakis Stadium (named after Georgios Karaiskakis, hero of the Greek War of Independence) 12. Quarter-finals (1998–9) 13. 10 years 14. Werder Bremen (2007–8) 15. Rivaldo.

PSV Eindhoven

1. What does PSV stand for?
2. How many Dutch teams, including PSV of course, have won the European Cup?
3. Who did PSV defeat in the 1988 European Cup Final?
4. What is the team's nickname in Holland?
5. Which famous manager led the team to their first European Cup in 1988?
6. Which legendary Dutch goalkeeper saved a penalty to win the 1988 European Cup?
7. What was unusual about PSV's European Cup run?
8. Which Englishman took over from Guus Hiddink as coach?
9. In 2002, which manager helped PSV reclaim the Dutch title?
10. How many of the four Dutch League titles did PSV win between 2004 and 2008?
11. True or false: Bobby Robson was fired for underperforming in Europe despite winning the Dutch League twice in his first two years (1990–1 and 1991–2)?
12. True or false: Hans Westerhof, who replaced Robson, won the league in his first season?
13. What is unique about PSV's shirt sponsor?
14. Who did the club beat in the 1978 UEFA Cup Final?
15. When PSV won the European Cup in 1988, whose title did they inherit?

1. Philips Sport Vereniging (Philips Sports Union) 2. Three (Ajax, PSV and Feyenoord) 3. Benfica 4. Boeren (Farmers or Peasants) 5. Guus Hiddink 6. Hans van Breukelen 7. They didn't actually win any of their final five fixtures (all were won on away goals and penalties) 8. Bobby Robson 9. Guus Hiddink 10. All four 11. True 12. False. Hans Westerhof's team came second 13. It has never changed. It has been Philips since the first year, 1982 14. SC Bastia 15. FC Porto.

Real Madrid

1. True or false: Real Madrid is an older club than Barca?
2. What is the full name of Real's famous stadium?
3. What unique and prestigious title did FIFA award the club in 2000?
4. After which group of nomadic warriors and which crusty dessert does the club get its nicknames?
5. True or false: when Real won La Liga in 1931–2 they were the second team to do so?
6. What was the name of the club's first proper ground?
7. In what year was the club granted a royal seal by the King of Spain?
8. Between 1950 and 1960, how many consecutive European Cups did Real Madrid put together?
9. During the 1980s, Madrid re-established national dominance with the help of a group of five star players known as 'La Quinta del Buitre'. From which member did the name derive?
10. Name two of the other four players that made up 'La Quinta del Buitre'?
11. The club has its own anthem. What is it called?
12. The team badge contains a Royal Crown to symbolize the royal seal. But what does the dark band represent?
13. At the beginning of 2008–9, which goalkeeper held the record for the most games played for Real?
14. Who is the club's all-time top scorer?
15. How many La Liga titles had Real won up to and including 2007–8?

1. False. They were founded three years later, in 1902 2. Santiago Bernabéu Stadium (named after a former President) 3. The Best Club of the 20th Century 4. Los Vikingos (The Vikings); Los Merengues (The Meringues) 5. False. Barca won the first, Athletic Bilbao won the second and third. Real won the fourth. 6. Campo de Rose 7. 1920 8. Five, 1955–60 9. Emilio Butragueño 10. Manolo Sanchís, Martín Vázquez, Míchel and Miguel Pardeza 11. 'Himno del Real Madrid' 12. It is the band of the Region of Castile 13. Iker Casillas 14. Alfredo Di Stefano, with 307 goals 15. 31.

Roma

1. How many times did Roma win Serie A prior to their win in the 2000–1 season?
2. Who beat Roma on penalties in the Champions League Final in 1984?
3. What is the name of the club's stadium?
4. Roma had five managers between the time Fabio Capello left in 2004 and the end of the 2005–6 season. Name one of them.
5. Four Englishmen have managed Roma. Name one of them.
6. Who captained Roma at the start of the 2007–8 season?
7. Which famous Brazilian wore the now retired Number 6 shirt?
8. Which future England manager coached the side between 1984 and 1986?
9. In March 2008, the club record for appearances was held by whom?
10. The same player holds the record for Serie A appearances. But whose record did he beat?
11. Who is the club's all–time leading scorer?
12. Which fashion label was Roma's first shirt sponsor in 1970–1?
13. How is the local derby between Roma and Lazio known?
14. Up to and including 2007–8, how many Serie A titles had Roma won?
15. How many Serie B titles have the club won?

1. Two: 1941–2 and 1982–3 2. Liverpool 3. Stadio Olimpico 4. Cesare Prandelli, Rudi Völler, Luigi Del Neri, Bruno Conti, Luciano Spalletti 5. William Garbutt, Herbert Burgess, Jesse Carver, Alec Stock 6. Francesco Totti 7. Aldair, centre-back, 1990–2003 8. Sven-Göran Eriksson 9. Francesco Totti (496) 10. Giacomo Losi 11. Francesco Totti (165 goals by the end of 2007–8; he is also leading Serie A scorer) 12. Lacoste 13. Derby della Capitale 14. Three (1941–2; 1982–3; 2000–01) 15. One (1951–2).

Rosenborg

1. The club's full title is Rosenborg BK. What does BK stand for?
2. In which city are the club based?
3. True or false: Rosenborg's run of 13 consecutive League titles up until 2005 was the longest ever in world football?
4. What strange word gave its name to Rosenborg when the club was first founded?
5. In what year was the club founded?
6. Since 1957 the club has played in which stadium?
7. What is the team's nickname?
8. In what year did Rosenborg first qualify for the Champions League?
9. Before 2004, Rosenborg had a proud Champions League record. What was it?
10. Which Italian giants did Rosenborg beat away from home to progress to the Champions League quarter-finals in 1996–7?
11. Which former Rosenborg Championship winner attracted the attention of Liverpool in 1994?
12. Which former player won the Spanish League and lost in a Champions League Final with Valencia?
13. Against whom did Rosenborg record their then highest victory (10–0), in 1996?
14. Who scored a record 30 goals for the club in the 1968–9 season?
15. In the same season, the same player scored a club-record number of goals in one game. How many?

1. Ballklub 2. Trondheim 3. False. Skonto Riga of Latvia achieved 14 consecutive titles that same year 4. The team was called 'Odd' 5. 1917 6. Lerkendal Stadion 7. Troillongan (The Troll Kids or The Rascals in local dialect) 8. 1995 9. They qualified for eight consecutive tournaments, a record that Manchester United broke in 2004 10. AC Milan 11. Stig Inge Bjørnebye 12. John Alieu Carew 13. SK Brann 14. Odd Iversen 15. Six, against Vålerenga IF Fotbal.

Sporting Lisbon

1. Sporting Lisbon is not the team's official name. What should it be?
2. Which club is Sporting's main rival in the local derby?
3. From which mammal, depicted on the team badge, do the club derive their nickname?
4. In which year was Sporting founded?
5. Sporting play their games at which stadium?
6. Who started the 2008–9 season as Sporting manager?
7. Prior to 2008–9, how many league titles had the club won?
8. Name two players, trained in the Sporting academy, that went on to win the Champions League with Manchester United in 2007–8.
9. Name two of the six British coaches that have managed Sporting.
10. Which famous player and coach of Sporting had both Spanish and Argentine nationality during his life?
11. When did Sporting win their first league title?
12. Who beat Sporting in the final of the 2004–5 UEFA Cup?
13. What colour normally dominates the Sporting away kit?
14. Which is the only European trophy that the Lions have won?
15. Which former manager of Sporting went on to manage the Welsh national team?

1. Sporting Clube de Portugal 2. Benfica 3. Leões (Lions) 4. 1906 5. Estádio José Alvalade 6. Paulo Bento 7. Eighteen 8. Cristiano Ronaldo and Nani 9. Malcolm Allison, Keith Burkinshaw, Sir Bobby Robson, Randolph Galloway, Jimmy Hagan, John Toshack 10. Alfredo Di Stefano 11. 1941 12. CSKA Moscow 13. Black 14. The Cup Winners' Cup, 1964 15. John Toshack.

Valencia

1. In which two years did Valencia lose in the Champions League Final?
2. Which Spanish side beat them in their first final?
3. True or false: Valencia's nickname, 'Los Che' comes from the club's close association with the Argentine Revolutionary?
4. Valencia expect to move to a new stadium in 2009, but where have they been playing in the meantime?
5. Who was the first Valencia player to be picked to play for Spain?
6. Which Scottish team were invited to Valencia's brand-new stadium in 1923 and beat the home team two days in a row?
7. What was the first national trophy that Valencia won?
8. Before the new millenium Valencia hadn't won La Liga since 1970–1. Which inspirational legend built that successful team?
9. Which Valencian superstar was integral to the 1978 World Cup-winning Argentina side?
10. Who did Valencia beat when they became the first Spanish team to win the European Super Cup in 1981?
11. In which year did poor performances and massive debts culminate in relegation for the club?
12. What was Mario Kempes' nickname?
13. Which two English teams did Valencia beat in the quarter-finals and semi-finals of the 2000–1 Champions League?
14. Which mammal appears on the team badge and is closely associated with both the club and their region of Spain?
15. Who missed a penalty in the shoot-out against Bayern Munich when Valencia finished runners-up in the Champions League?

1. 2000 and 2001 2. Real Madrid 3. False. It is a common multipurpose term used in the local dialect. 4. Estadio Mestalla 5. Eduardo Cubells 6. Dundee United 7. The 1941 Copa del Rey, versus Español 8. Alfredo Di Stefano 9. Mario Kempes 10. Nottingham Forest 11. 1986 12. The Matador 13. Arsenal and Leeds United 14. A bat 15. Mauricio Pellegrino.

Werder Bremen

1. True or false: the Nazis branded Bremen the 'Jew's Club' and forced both the president and coach out of the country?
2. True or false: Bremen is an older club than Bayern Munich?
3. True or false: Bremen was set up by a group of students?
4. When translated, the word 'Werder's' meaning is the same as a British high street clothing store's name. Which one?
5. What does the SV stand for in the team name, SV Werder Bremen?
6. How many league titles had the side won up to and including 2007–8?
7. True or false: Bremen have never won a European honour?
8. Which German and one–time Bremen striker won the 2006 World Cup's Golden Boot Award?
9. Which of the club's former potent strikers was sent off during a World Cup for a now infamous spitting incident?
10. Which Japanese international made a major contribution to Bremen's successful 1970s side?
11. True or false: Bremen conceded the Bundesliga's first–ever goal?
12. Which French side crushed Bremen 10–2 on aggregate in the 2004–5 Champions League?
13. Which little–known Serbian side did Bremen beat to win the Intertoto Cup in 1998?
14. True or false: when Bremen defeated Monaco in the 1991–2 Cup Winners' Cup Final, both sides were first–time finalists?
15. Which Canadian represented Bremen for seven years, before playing right–back for Tottenham Hotspur?

1. False. It was Bayern Munich who suffered this fate 2. True. It was founded one year earlier in 1899 as Fußballverein Werder 3. True. Sixteen vocational high school students won a prize of sports equipment which they put to good use 4. River Island 5. Sportverein 6. Four (1964–5, 1987–8, 1992–3, 2003–4) 7. False. They won the Cup Winners' Cup in 1991–2 and the Intertoto Cup in 1997–8 8. Miroslav Klose 9. Rudi Völler 10. Yasuhiko Okudera 11. True. Against Borussia Dortmund 12. Olympique Lyonnais 13. FK Vojvodina 14. True 15. Paul Stalteri.

Back to the Sixties

Quiz 1

1. In which year did Brian Kidd make his debut for Manchester United?
2. How many teams in the Premier League in 2001–2 were in Division Two in 1960–1?
3. Which 2003–4 Premier League side, based in the North East, were relegated from Division Two in 1965–6?
4. Which Nottinghamshire-based side didn't lose a home game in Division Three in 1963–4?
5. Which London team finished third in Division One in 1961–2?
6. Which Cheshire-based club won only once away from home in Division Three in 1963–4?
7. Which team won only one away game in Division One in 1961–2?
8. Who in 1964 became QPR's youngest-ever league player?
9. In which year did Torquay United draw eight league games in a row?
10. Who scored 37 goals for Tottenham Hotspur in the 1962–3 league season?
11. In which season did West Ham United draw five league games in a row?
12. In which season did York City win seven league games in a row?
13. In which year did Fulham's run of 11 league defeats in a row end?
14. Who, in September 1965, became Leyton Orient's youngest-ever player in a league game?
15. Which year saw a sequence of seven league wins for Colchester United end?

1. 1967 2. Eight 3. Middlesbrough 4. Mansfield Town 5. Tottenham Hotspur 6. Crewe Alexandra 7. Nottingham Forest 8. Frank Sibley 9. 1969 10. Jimmy Greaves 11. 1968–9 12. 1964–5 13. 1962 14. Paul Went 15. 1969.

Quiz 2

1. Which team won Division Two in 1962–3 by one point from Chelsea?
2. Which London club finished as runners-up in Division Two in 1961–2?
3. Which team avoided relegation to Division Two by one point in 1960–1?
4. Which pair scored Liverpool's goals in the 2–1 1965 FA Cup Final victory over Leeds United?
5. In which year did Nobby Stiles make his first-team debut for Manchester United?
6. For which team did Howard Kendall play in the 1964 FA Cup Final?
7. Which London-based club didn't lose a home game in Division One in 1964–5?
8. Aston Villa's longest sequence of league defeats was in which year of the 1960s?
9. Who scored 34 league goals for Bradford City in 1961–2?
10. Who replaced Raich Carter as manager of Middlesbrough in 1966?
11. Who was boss of Gillingham when they won the Division Four championship in 1963–4?
12. In which season did Cliff Holton score 36 goals in Division Three for Northampton Town?
13. In which season did York City lose eight league games in a row?
14. Which team lost 5–0 in the 1963–4 Scottish League Cup Final?
15. In which season did Terry Harkin hit 35 league goals for Crewe Alexandra in Division Four?

1. Stoke City 2. Leyton Orient 3. Blackpool 4. Ian St. John and Roger Hunt 5. 1960 6. Preston North End 7. Tottenham Hotspur 8. 1963 9. David Layne 10. Stan Anderson 11. Freddie Cox 12. 1961–2 13. 1966–7 14. Morton 15. 1964–5.

Quiz 3

1. For which club did Ronnie Clayton appear in the 1960 FA Cup Final?
2. Who kept goal for Tottenham Hotspur in the 1967 FA Cup Final?
3. Which two teams, at opposite ends of the country, won only once away from home in Division One in 1967–8?
4. Which team were unbeaten at home in Division Two in 1964–5?
5. Which club from the North West didn't draw at home in Division One in 1963–4?
6. For which team did Don Megson play in the 1966 FA Cup Final?
7. Which 2007 Premier League side finished bottom of Division One in 1965–6?
8. Which Birmingham City player became their manager in 1960?
9. In which year of the 1960s did Bury lose six league games in a row?
10. Who scored five goals for Charlton Athletic against Portsmouth in a 1960 league game?
11. Which team beat Hartlepools United 10–1 in a 1962 Division Four match?
12. Who in 1962 became Leeds United's youngest-ever league player?
13. In which season did Halifax Town have a run of 17 league matches unbeaten?
14. In which year did Luton Town's run of 19 league matches unbeaten end?
15. Against which team in November 1965 did John Toshack become Cardiff City's youngest-ever league player?

1. Blackburn Rovers 2. Pat Jennings 3. Coventry City and Newcastle United 4. Northampton Town 5. Liverpool 6. Sheffield Wednesday 7. Blackburn Rovers 8. Gil Merrick 9. 1967 10. John Summers 11. Wrexham 12. Peter Lorimer 13. 1968–9 14. 1969 15. Leyton Orient.

Quiz 4

1. In which year did Roger Hynd make his debut for Crystal Palace?
2. Which London-based club only won one away game in Division One in 1960–1?
3. Which team finished bottom of Division One in 1961–2?
4. Which club were unbeaten at home in Division Three in 1962–3?
5. Which two London-based teams only won once away from home in Division One in 1964–5?
6. In which year did Cyril Knowles make his debut for Tottenham Hotspur?
7. Which team won only once away from home in Division Two in 1962–3?
8. Who appeared for Aston Villa against Bolton in 1969 aged 15 years and 349 days?
9. In which year of the 1960s did Blackpool remain undefeated in 17 league games in a row?
10. Who, in April 1961, became Manchester City's youngest league player?
11. In which season did Northampton Town win eight league matches in a row?
12. Which Plymouth Argyle player scored five times against Charlton Athletic in a 1960–1 Division Two game?
13. Which club lost 9–2 to Leyton Orient in a 1962–3 League Cup game?
14. In which year did Coventry City win six league games in a row?
15. In which season did Bobby Hunt score 38 goals for Colchester United in Division Four?

1. 1969 2. West Ham United 3. Chelsea 4. Bournemouth & Boscombe 5. Tottenham Hotspur and Fulham 6. 1964 7. Luton Town 8. Jimmy Brown 9. 1968 10. Glyn Pardoe 11. 1960-1 12. Wilf Carter 13. Chester 14. 1964 15. 1961-2.

Quiz 5

1. Which London side were unbeaten at home in Division Three in 1965–6?
2. Which Yorkshire club failed to win away from home in Division Four in 1968–9?
3. Which team, in League One in 2008, were champions of Division Four in 1965–6?
4. Which two teams from the Midlands were relegated from Division One in 1964–5?
5. Which two teams won only once away from home in Division Three in 1962–3?
6. For which club did Bill Slater appear in the 1960 FA Cup Final?
7. Which team didn't win away from home in Division One in 1963–4?
8. In which year did Fred Cox sign Ted McDougall for Bournemouth & Boscombe?
9. In which year were Bradford City beaten 9–1 by Colchester United in Division Four?
10. Which club were Scottish First Division champions for the 1964–5 season?
11. In which season did Grimsby Town draw five league games in a row?
12. In which year did QPR's sequence of 20 games without a league win end?
13. In which season did Mansfield Town get to the sixth round of the FA Cup?
14. Which club did Scunthorpe United beat 8–1 in a 1964–5 Division Three game?
15. Which non-league team did Halifax Town beat 7–0 in a 1967 FA Cup match?

1. Millwall 2. Bradford Park Avenue 3. Doncaster Rovers 4. Wolverhampton Wanderers and Birmingham City 5. Carlisle United and Halifax Town 6. Wolverhampton Wanderers 7. Ipswich Town 8. 1969 9. 1961 10. Kilmarnock 11. 1964–5 12. 1969 13. 1968–9 14. Luton Town 15. Bishop Auckland.

Quiz 6

1. In which year did Ron Davies make his league debut for Southampton?
2. Which Midlands-based team won 17 of their 21 home games in Division One in 1960–1?
3. Which was the highest placed London team in Division One in 1968–9?
4. Which two teams were unbeaten at home in Division Four in 1967–8?
5. Which goalkeeper scored for Tottenham Hotspur against Manchester United in August 1967?
6. Who scored a goal for Leeds United in the 1965 FA Cup Final?
7. Which club finished bottom of Division Four in 1961–2?
8. In which year of the 1960s did Bristol Rovers lose eight league games in a row?
9. Who in 1961 became Notts County's youngest-ever league player?
10. Which team did Oldham Athletic beat 11–0 in a 1962 Division Four game?
11. Who scored 52 goals for Peterborough United in Division Four in 1960–1?
12. In which year did Sheffield Wednesday's run of 19 unbeaten league matches end?
13. Which West Midlands club did Leicester City beat 8–1 in a 1964–5 League Cup game?
14. Which team did Oxford United beat 7–0 in a 1964 Division Four game?
15. In which year of the 1960s did Darlington have a sequence of 17 league matches unbeaten?

1. 1966 2. Wolverhampton Wanderers 3. Arsenal 4. Barnsley and Crewe Alexandra 5. Pat Jennings 6. Billy Bremner 7. Chester 8. 1961 9. Tony Bircumshaw 10. Southport 11. Terry Bly 12. 1961 13. Coventry City 14. Barrow 15. 1968.

Quiz 7

1. In which year did John Boyle make his debut for Chelsea?
2. For which London-based club did Cliff Jones appear in the 1962 FA Cup Final?
3. Which South Coast team only won one away game in Division Two in 1960–1?
4. Which club from the North West didn't lose a home game in Division One in 1962–3?
5. Who scored a hat-trick for Tottenham Hotspur against Blackpool on his debut in 1961?
6. Which team finished bottom of Division Three in 1960–1?
7. In which position did Cardiff City finish in Division One in 1960–1?
8. In which year did Barry Murphy make his league debut for Barnsley?
9. In which year did Leeds United's run of 34 unbeaten league matches end?
10. Who in 1966 became Port Vale's youngest league player?
11. In which season did Mike O'Hara become Luton Town's youngest-ever league player?
12. Which club did Southampton beat 9–3 in Division Two in September 1965?
13. In which season did Shrewsbury Town draw six league games in a row?
14. Which team defeated Darlington 10–0 in Division Four in 1963–4?
15. Who scored five goals for Bury in a league game against Rotherham United in 1965?

1. 1965 2. Tottenham Hotspur 3. Portsmouth 4. Everton 5. Jimmy Greaves 6. Chesterfield 7. 15th 8. 1962 9. 1969 10. Malcolm McKenzie 11. 1960–1 12. Wolverhampton Wanderers 13. 1963–4 14. Doncaster Rovers 15. Ray Pointer.

Quiz 8

1. In which year did George Best make his debut for Manchester United?
2. Which East of England team were unbeaten at home in Division Three in 1968–9?
3. Which club from the North West were unbeaten at home in Division One in 1966–7?
4. Which goalkeeper scored for Leicester City against Southampton in October 1967?
5. Which Yorkshire-based team didn't lose a home game in Division Two in 1963–4?
6. Which club from the North West didn't lose a home game in Division Two in 1961–2?
7. Who kept goal for Leicester City in the 1961 FA Cup Final?
8. In which year of the 1960s did Bradford City remain unbeaten in 21 successive league games?
9. Which English team beat Floriana 10–0 in September 1962 in a European Cup game?
10. In which year of the 1960s did Northampton Town go 18 games without a league win?
11. Who captained Norwich City's League Cup-winning side of 1961–2?
12. In which year did Rochdale win eight league games in a row?
13. In which season of the 1960s did Barrie Thomas score 31 league goals in Division Two for Scunthorpe United?
14. Which team were beaten 8-1 by Coventry City in Division Three in 1963–4?
15. In 1961, which club did Southampton beat 7–1 in the FA Cup?

1. 1963 2. Luton Town 3. Manchester United 4. Peter Shilton 5. Leeds United 6. Liverpool 7. Gordon Banks 8. 1969 9. Ipswich Town 10. 1969 11. Ron Ashman 12. 1969 13. 1961–2 14. Shrewsbury Town 15. Ipswich Town.

Quiz 9

1. Which seaside-team finished bottom of Division One in 1966–7?
2. Which club finished bottom of Division Two in 1963–4?
3. For which First Division club did Anthony Burns play from 1963 to 1966?
4. For which club did Terry Dyson appear in the 1961 FA Cup Final?
5. Which Yorkshire side won only once away from home in Division Three in 1964–5?
6. Which seven teams in Division Four in 1960–1 were no longer in the league for the 2003–4 season?
7. Which club, in League Two in 2008, finished bottom of Division Two in 1960–1?
8. In which year of the 1960s did Arsenal draw six league games in a row?
9. In which season of the 1960s did Plymouth Argyle lose nine league games in a row?
10. In which year of the 1960s did Leyton Orient's sequence of 23 games without a league win end?
11. Which team did Ipswich Town beat 7–0 in a Division Two game in 1964?
12. In which season did Rochdale draw six league games in a row?
13. In which season of the 1960s did Hull City win ten league games in a row?
14. In which year did Southampton go 20 games without a league win?
15. In which year of the 1960s did Brentford beat Wrexham 9–0 in Division Three?

1. Blackpool 2. Scunthorpe United 3. Arsenal 4. Tottenham Hotspur 5. Barnsley 6. Chester, Barrow, Accrington Stanley, Southport, Aldershot, Workington and Bradford Park Avenue 7. Lincoln City 8. 1961 9. 1963–4 10. 1963 11. Portsmouth 12. 1968–9 13. 1965–6 14. 1969 15. 1963.

Quiz 10

1. Which team finished bottom of Division Three in 1963–4?
2. In which year did Frank McLintock make his debut for Arsenal?
3. Charlie Cooke scored on his debut for Chelsea in 1966. Against which London-based club?
4. For which team, based in the North West, did Tony Book play in the 1969 FA Cup Final?
5. Which two teams failed to win away from home in Division One in 1968–9?
6. For which team did Willie Stevenson play from 1962 to 1967?
7. Which team from the North West were unbeaten at home in Division Two in 1965–6?
8. Which club did Brighton & Hove Albion beat 10–1 in the 1965–6 FA Cup?
9. Who was manager of Nottingham Forest from 1960 to 1963?
10. In which year did Rotherham United draw six league games in a row?
11. Who scored five league goals for Fulham against Halifax Town in a Division Three match in 1969?
12. For which team did Phil O'Connor play on Boxing Day 1969 at the age of 16 years and 76 days?
13. Which player won a cap for the Republic of Ireland while at Exeter City in the 1960s?
14. In which year of the 1960s did Scunthorpe United win six league games in a row?
15. Who in 1966 became Everton's youngest league player?

1. Notts County 2. 1964 3. West Ham United 4. Manchester City 5. Stoke City and QPR 6. Liverpool 7. Manchester City 8. Wisbech 9. Andy Beattie 10. 1969 11. Steve Earle 12. Southend United 13. Dermot Curtis 14. 1969 15. Joe Royle.

Quiz 11

1. Which coastal side won only once away from home in Division Two in 1964–5?
2. Which two teams were beaten only once at home in Division Two in 1968–9?
3. In which year did Phil Beal make his debut for Tottenham Hotspur?
4. For which club did David Herd play in the 1963 FA Cup Final?
5. Who kept goal for Chelsea in the 1967 FA Cup Final?
6. For which club did Frank McLintock play in the 1963 FA Cup Final?
7. Which two South Eastern teams were unbeaten at home in Division Four in 1964–5?
8. Who was manager of Arsenal from 1962 to 1966?
9. In which year of the 1960s did Plymouth Argyle go 13 games without a league win?
10. In which season did Hartlepool United win seven league games in a row?
11. Who in 1969 became the youngest player for Stockport County in a league fixture?
12. In which season did Roger Hunt score 41 league goals for Liverpool?
13. In which year of the 1960s did Derby County have a sequence of 22 unbeaten league matches?
14. In which season did Sheffield United win eight league games in a row?
15. In which season did Bristol City beat Chichester City 11–0 in the FA Cup?

1. Portsmouth 2. Middlesbrough and Derby County 3. 1963 4. Manchester United 5. Peter Bonetti 6. Leicester City 7. Millwall and Brighton & Hove Albion 8. Billy Wright 9. 1963 10. 1967–8 11. Jimmy Collier 12. 1961–2 13. 1969 14. 1960–1 15. 1960–1.

Quiz 12

1. Who scored the winning goal for West Ham United in the 1964 FA Cup Final?
2. For which club did Tommy Cummings appear in the 1962 FA Cup Final?
3. Which was the highest-placed London team in Division One in 1965–6?
4. Which Midlands team finished second-bottom in Division Four in 1962–3?
5. For which team did Ernie Machin play from 1962 to 1972?
6. Which South East club didn't lose a home game in Division Four in 1963–4?
7. Which team from the London area did Blackpool beat 7–1 in the 1963–4 League Cup?
8. Which year saw a sequence of 25 unbeaten league matches end for Coventry City?
9. Which team beat Plymouth Argyle 9–0 in a December 1960 Division Two match?
10. In which season did QPR lose nine league games in a row?
11. In which season did Ipswich Town go 21 games without a single league win?
12. In which year did Tottenham Hotspur win 13 league games in a row?
13. In which season did Halifax Town win seven league games in a row?
14. Which Norwegian team did Leeds United beat 10–0 in a 1969 European Cup game?
15. Which club defeated Crewe Alexandra 13–2 in February 1960 in an FA Cup replay?

1. Ronnie Boyce 2. Burnley 3. Chelsea 4. Bradford City 5. Coventry City 6. Gillingham 7. Charlton Athletic 8. 1967 9. Stoke City 10. 1968–9 11. 1963–4 12. 1960 13. 1964 14. Lyn 15. Tottenham Hotspur.

Quiz 13

1. For which team did Len Glover play in the 1969 FA Cup Final?
2. Which Welsh side were unbeaten at home in Division Four in 1966–7?
3. Which was the highest placed London team in Division One in 1963–4?
4. How many teams in the Premier League in 2003–4 were in Division Three in 1960–1?
5. For which club did Tony Hateley play in 1967–8?
6. For which team did Bobby Hope play in the 1968 FA Cup Final?
7. Which London-based team lost only one home game in Division Three in 1964–5?
8. In which year of the 1960s did Blackburn Rovers lose seven league games in a row?
9. Who in 1967 became Chelsea's youngest league player when he appeared against Spurs aged 16 years and 138 days?
10. In which season did Luton Town go 16 games without a league win?
11. Which non-league team from Northamptonshire did Plymouth Argyle beat 6–0 in the 1965–6 FA Cup?
12. Which North West-based team defeated QPR 8–1 in Division One in 1969?
13. In which year did Phil Hoadley become Crystal Palace's youngest-ever league player?
14. Which Lancashire-based club beat West Ham United 8–2 in Division One on Boxing Day 1963?
15. In which year did Colchester United play 20 league games without winning?

1. Leicester City 2. Wrexham 3. Tottenham Hotspur 4. None 5. Liverpool 6. West Bromwich Albion 7. Brentford 8. 1966 9. Ian Hamilton 10. 1964–5 11. Corby Town 12. Manchester United 13. 1968 14. Blackburn Rovers 15. 1968.

Quiz 14

1. For which team did Ray Wilson play in the 1966 FA Cup Final?
2. Against which Midlands team did Denis Law score on his Manchester United debut in 1962?
3. Which Yorkshire side were unbeaten at home in Division One in 1968–9?
4. Which two teams were relegated from Division Two in 1964–5?
5. Which club scored 109 goals in Division Three in 1962–3?
6. Who kept goal for Everton in the 1968 FA Cup Final?
7. Which London-based team won away from home 11 times in Division One in 1965–6?
8. In which year did Peterborough United's run of 17 unbeaten league matches come to an end?
9. For which club did Geoff Morris became the youngest league player in September 1965?
10. Who scored six goals for West Ham United against Sunderland in a 1968–9 Division One game?
11. Who in 1966 became the youngest-ever league player for Hartlepool United?
12. In which season did Wrexham remain unbeaten for 16 league matches in a row?
13. In which year did Crystal Palace go 20 matches without a single league win?
14. Who in 1964 became the youngest-ever league player for Sunderland?
15. In which year did Bury remain unbeaten in 18 league games in a row?

1. Everton 2. West Bromwich Albion 3. Leeds United 4. Swindon Town and Swansea City 5. Northampton Town 6. Gordon West 7. Chelsea 8. 1961 9. Walsall 10. Geoff Hurst 11. John McGovern 12. 1966–7 13. 1962 14. Derek Forster 15. 1961.

Quiz 15

1. Which team, in League One in 2008, didn't draw at home in Division Three in 1961–2?
2. Which club, no longer in existence, won away from home only once in Division Four in 1967–8?
3. How many teams finished on 39 points in Division Two in 1961–2?
4. Which London-based team won 16 of their 21 away games in Division One in 1960–1?
5. For which team did Allan Clarke play from 1966 to 1968?
6. Which West Midlands club didn't lose a home game in Division Three in 1960–1?
7. Which two teams only lost once at home in Division One in 1962–3?
8. Which team defeated QPR 8–1 in Division Three in 1965?
9. In which year did Crystal Palace have a sequence of 18 unbeaten league matches?
10. Who scored five goals for Torquay United against Newport County in a 1963–4 Division Four league game?
11. Which team beat Sunderland 8–0 in Division One in 1968?
12. Which non-league team did York City beat 6–0 in the 1968–9 FA Cup?
13. In which year did Port Vale have a sequence of 19 unbeaten league matches?
14. Which club did Fulham beat 10–1 in a 1962–3 Division One game?
15. Who scored 41 league goals for Chelsea in 1960–61?

1. Peterborough United 2. Bradford Park Avenue 3. Eight 4. Tottenham Hotspur 5. Fulham 6. Walsall 7. Leicester City and Tottenham Hotspur 8. Mansfield Town 9. 1969 10. Robin Stubbs 11. West Ham United 12. South Shields 13. 1969 14. Ipswich Town 15. Jimmy Greaves.

Back to the Seventies

Quiz 1

1. For which club did Alan Gowling play from 1975 to 1978?
2. Which two teams in the 2007–8 Premier League were relegated from Division Two at the end of the 1970–1 season?
3. Against which club did Alan Curbishley score on his debut for West Ham United in 1975?
4. For which team did the forward Roger Gibbins play from 1976 to 1978?
5. Which London-based team lost only once at home in Division Two in 1972–3?
6. For which London club did Derek Hales play in 1977–8?
7. Which club failed to win away from home in Division Four in 1973–4?
8. For which Midlands team did Ray Graydon play from 1971 to 1977?
9. Which North West team finished as runners-up in Division One in 1976–7 by one point?
10. For which team did the winger Ronnie Goodlass play from 1971 to 1977?
11. For which London club did Peter Eastoe play from 1976 to 1979?
12. Which team lost only once at home in Division One in 1972–3?
13. For which Midlands club did the winger John Connolly play from 1976–8?
14. In which season did Bob Hazell make his debut for Wolverhampton Wanderers?
15. For which Midlands club did the midfielder Leslie Cartwright play from 1970 to 1977?

1. Newcastle United 2. Bolton Wanderers and Blackburn Rovers 3. Newcastle United 4. Norwich City 5. QPR 6. West Ham United 7. Mansfield Town 8. Aston Villa 9. Manchester City 10. Everton 11. QPR 12. Liverpool 13. Birmingham City 14. 1977-8 15. Coventry City.

Quiz 2

1. For which Midlands club did the forward David Cross play from 1973 to 1976?
2. Which was the only team to remain undefeated at home in Division One in 1975–6?
3. In which season did Tony Currie make his debut for Leeds United?
4. Which team from the South West lost only once at home in Division Three in 1971–2?
5. For which Midlands club did the forward John Deehan play from 1975 to 1979?
6. Which club won only once away from home in Division One in 1971–2?
7. In which season did John Gregory make his debut as a player for Aston Villa?
8. Which South East team failed to win away from home in Division Two in 1971–2?
9. Who scored 42 goals for Bournemouth & Boscombe in the 1970–1 league season?
10. In which 1970s season did Blackburn Rovers play 16 league games in a row without winning?
11. How many league games did Cardiff City win away from home in the 1972–3 season?
12. In which year did Jim Bone make his debut for Sheffield United?
13. In which season of the 1970s did Arsenal suffer seven league defeats in a row?
14. Who kept goal for Chelsea in the 1970 FA Cup Final?
15. In which season did Alan Birchenall make his league debut for Leicester City?

1. Coventry City 2. Queens Park Rangers 3. 1976–7 4. Bournemouth & Boscombe 5. Aston Villa 6. Everton 7. 1977–8 8. Watford 9. Ted MacDougall 10. 1978–9 11. None 12. 1973 13. 1976–7 14. Peter Bonetti 15. 1971–2.

Quiz 3

1. Which was the only team to remain undefeated at home in Division Four in 1976–7?
2. For which Midlands club did the forward Alan Green play from 1971 to 1979?
3. For which London club did Jeff Blockley play from 1972 to 1975?
4. For which North West club did Gerry Daly play from 1973 to 1977?
5. Against which Midlands team did Mick Buckley make his debut for Everton in March 1972?
6. Which team from the North West lost only once at home in Division Three in 1972–3?
7. For which club did the midfielder Dave Clements play from 1973 to 1976?
8. For which team did Keith Bertschin play from 1973 to 1977?
9. For which club did striker Wyn Davies make his debut against Derby County in 1972?
10. In which season did John Gorman make his debut for Carlisle United?
11. For which northern club did the defender Bill Green play from 1973 to 1976?
12. How old was Roger Hynd when he made his debut for Birmingham City in 1970?
13. Against which club did Mike Bernard make his league debut for Everton in August 1972?
14. Which team lost only once at home in Division Four in 1971–2?
15. For which team did John Beck play from 1976 to 1978?

1. Bradford City 2. Coventry City 3. Arsenal 4. Manchester United 5. Wolverhampton Wanderers 6. Bolton Wanderers 7. Everton 8. Ipswich Town 9. Manchester United 10. 1970–1 11. Carlisle United 12. 28 13. Norwich City 14. Lincoln City 15. Coventry City.

Quiz 4

1. For which Midlands club did midfielder Alan Campbell play from 1970 to 1976?
2. Which team failed to win away from home in Division Four in 1974–5?
3. Which Midlands club did the forward David Cross join in 1976?
4. For which club did Viv Busby play during the 1976–7 season?
5. In which season did Terry Curran make his debut for Derby County?
6. Which club won only once away from home in Division One in 1973–4?
7. For which team did Danny Bowers play from 1973 to 1979?
8. Against which football club did the midfielder Keith Eddy make his debut for Sheffield United in 1972?
9. Against which team did Brian Greenhoff make his final appearance for Manchester United in 1979?
10. Who was sacked as England manager in 1974?
11. In which season did John Gorman make his debut for Tottenham Hotspur?
12. In which season did the defender Bill Green make his debut for West Ham United?
13. Which was the only team to remain undefeated at home in Division Three in 1970–1?
14. For which Midlands club did the defender Peter Hindley play from 1974 to 1976?
15. Against which club did David Hay make his debut for Chelsea in August 1974?

1. Birmingham City 2. Scunthorpe United 3. West Bromwich Albion 4. Norwich City 5. 1977–8 6. Norwich City 7. Stoke City 8. Birmingham City 9. Wolverhampton Wanderers 10. Alf Ramsey 11. 1976–7 12. 1976–7 13. Preston North End 14. Coventry City 15. Carlisle United

Quiz 5

1. For which London club did John Hollins make his debut in August 1975?
2. Which Welsh team failed to win away from home in Division Two in 1972–3?
3. In which season of the 1970s did Ron Futcher make his debut for Luton Town?
4. In which season did winger Frank Carrodus make his debut for Aston Villa?
5. For which club did the forward Ray Hankin play from 1973 to 1976?
6. How old was Frank Clark when he made his debut for Nottingham Forest in August 1975?
7. For which club did the midfielder Terry Hibbitt play from 1971 to 1975?
8. How old was Terry Cooper when he made his debut for Middlesbrough in March 1975?
9. For which team did the winger Leighton James play his first game in December 1975?
10. Which team won only once away from home in Division One in 1972–3?
11. For which team did Colin Barrett play from 1970 to 1976?
12. Which was the only team to remain undefeated at home in Division Two in 1975–6?
13. For which club did Stewart Barrowclough make more than 200 league appearances between 1970 and 1978?
14. Which two teams remained undefeated at home in Division One in the 1978–9 season?
15. For which team did full-back Manny Andruszewski make more than 80 league appearances between 1973 and 1979?

1. Queens Park Rangers 2. Cardiff City 3. 1974–5 4. 1974–5 5. Burnley 6. 31 7. Newcastle United 8. 30 9. Derby County 10. West Bromwich Albion 11. Manchester City 12. Sunderland 13. Newcastle United 14. Liverpool and Nottingham Forest 15. Southampton.

Quiz 6

1. Which was the only team, based in the North West, to remain undefeated at home in Division One in 1976–7?
2. For which North East club did the forward Paul Cannell play from 1972 to 1978?
3. Which was the only team to remain undefeated at home in Division Four in the 1974–5 season?
4. For which team, based in the North West, did Peter Cormack play from 1972 to 1976?
5. In which season did Archie Gemmill make his debut for Nottingham Forest?
6. For which team did the striker David Geddis play his first game in May 1977?
7. Which Midlands club did the midfielder Terry Hibbitt join in 1975?
8. In which season did forward John Duncan make his debut for Tottenham Hotspur?
9. For which team did Phil Boyer play from 1974 to 1977?
10. In which season did Alan Ball make his league debut for Arsenal?
11. Which team won only once away from home in Division Three in 1973–4?
12. Which was the only team to remain undefeated at home in Division One in 1977–8?
13. In which year of the 1970s did Jim Brogan make his debut for Coventry City?
14. Which three teams were relegated from Division Two in 1976–7? Clue: there were two Uniteds and a side from the South Coast.
15. In which season did midfielder Ralph Coates make his debut for Tottenham Hotspur?

1. Liverpool 2. Newcastle United 3. Mansfield Town 4. Liverpool 5. 1977–8 6. Ipswich Town 7. Birmingham City 8. 1974–5 9. Norwich City 10. 1971–2 11. Rochdale 12. Nottingham Forest 13. 1975 14. Carlisle United, Hereford United and Plymouth Argyle 15. 1971–2.

Quiz 7

1. For which Midlands club did the winger John Farley play from 1974 to 1978?
2. In which season did Terry Curran make his debut for Southampton?
3. How old was the striker Wyn Davies when he made his debut for Manchester City in 1971?
4. Which team finished bottom of the Scottish Premier Division in 1975–6?
5. For which club did the forward David Cross play from 1971 to 1973?
6. In which season of the 1970s did Blackpool play 19 league games in a row without winning?
7. With which team did Martin Chivers start the 1978–9 season?
8. In which season did AFC Bournemouth play 14 league games in a row without winning?
9. Against which team did Stan Bowles play his last game for QPR in 1979?
10. In which season of the 1970s did Bradford City draw six league games in a row?
11. For which London team did Eamonn Bannon make his league debut in February 1979?
12. In which season of the 1970s did Bristol Rovers draw five league games in a row?
13. For which Midlands club did Brian Alderson play from 1975 to 1978?
14. Who in March 1972 became Bury's youngest league player when he took the field against Stockport County?
15. In which season did Stan Harland make his debut for Birmingham City?

1. Wolverhampton Wanderers 2. 1978–9 3. 29 4. St Johnstone 5. Norwich City 6. 1970–1 7. Norwich City 8. 1973–4 9. Wrexham 10. 1975–6 11. Chelsea 12. 1975–6 13. Leicester City 14. Brian Williams 15. 1971–2

Quiz 8

1. Which London team finished next to bottom in Division One in 1974–5?
2. In which season did Alan Foggon make his debut for Middlesbrough?
3. Which team finished bottom of the Scottish Premier League in 1976–7?
4. Against which Midlands team did Archie Gemmill make his debut for Derby County in 1970?
5. For which London club did Don Givens play from 1972 to 1978?
6. In which season did Brighton & Hove Albion go 15 games without a league win?
7. For which club did Welsh international Terry Hennessey play from 1970–3?
8. Which club did Cambridge United beat 6–0 in a league game in September 1971?
9. In which season did Glenn Hoddle make his debut for Tottenham Hotspur?
10. For which team did midfielder Bryan Hamilton play from 1975 to 1977?
11. Which club beat Jeunesse Hautcharage 13–0 in the European Cup-Winners' Cup in September 1971?
12. Against which club did the defender Alex Forsyth make his debut for Manchester United in 1973?
13. In which season did the midfielder David Hunt make his debut for Derby County against Leeds United?
14. In which 1970s season did the forward Billy Jennings make his debut for West Ham United?
15. Which was the only team, based in Yorkshire, to remain undefeated at home in Division One in 1971–2?

1. Chelsea 2. 1972–3 3. Kilmarnock 4. West Bromwich Albion 5. Queens Park Rangers 6. 1972–3 7. Derby County 8. Darlington 9. 1975–6 10. Everton 11. Chelsea 12. Arsenal 13. 1977–8 14. 1974–5 15. Leeds United.

Quiz 9

1. Which three teams were undefeated at home in Division Two in the 1971–2 season?
2. For which London club did Alan Hudson make his debut in 1977?
3. Which team failed to win away from home in Division Three in 1977–8?
4. For which club did the forward John Hawley play from 1978 to 1979?
5. Which club finished third in Division One in 1973–4?
6. In which season did Andy Crawford make his debut for Derby County?
7. Against which team did Brian Greenhoff make his debut for Manchester United in September 1973?
8. Which team finished bottom of the Scottish Premier League in 1978–9?
9. For which Midlands team did Bob Hatton play from 1971 to 1976?
10. How old was Johnny Giles when he made his debut for West Bromwich Albion in 1975?
11. Which team beat Cambridge United 6–0 in a Division Three game in April 1974?
12. Against which country did Aston Villa's John Gidman win his only international cap for England in 1977?
13. In which season of the 1970s did Colchester United draw six league games in a row?
14. For which London club did Peter Eustace play from 1970 to 1972?
15. In which season did the defender Graham Cross make his debut for Brighton & Hove Albion?

1. Birmingham City, Millwall and Norwich City 2. Arsenal 3. Hereford United 4. Leeds United 5. Derby County 6. 1977–8 7. Ipswich Town 8. Motherwell 9. Birmingham City 10. 34 11. Aldershot 12. Luxembourg 13. 1976–7 14. West Ham United 15. 1976–7.

Quiz 10

1. Which team finished sixth in Division One in 1973–4?
2. In which 1970s season did Brighton & Hove Albion suffer 12 league defeats in a row?
3. For which Midlands club did Alan Buckley play during the 1978–9 season?
4. Which two teams failed to win away from home in Division Four in 1976–7?
5. In which season did Keith Coleman make his debut for West Ham United?
6. Which was the only team to remain undefeated at home in Division Three in 1976–7?
7. For which club did Stan Cummins play from 1976–9?
8. In which 1970s season did Cambridge United go 14 league games without losing?
9. Against which club did the forward Roger Davies make his debut for Leicester City in December 1977?
10. For which Midlands club did the midfielder John Craven play from 1973 to 1977?
11. Which team finished 13th in Division One in 1978–9?
12. In which season of the 1970s did Blackpool draw five league games in a row?
13. In which season did striker Trevor Francis make his debut for Birmingham City?
14. In which year did Crewe Alexandra lose ten league games in succession?
15. In which season of the 1970s did Blackburn Rovers draw five league games in a row?

1. Burnley 2. 1972–3 3. Birmingham City 4. Halifax Town and Southport 5. 1973–4 6. Mansfield Town 7. Middlesbrough 8. 1972–3 9. Derby County 10. Coventry City 11. Bristol City 12. 1976–7 13. 1970–1 14. 1979 15. 1975–6.

Quiz 11

1. Which London team finished bottom of Division One in 1976–7?
2. In which season did Steve Daley make his debut for Wolverhampton Wanderers?
3. Which Midlands club finished third in Division One in 1978–9?
4. Who scored 32 goals for Brighton & Hove Albion in Division Three in 1976–7?
5. For which London club did Ron Abbott play from 1971 to 1979?
6. Which two teams were undefeated at home in Division Four in the 1975–6 campaign?
7. For which club did Phil Boersma play from 1975 to 1977?
8. In which 1970s season did Cambridge United win seven league games in a row?
9. For which Midlands club did goalkeeper John Burridge play from 1975 to 1978?
10. Which Irish team did Derby County beat 12–0 in a UEFA Cup game in September 1976?
11. In which season did Martin Dobson make his debut for Everton?
12. Which was the only team to remain undefeated at home in Division Four in the 1977–8 season?
13. In which year of the 1970s did Exeter City win seven league games in a row?
14. Who became Birmingham City's youngest league player when he took the field against Cardiff City in September 1970?
15. Who kept goal for Arsenal in the 1971 FA Cup Final?

1. Tottenham Hotspur 2. 1971-2 3. West Bromwich Albion 4. Peter Ward 5. Queens Park Rangers 6. Lincoln City and Northampton Town 7. Middlesbrough 8. 1976-7 9. Aston Villa 10. Finn Harps 11. 1974-5 12. Aldershot 13. 1977 14. Trevor Francis 15. Bob Wilson.

Quiz 12

1. For which London club did Chris Garland play from 1971 to 1975?
2. Which Yorkshire team failed to win away from home in Division Three in the 1975–6 season?
3. In which season did Bobby Gould make his debut for West Ham United?
4. Which of the Nottingham sides was the only team to remain undefeated at home in Division Four in 1970–1?
5. Against which Merseyside team did the midfielder Bryan Hamilton make his debut for Ipswich Town in August 1971?
6. In which year of the 1970s did Burnley go 24 games without a league win?
7. How old was Gordon Hill when he made his debut for Manchester United in 1975?
8. In which 1970s season did Bristol City lose seven league games in a row?
9. In which season did Geoff Hurst make his debut for Stoke City?
10. Which Midlands team failed to win away from home in Division One in the 1975–6 campaign?
11. For which Midlands club did Jeff Blockley play from 1975 to 1978?
12. For which team did Danis Salman take the field against Watford in November 1975 at the age of 15 years and 243 days?
13. Which club did Barnet beat 6–1 in the 1970–1 FA Cup first round?
14. Who scored in both the 1970 FA Cup Final and the subsequent replay for Leeds United?
15. In which year of the 1970s did Peter Brine make his debut for Middlesbrough?

1. Chelsea 2. Sheffield Wednesday 3. 1973–4 4. Notts County 5. Everton 6. 1979 7. 21 8. 1970–1 9. 1972–3 10. Aston Villa 11. Leicester City 12. Brentford 13. Newport County 14. Mick Jones 15. 1972.

Quiz 13

1. Which was the highest-placed London team in Division One at the end of the 1974–5 season?
2. For which London club did Steve Finnieston play from 1971 to 1978?
3. Which two teams won only once away from home in Division One in 1970–1?
4. In which season did the defender Tony Green make his debut for Newcastle United?
5. For which Midlands club did the midfielder Tommy Craig play from 1978 to 1979?
6. Against which team did the defender Mick Henderson make his debut for Sunderland in 1975?
7. Which riverside team finished bottom of the Scottish Premier Division in 1977–8?
8. Which two giants of the game were undefeated at home in Division One in 1970–1?
9. For which club did the winger John Connolly play from 1972 to 1976?
10. Which club failed to win away from home in Division Two in 1975–6?
11. In which season did Bobby Hope make his debut for Birmingham City?
12. Which Anglian team finished fourth in Division One in 1973–4?
13. In which 1970s season did Bournemouth & Boscombe win seven league games in a row?
14. Who became Bradford City's youngest league player when he took the field against Mansfield Town in April 1970?
15. For which Midlands club did forward Chris Chilton play from 1971 to 1973?

1. Queens Park Rangers 2. Chelsea 3. Blackpool and West Bromwich Albion 4. 1971-2 5. Aston Villa 6. York City 7. Clydebank 8. Arsenal and Liverpool 9. Everton 10. Plymouth Argyle 11. 1972-3 12. Ipswich Town 13. 1970-1 14. Robert Cullingford 15. Coventry City.

Quiz 14

1. Which team failed to win away from home in Division One in the 1976–7 season?
2. In which year did Jim Bone make his debut for Norwich City?
3. Which was the only team to remain undefeated at home in Division Four in 1973–4?
4. In which season did Jimmy Conway make his debut for Manchester City?
5. Against which team did Stan Bowles score for QPR on his debut in 1972?
6. For which club did the goalkeeper Dai Davies play from 1970 to 1977?
7. In which year of the 1970s did Steve Bryant make his debut for Birmingham City?
8. Against which team did Charlie George score on his debut for Derby County in August 1975?
9. In which season did defender Kenny Burns make his debut for Birmingham City?
10. Against which London club did the striker Derek Hales make his debut for Derby County in December 1976?
11. Which North East side lost only once at home in Division Two in 1973–4?
12. Which club failed to win away from home in Division Four in the 1977–8 campaign?
13. In which season did Mick Burns make his debut for Newcastle United?
14. Which team failed to win away from home in Division One in 1978–9?
15. Against which London club did Brian Alderson make his league debut for Coventry City in September 1970?

1. Derby County 2. 1972 3. Peterborough United 4. 1976–7 5. Nottingham Forest 6. Everton 7. 1974 8. Sheffield United 9. 1971–2 10. Arsenal 11. Middlesbrough 12. Rochdale 13. 1974–5 14. Norwich City 15. Chelsea.

Quiz 15

1. For which team did the forward Steve Earle play from 1973 to 1978?
2. Which North West team failed to win away from home in Division Four in 1971–2?
3. In which year of the 1970s did Bristol Rovers' sequence of 32 unbeaten league matches end?
4. Which London club did John Craven leave in 1973?
5. Which club beat Cambridge United 6–0 in a league game in September 1974?
6. Which three teams lost only once at home in Division One in 1973–4?
7. In which season did the defender Steve Harrison make his debut for Blackpool?
8. Who in November 1976 became Fulham's youngest league player when he took the field against Cardiff City?
9. Which North West team failed to win away from home in Division Two in 1974–5?
10. In which season of the 1970s did Gillingham enjoy a run of 20 unbeaten league matches?
11. Who became Grimsby Town's youngest league player when he took the field against Walsall in October 1975?
12. Which London club was the only team to remain undefeated at home in Division Two in 1976–7?
13. Which coastal non-league team lost 11–0 to AFC Bournemouth in the 1971–2 FA Cup first round?
14. In which season did the defender Tommy Carroll make his debut for Birmingham City?
15. Which was the only team to remain undefeated at home in Division Three in the 1978–9 season?

1. Leicester City 2. Chester 3. 1974 4. Crystal Palace 5. Darlington 6. Leeds United, Liverpool and Derby County 7. 1971-2 8. Tony Mahoney 9. Oldham Athletic 10. 1973-4 11. Tony Ford 12. Chelsea 13. Margate 14. 1971-2 15. Shrewsbury Town.

Back to the Eighties

Quiz 1

1. To which team did Dave Beasant transfer from Wimbledon in 1988?
2. Which goalkeeper scored for Watford against Coventry City in January 1984?
3. Who was the top league goalscorer for Millwall in 1988–9?
4. Which London team did Liverpool beat 5–0 at home in the league in the 1988–9 season?
5. Which two teams from the Midlands were relegated from Division 1 in 1985–6?
6. For which team did Dale Jasper play from 1982 to 1986?
7. Which team did Preston North End beat 6–0 at home in Division Three in the 1988–9 season?
8. Which player scored the most league goals for Middlesbrough in 1988–9?
9. For which team did Peter Barnes play from 1981 to 1984?
10. Which team were runners-up in the World Cup in both 1982 and 1986?
11. Which player scored the most league goals for West Ham United in 1988–9?
12. From which club did Viv Anderson move to Manchester United in 1987?
13. Which 2000–1 Premier League team finished 14th in Division Four in 1980–1?
14. For which London team did Steve Walford play from 1983 to 1989?
15. Which team finished bottom of the Scottish Premier League in 1980–1?

1. Newcastle United 2. Steve Sherwood 3. Tony Cascarino 4. Luton Town 5. Birmingham City and West Bromwich Albion 6. Chelsea 7. Chesterfield 8. Bernie Slaven 9. Leeds United 10. W Germany 11. Leroy Rosenior 12. Arsenal 13. Bradford City 14. West Ham United 15. Heart of Midlothian.

Quiz 2

1. Which team did Rotherham United beat 6–0 at home in Division Four in the 1988–9 season?
2. For which team did Martin Allen play from 1983 to 1989?
3. Of the five encounters in the 1988–9 season between Dundee and Dundee United, how many did Dundee United win?
4. To which team did John Hendrie transfer from Bradford City in 1988?
5. Which player scored the most league goals for QPR in 1988–9?
6. Which team finished bottom of the B&Q Scottish League Premier Division in 1988–9?
7. Who started all 38 league games for Southampton in 1988–9?
8. In which year did Pat Jennings make his 100th international appearance?
9. Which was the only team not to lose at home in Division One in 1982–3?
10. To which team did Nigel Gleghorn transfer from Ipswich in 1988?
11. How many England caps did Peter Davenport win in the 1980s?
12. Which Welsh team finished sixth in Division One in 1981–2?
13. Which team finished bottom of Division Four in 1980–1?
14. Clubs from which city finished bottom and next to bottom in Division Two in 1980–1?
15. Which team finished bottom of the Scottish Premier League in 1983–4?

1. Hereford United 2. QPR 3. Five 4. Newcastle United 5. Mark Falco 6. Hamilton Academical 7. Rod Wallace 8. 1983 9. Manchester United 10. Manchester City 11. One 12. Swansea City 13. York City 14. Bristol 15. Motherwell

Quiz 3

1. To the nearest 5000, what was the average league gate in the 1988–9 season at Arsenal?
2. Which team finished bottom of the B&Q Scottish League Second Division in 1988–9?
3. To which team did Jim Leighton transfer from Aberdeen in 1988?
4. Which team beat Chelsea 4–0 in the 1988–9 FA Cup third round?
5. Which two players started all 46 league games for Watford in 1988–9?
6. Who was the highest goalscorer in the league for Wimbledon in 1988–9?
7. In which year did Alan Davies make his debut for Manchester United?
8. For which team did goalkeeper Chris Turner play from 1985 to 1988?
9. For which team did Paul Walsh play from 1984 to 1988?
10. How many games did Stoke City win in Division One in 1984–5?
11. At which two clubs was Terry Fenwick playing when he won 20 England caps during the 1980s?
12. To which team did Imre Varadi transfer from Manchester City in 1988?
13. Which was the only team not to lose at home in Division Four in 1980–1?
14. Which 2008–9 Premier League team finished 18th in Division Two in 1985–6?
15. Against which club did Paul Mariner make his debut for Arsenal in 1984?

1. 35,000 (35,595) 2. Stenhousemuir 3. Manchester United 4. Barnsley 5. Tony Coton and Nigel Gibbs 6. John Fashanu 7. 1982 8. Manchester United 9. Liverpool 10. Three 11. QPR and Tottenham Hotspur 12. Sheffield Wednesday 13. Southend United 14. Sunderland 15. Aston Villa.

Quiz 4

1. Which goalkeeper scored for Coventry City against Sheffield Wednesday in October 1986?
2. Which team did Norwich beat 8–0 in the 1988–9 FA Cup fourth round?
3. Who scored both goals for Liverpool in their 2–1 victory over Wimbledon in the 1988 FA Charity Shield?
4. Clive Allen won five England caps during the 1980s while playing for which two clubs?
5. Which player scored the most league goals for Arsenal in 1988–9?
6. Which team did Luton Town beat 6–1 at home in the league in the 1988–9 season?
7. To which team did Andy Townsend transfer from Southampton in 1988?
8. Which footballer netted the most league goals for Liverpool in 1988–9?
9. For which team did Steve Francis keep goal from 1981 to 1987?
10. For which club did Ian Banks play from 1983 to 1986?
11. Which top-flight side were knocked out of the FA Cup by Brighton & Hove Albion for two successive seasons in the 1980s?
12. Who were the semi-finalists in the 1988–9 SIMOD Cup?
13. Which was the only team not to lose at home in Division Three in 1980–1?
14. Which 'City' finished bottom of Division Three in 1981–2?
15. Which 2008–9 Premier League side finished 16th in Division Two in 1982–3?

1. Steve Ogrizovic 2. Sutton United. 3. John Aldridge 4. QPR and Tottenham Hotspur 5. Alan Smith 6. Southampton 7. Norwich City 8. John Aldridge 9. Chelsea 10. Leicester City 11. Liverpool 12. Crystal Palace, Everton, Nottingham Forest and QPR 13. Rotherham United 14. Chester City 15. Middlesbrough.

Quiz 5

1. Which London team did Chester City beat 7–0 at home in Division Three in the 1988–9 season?
2. Which team finished bottom of the B&Q Scottish League First Division in 1988–9?
3. Which London side was the only team not to win away from home in Division One in 1980–1?
4. By how many points did Everton win the Division One title in 1984–5?
5. Who were the highest placed London team in Division One in 1987–8?
6. For which team did goalkeeper Jim Arnold make his debut in August 1981?
7. For which South Coast team did Ian Baird play in 1987–8?
8. In which year did John Barnes score in England's 2–0 victory over Brazil?
9. Which team did Manchester United beat 4–0 in the 1988–9 FA Cup fourth round?
10. To which team did Peter Jackson transfer from Newcastle United in 1988?
11. For which team did Ken Armstrong play from 1984 to 1986?
12. Which team did Burnley beat 6–0 at home in Division Four in the 1988–9 season?
13. For which London club did Neil Orr play from 1982 to 1987?
14. Which Division Two team won away from home only once in 1981–2?
15. Which team finished bottom of the Scottish Premier League in 1985–6?

1. Fulham 2. Queen of the South 3. Crystal Palace 4. 13 5. QPR 6. Everton 7. Portsmouth 8. 1984 9. Oxford United 10. Bradford City 11. Birmingham City 12. York City 13. West Ham United 14. Shrewsbury Town 15. Clydebank.

Quiz 6

1. In which year did Aiden Butterworth make his debut for Leeds United?
2. What nationality was the 1980s Manchester United player John Sivebaek?
3. To which team did Derek Mountfield transfer from Everton in 1988?
4. Which team knocked Barnsley out of the 1988–9 FA Cup?
5. Who won 14 England caps in the 1980s while with Watford and AC Milan?
6. For which team did Sam Allardyce play in 1983–4?
7. Which rivals finished first and second in Division One in 1986–7?
8. Which team did Leyton Orient beat 8–0 at home in Division Four in the 1988–9 season?
9. From which club did John Barnes move to Liverpool in 1987?
10. Which team knocked Blackburn Rovers out of the 1988–9 FA Cup?
11. Who were the highest placed London team in Division One in 1985–6?
12. Which 2007–8 Championship side finished 17th in Division Two in 1982–3?
13. For which London club did Vladimir Petrovic play in 1982–3?
14. Exeter City failed to win an away game in Division Four in 1986–7. In which position did they finish?
15. In which year did Remi Moses make his debut for Manchester United?

1. 1981 2. Danish 3. Aston Villa 4. Everton 5. Luther Blissett 6. Coventry City 7. Everton and Liverpool 8. Colchester United 9. Watford 10. Brentford 11. West Ham United 12. Charlton Athletic 13. Arsenal 14. 14th 15. 1981.

Quiz 7

1. How many England caps did Sammy Lee win in the 1980s while with Liverpool?
2. Which player scored the most league goals for Tottenham in 1988–9?
3. Which player started all 46 league games for Wolves in 1988–9?
4. Which Italian side signed Joe Jordan from Manchester United in 1981?
5. Which three teams were relegated from Division One in 1982–3?
6. Which was the only team, based in the North West, not to win away from home in Division One in 1986–7?
7. For which team did Ian Allinson play from 1983 to 1987?
8. To which team did Brett Angell transfer from Derby County in 1988?
9. For which team did Paul Canoville play from 1981 to 1986?
10. Who scored the winning goal for Spurs against QPR in the 1982 FA Cup Final replay?
11. How many England caps did Mike Duxbury win in the 1980s?
12. Which team knocked Sheffield United out of the 1988–9 FA Cup?
13. For which Division One club did Paul Wilkinson play from 1985 to 19877?
14. Which 2003–4 Premier League side finished bottom of Division Two in 1982–3?
15. For which London club did Danny O'Shea play from 1980 to 1984?

1. 14 2. Chris Waddle 3. Andy Thompson 4. AC Milan 5. Manchester City, Swansea City and Brighton & Hove Albion 6. Manchester City 7. Arsenal 8. Stockport County 9. Chelsea 10. Glenn Hoddle 11. Ten 12. Norwich City 13. Everton 14. Bolton Wanderers 15. Arsenal.

Quiz 8

1. For which North West team did Arthur Graham play from 1983 to 1985?
2. For which team did John Aldridge play from 1984 to 1987?
3. Which rivals finished third and fourth in Division One in 1986–7?
4. What happened after the Scottish Cup Final between Rangers and Celtic in 1980, which the Bhoys won 1–0?
5. Which player started all 46 league games for West Brom in 1988–9?
6. Who was the top league goalscorer for Norwich City in 1988–9?
7. Brighton & Hove Albion's Steve Foster won three England caps in which year?
8. Who were the semi-finalists in the 1988–9 Littlewoods Cup?
9. To which team did Peter Davenport transfer from Manchester United in 1988?
10. Which University town's team finished 18th in Division One in 1986–7?
11. Who was the highest goalscorer in the league for Newcastle United in 1988–9?
12. Midfielder Gordon Cowans gained nine England caps in the 1980s. Which two clubs was he with?
13. Which two teams failed to win an away game in Division Two in 1983–4?
14. Which team finished bottom of the Scottish Premier League in 1982–3?
15. Which 2007–8 London-based Premier League team finished bottom of Division Two in 1985–6?

1. Manchester United 2. Oxford United 3. Tottenham Hotspur and Arsenal 4. After a pitch invasion during which 210 fans were arrested, the sale of alcohol was banned at all Scottish grounds 5. Stacey North 6. Robert Fleck 7. 1982 8. Bristol City, Luton Town, Nottingham Forest and West Ham United 9. Middlesbrough 10. Oxford United 11. Mirandinha 12. Aston Villa and Bari 13. Swansea City and Cambridge United 14. Kilmarnock 15. Fulham.

Quiz 9

1. To which team did Kenny Sansom transfer from Arsenal in 1988?
2. Who scored the fourth goal from the penalty spot for Manchester United in their 4–0 win over Brighton & Hove Albion in the 1983 FA Cup Final replay?
3. For which team did Brian Attley play from 1982 to 1984?
4. Which four teams were relegated from Division One in 1987–8?
5. To which team did Russell Osman transfer from Leicester City in 1988?
6. Which team knocked Hull City out of the 1988–9 FA Cup?
7. Which club was John Gregory playing for when he won six England caps in the 1980s?
8. Who was the top league goalscorer for Nottingham Forest in 1988–9?
9. How many caps did Paul Bracewell win in the 1980s while he was with Everton?
10. Which player scored the most league goals for Everton in 1988–9?
11. Which team scored the fewest goals in Division One in 1983–4?
12. Which was the only team not to lose at home in Division One in 1987–8?
13. Which team failed to win an away game in Division Three in 1983–4?
14. For which Division One club did Peter Reid play from 1982 to 1989?
15. Which seaside Division Four team won away from home only once in 1985–6?

1. Newcastle United 2. Arnold Muhren 3. Derby County 4. Oxford United, Watford, Portsmouth and Chelsea 5. Southampton 6. Liverpool 7. QPR 8. Nigel Clough 9. Three 10. Tony Cottee 11. Wolverhampton Wanderers 12. Liverpool 13. Scunthorpe United 14. Everton 15. Torquay United.

Quiz 10

1. Trevor Francis won England caps in the 1980s while he was with which three clubs?
2. To which team did Wimbledon lose 5–1 at home in the league in the 1988–9 season?
3. Which two players started all 38 league games for Spurs in 1988–9?
4. Which two Premier League teams of 2007–8 were in Barclays Division Three in the 1988–9 season?
5. Which was the highest placed London team in Division One in 1984–5?
6. For which team did Mark Aizlewood play from 1982 to 1987?
7. For which team did John Gidman play from 1981 to 1986?
8. Who won the League Cup in 1986–7?
9. Which team won the English First Division in 1984–5?
10. Who was sacked as manager by Manchester United in 1981 despite winning his last seven games?
11. Which team finished bottom of the Scottish Premier League in 1981–2?
12. For which Division One club did Steve McMahon play from 1979 to 1983?
13. Who kept goal for Manchester City in the 1981 FA Cup Final?
14. Who became manager of Aston Villa in 1982?
15. Who kept goal for Everton in the 1984 FA Cup Final?

1. Nottingham Forest, Manchester City and Sampdoria 2. Arsenal 3. Gary Mabbutt and Chris Waddle 4. Fulham and Bolton Wanderers 5. Tottenham Hotspur 6. Charlton Athletic 7. Manchester United 8. Arsenal 9. Everton 10. Dave Sexton 11. Airdrieonians 12. Everton 13. Joe Corrigan 14. Tony Barton 15. Neville Southall.

Quiz 11

1. For which London club did defender Paul Elliott play from 1981 to 1983?
2. In which year did Arnold Muhren join Manchester United from Ipswich Town?
3. For which team did Ossie Ardiles play in 1988–9?
4. Which millionaire bought Chelsea FC for £1 in 1982?
5. Which team, in the Championship in 2007–8, was the only team not to win away from home in Division One in 1984–5?
6. Which three teams were relegated from Division One in 1981–2?
7. Who became Chairman of Chelsea FC in 1982?
8. Who was the highest goalscorer in the league for Reading in 1988–9?
9. How many England caps did Kerry Dixon win in the 1980s?
10. In which season did Kevin Langley play for Everton?
11. Which 2008–9 Premier League team finished second bottom of Division Two in 1985–6?
12. Which team finished bottom of the Scottish Premier League in 1984–5?
13. For which North East team did Wesley Saunders play from 1981 to 1985?
14. Who kept goal for Everton in the 1986 FA Cup Final?
15. In which year of the 1980s did forward Peter Ward make his debut for Nottingham Forest?

1. Charlton Athletic 2. 1982 3. QPR 4. Ken Bates; he later sold the club to Roman Abramovich for £17m 5 Stoke City 6. Leeds United, Wolverhampton Wanderers and Middlesbrough 7. Ken Bates 8. Trevor Senior 9. Eight 10. 1986–7 11. Middlesbrough 12. Morton 13. Newcastle United 14. Bobby Mimms 15. 1980.

Quiz 12

1. Which giant club from the North West knocked minnows AFC Bournemouth out of the 1988–9 FA Cup?
2. To which London team did Neil Ruddock transfer from Tottenham in 1988?
3. For which team did Paul McGrath play from 1982 to 1989?
4. Against which team did Raddy Antic make his final appearance for Luton Town in 1984?
5. For which team did Doug Rougvie play from 1984 to 1987?
6. Which was the only team, based in London, not to lose at home in Division One in 1980–1?
7. Which team did Northampton Town beat 6–0 at home in Division Three in the 1988–9 season?
8. In which year of the 1980s did Eric Gates win two England caps?
9. The champions of Division Four in 1981–2 didn't lose a single league game at home. They played in the Championship in 2008–9. Who were they?
10. Which 2008–9 Championship team finished 18th in Division Three in 1985–6?
11. Against which Anglian team did Steve Wigley score his first goal for Nottingham Forest in 1984?
12. In which year of the 1980s did Ian Wallace make his debut for Nottingham Forest?
13. For which team did John Wark play from 1984 to 1988?
14. For which club did Jeff Wealands keep goal from 1983 to 1985?
15. For which Scottish club did Maurice Johnston play from 1984 to 1987?

1. Manchester United 2. Millwall 3. Manchester United 4. West Bromwich Albion 5. Chelsea 6. Arsenal 7. Aldershot 8. 1981 9. Sheffield United 10. Bolton Wanderers 11. Ipswich Town 12. 1980 13. Liverpool 14. Manchester United 15. Celtic

Quiz 13

1. Which player scored the most league goals for Aston Villa in 1988–9?
2. Which team knocked Watford out of the 1988–9 FA Cup?
3. To which team did Roy Wegerle transfer from Chelsea in 1988?
4. For which team did Graeme Hogg play from 1982 to 1988?
5. For which team did Warren Aspinall play in the 1987–8 season?
6. In 1980 which record goalscorer was signed by Liverpool?
7. Which future Inter Milan boss managed Bristol City in 1982?
8. Which footballer netted the most league goals for Manchester United in 1988–9?
9. Which 2007–8 Premier League team finished 19th in Division Two in 1985–6?
10. Which was the only team, based in London, not to lose at home in Division Three in 1984–5?
11. Against which London side did Steve Williams make his debut for Arsenal on New Year's Day 1985?
12. Which Top Four 2007–8 Premier League side finished 18th in Division Two in 1982–3?
13. For which club did Nigel Winterburn play from 1983 to 1987?
14. For which club did forward Kevin Wilson play in the 1980s between spells at Derby County and Chelsea?
15. For which Division One club did Ian Wilson play from 1987 to 1989?

1. Alan Mcnally 2. Nottingham Forest 3. Luton Town 4. Manchester United 5. Aston Villa 6. Ian Rush 7. Roy Hodgson 8. Mark Hughes 9. Blackburn Rovers 10. Millwall 11. Tottenham Hotspur 12. Chelsea 13. Wimbledon 14. Ipswich Town 15. Everton.

Quiz 14

1. For which London team did Tommy Caton play from 1983 to 1987?
2. Who was the top league goalscorer for Coventry City in 1988–9?
3. Which team lost 8–0 at home to Celtic in the B&Q Scottish League Premier Division in 1988–9?
4. For which team did Chris Woods keep goal from 1981 to 1986?
5. Which former Arsenal hero was manager of Brentford from 1984 to 1987?
6. Which London team finished fifth in Division One in 1983–4 after winning the second division in 1982–3?
7. For which team did Reuben Agboola play from 1980 to 1985?
8. For which team did George McCluskey play from 1983 to 1986?
9. To which team did Andy Dibble transfer from Luton Town in 1988?
10. Which London team knocked Grimsby Town out of the 1988–9 FA Cup?
11. For which team did Frank Worthington play in 1983–4?
12. Which 2007–8 Premier League team finished third in Division Three in 1985–6?
13. Against which club did Charlie Nicholas make his debut for Arsenal in 1983?
14. Which was the only team not to lose at home in Division Four in 1983–4?
15. For which London team did Darren Wood play from 1984 to 1989?

1. Arsenal 2. David Speedie 3. Hamilton Academical 4. Norwich City 5. Frank McLintock 6. QPR 7. Southampton 8. Leeds United 9. Manchester City 10. Wimbledon 11. Southampton 12. Derby County 13. Luton Town 14. Reading 15. Chelsea.

Quiz 15

1. In which year did John Sheridan make his debut for Leeds United?
2. Which London team had a surprise sixth–place finish in Division One in 1986–7?
3. Which was the only team, based in Wales, not to win away from home in Division One in 1982–3?
4. Which club was managed by Ron Saunders from 1982 to 1986?
5. Which team lost 7–0 at home to Chelsea in Division Two in the 1988–9 season?
6. Which London team knocked Charlton Athletic out of the 1988–9 FA Cup?
7. For which team did David Hodgson play from 1982 to 1984?
8. How many points adrift of Scunthorpe United were Crewe Alexandra in last place in Division Four in 1981–2?
9. Which 'City' finished second bottom of Division Three in 1981–2?
10. For which London club did Mark Ward play from 1985 to 1989?
11. Which team finished bottom of the Scottish Premier League in 1986–7?
12. Which Midlands side were champions of Division Four in 1987–8?
13. Which 2003–4 Premier League team finished 14th in Division Two in 1985–6?
14. For which Midlands club did Romeo Zondervan play from 1982 to 1984?
15. For which English club did Scottish defender Willie Young play from 1981 to 1983?

1. 1982 2. Wimbledon 3. Swansea City 4. Birmingham City 5. Walsall 6. West Ham United 7. Liverpool 8. 15 9. Bristol City 10. West Ham United 11. Hamilton Academical 12. Wolverhampton Wanderers 13. Leeds United 14. West Bromwich Albion 15. Nottingham Forest.

Back to the Nineties

Quiz 1

1. Who was the highest goalscorer in the league for Wolves in 1995–6?
2. Everton's biggest home win in Division One in 1991–2 was 4–0. Against which London team?
3. Which 2008–9 Premier League side avoided relegation from Division One to Division Two in 1992–3 by one point?
4. Which other North West team did Manchester United beat 6–0 away from home in the 1995–6 Premier League?
5. Which 2003–4 Premier League player scored 19 goals for Crewe Alexandra in all competitions in 1991–2?
6. Which London side knocked QPR out of the 1995–6 FA Cup?
7. Which club had the highest gate in the Premier League in 1994–5?
8. Who was the top goalscorer in the league for QPR in 1993–4?
9. Swindon Town lost 5–0 at home twice in the Premier League in 1993–4. To which clubs?
10. Which club had the highest gate in Division Three in 1994–5?
11. Lee Makel joined Blackburn Rovers in July 1992. Which club did he leave to join them?
12. From which club did Imre Varadi join Rotherham United in March 1993?
13. Which Midlands club finished 19th in the GM Vauxhall Conference in 1991–2?
14. Who were the semi-finalists in the 1993–4 League Cup?
15. Who was the league's top goalscorer for Leicester City in 1993–4?

1. Don Goodman 2. West Ham United 3. Sunderland 4. Bolton Wanderers 5. Craig Hignett 6. Chelsea 7. Manchester United 8. Les Ferdinand 9. Leeds United and Liverpool 10. Carlisle United 11. Newcastle United 12. Leeds United 13. Kidderminster Harriers 14. Aston Villa, Manchester United, Sheffield Wednesday and Tranmere Rovers 15. Iwan Roberts.

Quiz 2

1. From which London club did Lee Chapman join Ipswich Town in January 1995?
2. Who came top of the goalscorers' league for Luton Town in 1993–4?
3. Which side surprised Everton by knocking them out of the 1995–6 FA Cup?
4. Who was the top goalscorer in the league for Millwall in 1993–4?
5. From which club did Graeme Le Saux join Blackburn Rovers in March 1993?
6. Who scored the most goals in the league for Sheffield United in 1994–5?
7. To which Yorkshire-based team did Sheffield Wednesday lose 6–1 at home in Division One in 1991–2?
8. Who netted the most goals in the league for Barnsley in 1995–6?
9. Which 2008–9 Championship team finished runner-up in Division One in 1995–6?
10. How many home games did Everton lose in the Premier League in 1996–7?
11. Which 2008–9 Championship side finished fourth in Division One in 1996–7?
12. Which South Coast team knocked Reading out of the 1996–7 FA Cup?
13. Who were the semi-finalists in the 1995–6 League Cup?
14. Who was the top goalscorer in the league for Liverpool in 1993–4?
15. Which London side beat Brentford in the 1995–6 FA Cup?

1. West Ham United 2. Kerry Dixon 3. Port Vale 4. Alex Rae 5. Chelsea 6. Nathan Blake 7. Leeds United 8. Andy Payton 9. Derby County 10. Eight 11. Ipswich Town 12. Portsmouth 13. Arsenal, Aston Villa, Birmingham City and Leeds United 14. Ian Rush 15. Charlton Athletic

Quiz 3

1. Which team lost 5–0 at home to Birmingham City in Division One in 1995–6?
2. Which North West side put Coventry City out of the 1995–6 FA Cup?
3. Which team finished runner-up in Division Two in 1996–7?
4. Which club had the lowest gate in the Premier League in 1993–4?
5. Who netted the most goals for Everton in 1993–4?
6. From which club did Iain Dowie join Crystal Palace in January 1995?
7. Mark Bright was the top league goalscorer for which team in 1993–4?
8. Which player started all 42 Premier League matches for Manchester City in 1992–3?
9. Who did Blackburn Rovers beat 7–1 at home in the 1992–3 Premier League?
10. Paul Bracewell left Sunderland in June 1995. Which club did he join?
11. From which club did Dean Kerslake join Leeds United in March 1993?
12. Who was the top goalscorer in the league for Tranmere Rovers in 1994–5?
13. Who bagged the most goals for Norwich City in 1994–5?
14. How many times did Luton Town score more than twice in a game in Division One in 1991–2?
15. Which North East team finished runner-up in the Premier League in 1995–6?

1. Barnsley 2. Manchester City 3. Stockport County 4. Wimbledon 5. Tony Cottee 6. Southampton 7. Sheffield Wednesday 8. David White 9. Norwich City 10. Newcastle United 11. Swindon Town 12. John Aldridge 13. Ashley Ward 14. None 15. Newcastle United.

Quiz 4

1. Who was the top goalscorer in the league for Stoke City in 1994–5?
2. How many home games did West Bromwich Albion lose in Division One in 1996–7?
3. Aston Villa were put out of the 1996–7 FA Cup by which team?
4. Who was Chelsea's leading goal scorer in the league in 1996–7?
5. Which London team knocked Barnsley out of the 1996–7 FA Cup?
6. Who did Blackburn Rovers beat 7–0 at home in the 1995–6 Premier League?
7. Which London side knocked Middlesbrough out of the 1995–6 FA Cup?
8. Who was the top goalscorer in the league for Wolves in 1996–7?
9. Which club had the lowest gate in Division Two in 1993–4?
10. Who was the top goalscorer in the league for Leeds United in 1993–4?
11. From which club did 6ft 7in striker Kevin Francis join Birmingham City in January 1995?
12. Which four players started all 42 Premier League matches for Aston Villa in 1992–3?
13. Which three teams were relegated from the Premier League in 1992–3?
14. From which club did Robert Fleck join Chelsea in August 1992?
15. Who was the top goalscorer in the league for Chelsea in 1994–5?

1. Paul Peschisolido 2. Nine 3. Derby County 4. Gianluca Vialli 5. QPR 6. Nottingham Forest 7. Wimbledon 8. Steve Bull 9. Hartlepool United 10. Rod Wallace 11. Stockport County 12. Earl Barrett, Paul McGrath, Kevin Richardson and Steve Staunton 13. Crystal Palace, Middlesbrough and Nottingham Forest 14. Norwich City 15. John Spencer.

Quiz 5

1. Which North West team finished bottom of the Premier League in 1995–6?
2. Who was the top goalscorer in the league for Derby County in 1994–5?
3. West Ham United's biggest home win in the First Division in 1991–2 was 4–0. Against which team?
4. Who scored the only goal for Scotland in their 1–0 win over the USA in May 1992?
5. Which England players scored the goals that beat Mexico 2–0 in a friendly in March 1997?
6. Which Welsh team knocked Peterborough United out of the 1996–7 FA Cup?
7. Who were the semi-finalists in the 1991–2 League Cup?
8. Which Yorkshire team knocked Arsenal out of the 1996–7 FA Cup?
9. Which 2008–9 Championship side finished 15th in Division One in 1996–7?
10. Who scored the only goal for Scotland in their 1–0 win over Northern Ireland in February 1992?
11. Aston Villa's biggest home win in Division One in 1991–2 was 4–0. Against which team?
12. Who was the top goalscorer in the league for Derby County in 1995–6?
13. Who was the top goalscorer in the league for Tottenham Hotspur in 1994–5?
14. From which club did Simon Garner join West Bromwich Albion in August 1992?
15. Who was the top Division Three goalscorer in 1992–3?

1. Bolton Wanderers 2. Marco Gabbiadini 3. Norwich City 4. Pat Nevin 5. Teddy Sheringham and Robbie Fowler 6. Wrexham 7. Manchester United, Middlesbrough, Nottingham Forest and Tottenham Hotspur 8. Leeds United 9. Charlton Athletic 10. Ally McCoist 11. Luton Town 12. Dean Sturridge 13. Jürgen Klinsmann 14. Blackburn Rovers 15. Darren Foreman of Scarborough.

Quiz 6

1. Which local lad started all 46 Division One games for Newcastle United in 1992–3?
2. From which London club did Jason Cundy join Spurs in 1992?
3. Who was the top goalscorer in the league for Bristol Rovers in 1995–6?
4. How many home games did Manchester United lose in the Premier League in 1996–7?
5. Who did Liverpool beat 6–0 at home in the 1995–6 Premier League?
6. Which side knocked Oxford United out of the 1995–6 FA Cup?
7. Who was the top goalscorer in the league for Wimbledon in 1996–7?
8. Who was the top goalscorer in the league for Aston Villa in 1993–4?
9. What was Swindon Town's goal difference in the 1993–4 season?
10. From which club did Ian Snodin join Oldham Athletic in January, 1995?
11. Which three players started all 42 Premier League matches for Norwich City in 1992–3?
12. How many of the 2003–4 Premier League sides were in Division One in 1992–3?
13. From which club did Robert Rosario join Nottingham Forest in March 1993?
14. Who was the top goalscorer in the league for Manchester United in 1994–5?
15. Manchester City's biggest home wins in Division One in 1991–2 were both 4–0. Against which two teams did they achieve this?

1. Lee Clark 2. Chelsea 3. Marcus Stewart 4. Two 5. Manchester City 6. Nottingham Forest 7. Efan Ekoku 8. Dean Saunders 9. –53 10. Everton 11. Mark Bowen, Bryan Gunn and David Phillips 12. Six 13. Coventry City 14. Andrei Kanchelskis 15. Luton Town and Leeds United.

Quiz 7

1. Who was the top goalscorer in the league for Blackburn Rovers in 1995–6?
2. Who did Coventry City beat 5–0 at home in the Premier League in 1995–6?
3. How many home games did Grimsby Town lose in Division One in 1996–7?
4. Which London team knocked Liverpool out of the 1996–7 FA Cup?
5. Which team did Wrexham beat 7–0 at home in Division Two in 1995–6?
6. Which side knocked Bolton Wanderers out of the 1995–6 FA Cup?
7. Who was the top goalscorer in the league for QPR in 1996–7?
8. Who was the top goalscorer in the league for Hull City in 1993–4?
9. From which club did Phil Starbuck join Sheffield United in January 1995?
10. Which player started all 42 Premier League matches for Southampton in 1992–3?
11. From which club did Darren Anderton join Spurs in June 1992?
12. Who was the top goalscorer in the league for Wolves in 1994–5?
13. Which team did Arsenal beat 7–1 at home in the First Division in 1991–2?
14. Which team knocked Everton out of the 1996–7 FA Cup?
15. Who was the top goalscorer in the league for Charlton Athletic in 1996–7?

1. Alan Shearer 2. Blackburn Rovers 3. Nine 4. Chelsea 5. Rotherham United 6. Leeds United 7. John Spencer 8. Dean Windass 9. Huddersfield Town 10. Tim Flowers 11. Portsmouth 12. Steve Bull 13. Sheffield Wednesday 14. Bradford City 15. Carl Leaburn.

Quiz 8

1. Which three teams were relegated from Barclays League Division One in 1991–2?
2. Which side knocked Walsall out of the 1995–6 FA Cup?
3. Who was the top goalscorer in the league for Newcastle United in 1996–7?
4. Who was the top goalscorer in the league for Norwich City in 1993–4?
5. Which three players started all 42 Premier League matches for Manchester United in 1992–3?
6. Who did Manchester City beat 4–0 at home in the 1992–3 Premier League?
7. Who was the top Division Two goalscorer in 1992–3?
8. From which club did Bernie Slaven join Port Vale in 1993?
9. Who was the top goalscorer in the league for Huddersfield Town in 1994–5?
10. Who scored the only goal for Argentina in their 1–0 win over Wales in June 1992?
11. How many home games did Bolton Wanderers lose in Division One in 1996–7?
12. Which team knocked Bolton Wanderers out of the 1996–7 FA Cup?
13. Which team finished runner-up in Division Two in 1995–6?
14. Which team did Crystal Palace beat 5–0 at home in Division One in 1995–6?
15. Which side knocked Shrewsbury Town out of the 1995–6 FA Cup?

1. Luton Town, Notts County and West Ham United 2. Ipswich Town 3. Alan Shearer 4. Chris Sutton 5. Steve Bruce, Gary Pallister and Peter Schmeichel 6. Leeds United 7. Bob Taylor of West Bromwich Albion 8. Middlesbrough 9. Andy Booth 10. Gabriel Batistuta 11. One 12. Chesterfield 13. Oxford United 14. Grimsby Town 15. Liverpool.

Quiz 9

1. Which London team did Sunderland beat 6–0 at home in Division One in 1995–6?
2. From which club did Steve Claridge join Luton Town in July 1992?
3. Which team finished runner-up in the Premier League in 1996–7?
4. Who was the top goalscorer in the league for Arsenal in 1993–4?
5. From which club did Earl Barrett join Everton in January 1995?
6. Which three players started all 46 First Division games for West Ham United in 1992–3?
7. From which club did Paul Walsh join Portsmouth in June 1992?
8. From which club did Dean Holdsworth join Wimbledon in August 1992?
9. Who did Sheffield United beat 6–0 at home in the 1992–3 Premier League?
10. Who was the top goalscorer in the league for Oxford United in 1994–5?
11. Which team finished bottom of Division Three in 1995–6?
12. Who was the top goalscorer in the league for Wimbledon in 1994–5?
13. Which team knocked Stockport County out of the 1996–7 FA Cup?
14. Who were the semi-finalists in the 1996–7 League Cup?
15. Which Yorkshire side knocked Carlisle United out of the 1996–7 FA Cup?

1. Millwall 2. Cambridge United 3. Newcastle United 4. Ian Wright 5. Aston Villa 6. Kevin Keen, Steve Potts and Ludek Miklosko 7. Tottenham Hotspur 8. Brentford 9. Tottenham Hotspur 10. Paul Moody 11. Torquay United 12. Efan Ekoku 13. Birmingham City 14. Leicester City, Middlesbrough, Stockport County and Wimbledon 15. Sheffield Wednesday.

Quiz 10

1. Which side knocked Peterborough out of the 1995–6 FA Cup?
2. Three of the top six teams in Division Two in 1991–2 were in the Premier League in 2003–4. Which three?
3. Who was the top goalscorer in the league for Spurs in 1996–7?
4. Who was the top goalscorer in the league for Chelsea in 1993–4?
5. From which club did Lee Nogan join Reading in January 1995?
6. Which player started all 42 Premier League matches for Blackburn Rovers in 1992–3?
7. Who was the top goalscorer in the league for Barnsley in 1993–4?
8. QPR's biggest home win in Division One in 1991–2 was 4–0. Against which team?
9. How many home games did Bury lose in Division Two in 1996–7?
10. Which team knocked Hednesford Town out of the 1996–7 FA Cup?
11. Liverpool's biggest home win in Division One in 1991–2 was 4–0. Against which team?
12. Which team knocked Blackburn Rovers out of the 1996–7 FA Cup?
13. Which side knocked Sheffield United out of the 1995–6 FA Cup?
14. Who was the top goalscorer in the league for Southampton in 1996–7?
15. Who was the top goalscorer in the league for Spurs in 1993–4?

1. Huddersfield Town 2. Blackburn Rovers, Leicester City and Middlesbrough 3. Teddy Sheringham 4. Mark Stein 5. Watford 6. Bobby Mimms 7. Andy Payton 8. Manchester City 9. None 10. Middlesbrough 11. Notts County 12. Coventry City 13. Aston Villa 14. Matt Le Tissier 15. Teddy Sheringham.

Quiz 11

1. Which side knocked Oldham Athletic out of the 1995–6 FA Cup?
2. Which two 2003–4 Premier League teams were in the Third Division in 1991–2?
3. From which club did Gary Charles join Aston Villa in January 1995?
4. Who was the top goalscorer in the league for Blackburn Rovers in 1993–4?
5. Which London team finished runner-up in Division One in 1996–7?
6. Who was the top goalscorer in the league for Ipswich Town in 1993–4?
7. Which side knocked West Ham United out of the 1995–6 FA Cup?
8. From which club did Neil Ruddock join Tottenham Hotspur in July 1992?
9. From which club did Jonathan Gould join Coventry City in July 1992?
10. Who was the top goalscorer in the league for Millwall in 1994–5?
11. Who did Chelsea beat 4–0 at home in the 1992–3 Premier League?
12. From which club did Mark Robins join Leicester City in January 1995?
13. Who was the top goalscorer in the league for Bristol City in 1993–4?
14. From which club did Barry Horne join Everton in July 1992?
15. Which London team knocked Manchester United out of the 1996–7 FA Cup?

1. Swindon Town 2. Bolton Wanderers and Fulham 3. Derby County 4. Alan Shearer 5. Barnsley 6. Ian Marshall 7. Grimsby Town 8. Southampton 9. West Bromwich Albion 10. Alex Rae 11. Middlesbrough 12. Norwich City 13. Wayne Allison 14. Southampton 15. Wimbledon.

Quiz 12

1. Who were the semi-finalists in the 1992–3 League Cup?
2. Which England players scored the goals that beat South Africa 2–1 in a friendly in May 1997?
3. Who was the top goalscorer in the league for Crystal Palace in 1995–6?
4. From which club did Scott Sellars join Newcastle United in March 1993?
5. Which player started all 42 Premier League matches for Ipswich Town in 1992–3?
6. Which club had the lowest gate in Division One in 1993–4?
7. Which side knocked Crewe Alexandra out of the 1995–6 FA Cup?
8. Which team finished runner-up in Division Three in 1996–7?
9. Who was the top goalscorer in the league for Coventry City in 1993–4?
10. Who did Manchester United beat 5–0 at home in the 1992–3 Premier League?
11. Which team finished bottom of the Second Division in 1995–6?
12. Which team knocked Newcastle United out of the 1996–7 FA Cup?
13. Who was the top goalscorer in the league for Tranmere Rovers in 1995–6?
14. From which club did Stuart Ripley join Blackburn Rovers in July 1992?
15. Who was the top goalscorer in the league for Manchester United in 1993–4?

1. Arsenal, Blackburn Rovers, Crystal Palace and Sheffield Wednesday 2. Ian Wright and Robert Lee 3. Dougie Freedman 4. Leeds United 5. David Linighan 6. Southend United 7. Southampton 8. Fulham 9. Peter Ndlovu 10. Coventry City 11. Hull City 12. Nottingham Forest 13. John Aldridge 14. Middlesbrough 15. Eric Cantona.

Quiz 13

1. Who was the top goalscorer in the league for Sheffield Wednesday in 1996–7?
2. Which team did Stoke City beat 5–0 at home in Division One in 1995–6?
3. Which side knocked Reading out of the 1995–6 FA Cup?
4. Who was the top goalscorer in the league for West Ham United in 1996–7?
5. Which two players started all 46 First Division games for Swindon Town in 1992–3?
6. Which team finished bottom of the First Division in 1995–6?
7. Who were the semi-finalists in the 1994–5 League Cup?
8. Manchester United lost twice at home in the First Division in 1991–2. Against which teams?
9. Who was the top goalscorer in the league for Walsall in 1994–5?
10. Who was the top Division One goalscorer in 1992–3?
11. How many home games did Rotherham United lose in Division Two in 1996–7?
12. From which club did Perry Groves join Southampton in August 1992?
13. How many home games did Sheffield Wednesday lose in the Premier League in 1996–7?
14. Which side knocked Wolves out of the 1995–6 FA Cup?
15. Which club had the lowest gate in Division Three in 1993–4?

1. Andy Booth 2. Luton Town 3. Manchester United 4. Paul Kitson 5. Colin Calderwood and Shaun Taylor 6. Luton Town 7. Bolton Wanderers, Crystal Palace, Liverpool and Swindon Town 8. Nottingham Forest and QPR 9. Kyle Lightbourne 10. Guy Whittingham of Portsmouth 11. Twelve 12. Arsenal 13. One 14. Tottenham Hotspur 15. Scarborough.

Quiz 14

1. Who was the top goalscorer in the league for Manchester United in 1991–2?
2. Who was the top goalscorer in the league for Watford in 1996–7?
3. Which club had the highest gate in Division Two in 1994–5?
4. Who did Liverpool beat 5–0 at home in the 1992–3 Premier League?
5. Who was the top goalscorer in the league for Leeds United in 1994–5?
6. How many home games did Notts County lose in Division Two in 1996–7?
7. Who scored the only goal for Wales in their 1–0 win over the Republic of Ireland in February 1992?
8. Who was the top goalscorer in the league for Newcastle United in 1994–5?
9. Who was the top goalscorer in the league for West Bromwich Albion in 1994–5?
10. From which club did Neil Shipperley join Southampton in January 1995?
11. Who was the top goalscorer in the league for Stoke City in 1996–7?
12. Which team knocked Norwich City out of the 1996–7 FA Cup?
13. How many home games did Chelsea lose in the Premier League in 1996–7?
14. How many goals did Robert Fleck score in the Rumbelows League Cup competition for Norwich City in 1991–2?
15. Luton Town lost 5–0 twice away from home in the First Division in 1991–2. Against which teams?

1. Brian McClair 2. Tommy Mooney 3. Birmingham City 4. Crystal Palace 5. Tony Yeboah 6. Ten 7. Mark Pembridge 8. Peter Beardsley 9. Andy Hunt 10. Chelsea 11. Mike Sheron 12. Leicester City 13. Two 14. Six 15. Manchester United and Coventry City.

Quiz 15

1. Who was the top goalscorer in the league for Bolton Wanderers in 1993–4?
2. Which club had the highest gate in Division One in 1994–5?
3. Which current league club finished next to bottom of the GM Vauxhall Conference in 1991–2?
4. Which player started all 42 Premier League matches for Oldham Athletic in 1992–3?
5. From which club did Steve Nicol join Notts County in January 1995?
6. Which team finished runner-up in Division Three in 1995–6?
7. From which club did Efan Ekoku join Norwich City in March 1993?
8. Which team knocked Watford out of the 1996–7 FA Cup?
9. How many home games did Oldham Athletic lose in Division One in 1996–7?
10. Who was the top goalscorer in the league for Crystal Palace in 1993–4?
11. Which player started all 42 Premier League matches for Wimbledon in 1992–3?
12. From which club did Paul Trollope join Derby County in January 1995?
13. Who was the top goalscorer in the league for Rotherham United in 1994–5?
14. Which Shearer headed the Division Two goalscoring chart for Blackburn Rovers in 1991–2?
15. Which three players each scored 13 league goals for Derby County in 1993–4?

1. John McGinlay 2. Wolves 3. Cheltenham Town 4. Mike Milligan 5. Liverpool 6. Gillingham 7. AFC Bournemouth 8. Manchester City 9. Nine 10. Chris Armstrong 11. Robbie Earle 12. Torquay United 13. Shaun Goater 14. Duncan Shearer 15. Paul Kitson, Tommy Johnson and Marco Gabbiadini.

THE NOUGHTIES

Premiership 2007–8

1. How many different teams had won the Premiership by the start of the 2008–9 season?
2. Of the ten all-time Premiership top scorers, how many were English at the beginning of the 2008–9 season?
3. Name the only one of the Premiership's top ten scorers of all time that is not European.
4. Manchester United won the league in 2007–8. But by how many points did they beat Chelsea?
5. Which two Premiership teams suffered the fewest defeats in 2007–8?
6. How many places did Liverpool finish above Everton in 2007–8?
7. Which London team dramatically escaped relegation on goal difference on the last day of the season?
8. Who scored the first goal of the 2007–8 season?
9. Which side had the fewest wins in the 2007–8 season?
10. How many did they have?
11. Which Sunderland player scored at the latest point in a match during the 2007–8 season?
12. The widest winning margin in the 2007–8 season was seven goals – 8–1. Which teams featured in the match?
13. Who played in the Permiership's only 11-goal thriller in 2008 and what was the score?
14. Who scored 2007–8's first hat-trick?
15. Which two players scored four goals in one game in the 2007–8 season?

1. Four – Manchester United, Arsenal, Chelsea and Blackburn 2. Seven 3. Dwight Yorke 4. Two 5. Arsenal and Chelsea (three) 6. One place. They were fourth and fifth respectively 7. Fulham 8. Michael Chopra for Sunderland against Tottenham Hotspur 9. Derby County 10. One 11. Andy Reid (90+6 minutes) 12. Middlesbrough 8–1 Manchester City 13. Portsmouth 7–4 Reading 14. Emmanuel Adebayor for Arsenal against Derby County, 22 September 15. Dimitar Berbatov and Frank Lampard.

Premiership 2006–7

1. Who did Manchester United beat into second place in the 2006–7 season?
2. The biggest win in 2006–7 was 6–0. Who was the match between?
3. Only one side remained unbeaten at home in 2006–7. Who?
4. Name the two Englishmen to finish in the top ten scorers in 2006–7.
5. One Irishman was also in the top ten scorers of 2006–7. Who did he play for?
6. The same player scored the fastest league goal (16 seconds) that season. Against who?
7. How did Moritz Volz earn the nickname '15,000 Volz' in 2006–7?
8. Which Premiership manager took over as England manager at the start of the 2006–7 season and who did he appoint as his captain?
9. Destined for the Premiership, which Welsh defender was named the Football League Young Player of the Year in March 2007?
10. After Alex Ferguson, which manager won most Manager of the Month awards in 2006–7?
11. Who won the season's first silverware after coming out victorious in the FA Community Shield at the Millennium Stadium in Cardiff?
12. Which Arsenal player was Player of the Month in January 2007?
13. Who was the 2006–7 Player of the Year?
14. Who won the Barclays Golden Glove Award in the same year?
15. With a capacity of 19,920, which team had the smallest ground in 2006–7?

1. Chelsea 2. Reading 6–0 West Ham United 3. Chelsea 4. Wayne Rooney and Darren Bent 5. Kevin Doyle (Reading) 6. Sheffield United 7. He scored the league's 15,000th goal in December, against Chelsea 8. Steve McClaren, John Terry 9. Gareth Bale 10. Steve Coppell (Reading) 11. Liverpool. They beat Chelsea 2–1 12. Cesc Fabregas 13. Cristiano Ronaldo 14. José Manuel Reina 15. Watford, Vicarage Road.

The Championship

1. Who was top scorer in the 2004–5 season?
2. Which ground had the biggest capacity in 2007–8?
3. Which club had the lowest capacity ground in 2007–8?
4. Who was the top scorer in 2007–8?
5. Which three teams were relegated in 2005–6?
6. What was the score of the 2006–7 play-off final?
7. How many goals did Hull put past Watford in the 2007 play-off semi-final?
8. Sunderland won the 2004–5 Championship. Who was their manager?
9. Who finished runner-up in 2004–5?
10. Which three teams were relegated in 2007–08?
11. Which Welsh side started the 2008–9 season as the recently promoted League One winners?
12. Which team managed to make it into the 2007–8 play-offs despite having a goal difference of just one?
13. Jamie Cureton was top scorer in the 2006–7 Championship. For which team did he play?
14. Which team signed Nathan Ellington following the 2004–5 season in which he finished top scorer?
15. Ninian Park is rare for a Championship ground as it contains terracing. Which team plays there?

1. Nathan Ellington, Wigan Athletic 2. Hillsborough (39,814) 3. Blackpool, Bloomfield Road (9,612) 4. Sylvan Ebanks-Blake, Wolverhampton Wanderers (23) 5. Crewe Alexandra, Millwall, Brighton & Hove Albion 6. Derby County 1-0 West Bromwich Albion 7. Four. Hull City 4-1 Watford 8. Mick McCarthy 9. Wigan Athletic 10. Leicester City, Scunthorpe United, Colchester United 11. Swansea City 12. Bristol City 13. Colchester United (23 goals) 14. West Brom 15. Cardiff City.

League One

1. Luton and Hull took the automatic promotion places in 2004–5. Who got the play-off place?
2. Which manager of Hull continued the club's amazing record with their 2004–5 promotion?
3. Who did Barnsley beat on penalties to win the 2005–6 play-offs?
4. By what score did Yeovil Town beat Nottingham Forest in the second leg of the 2006–7 play-off semi-final?
5. Which four teams were relegated in 2006–7?
6. What was most unusual about Nottingham Forest's entry into League One, after relegation, in 2004–5?
7. Which two players were top scorers in 2004–5?
8. Which two players were top scorers in 2005–6?
9. Billy Sharp was top scorer in 2006–7. Which club did he move to?
10. Which team had the highest stadium capacity in 2008–9?
11. Which team had the lowest stadium capacity in 2008–9?
12. Which side did Dean Windass move to after leaving Bradford City?
13. Who beat Leeds United 1–0 in the 2007–8 play-offs?
14. Which four teams were relegated in 2007–8?
15. Who managed Swansea's 2007–8 League One-winning side?

1. Sheffield Wednesday 2. Peter Taylor 3. Swansea City 4. 5–2 5. Chesterfield, Bradford City, Rotherham United, Brentford 6. They became the first former European Cup winners to slide into the third tier of their domestic league 7. Stuart Elliott and Dean Windass 8. Freddy Eastwood and Billy Sharp 9. Sheffield United 10. Leeds United, Elland Road (40,242) 11. Cheltenham Town, Whaddon Road (7,066) 12. Hull 13. Doncaster Rovers 14. Bournemouth, Gillingham, Port Vale, Luton Town. 15. Roberto Martínez.

League Two

1. Who got into League Two by finishing top of the Conference in 2007–8?
2. Who won League Two in 2004–5?
3. Who was the league's top scorer in 2004–5?
4. Only one player in the top ten scorers of 2004–5 wasn't from Britain. Who was he?
5. Which two teams were relegated in 2004–5?
6. Which two teams were relegated in 2006–7?
7. Three teams in 2008–9 had grounds that held more than 25,000 people. Who were they?
8. Who won the play-offs in 2006–7?
9. Who managed MK Dons to their 2007–8 league win?
10. Who took his place for the 2008–9 season?
11. Aaron McLean was top scorer in 2007–08, but where did his team, Peterborough finish in the league?
12. True or false: in the 2008–9 season more League Two clubs had terracing than those that did not?
13. In what year were Grimsby Town beaten 1–0 by Cheltenham Town in the play-off final?
14. In 2004–5 Coca-Cola replaced the old league sponsors. Who were the previous sponsors of the league?
15. Accrington Stanley have the smallest crowd capacity in League Two. What is their ground called?

1. Aldershot Town 2. Yeovil Town 3. Phil Jevons 4. Junior Agogo, Bristol Rovers (19 goals) 5. Kidderminster Harriers, Cambridge United 6. Boston United, Torquay United 7. Bradford City, Darlington, Rotherham United 8. Bristol Rovers 9. Paul Ince 10. Roberto Di Matteo 11. Second/Runners-up 12. False. There were 12 with and 12 without terracing 13. 2006 14. Nationwide Building Society 15. The Crown Ground (5,057).

Quiz 1

1. Which team began 2006–7 with five straight defeats, but still won their division?
2. Which two players have scored hat-tricks for three separate Premiership clubs?
3. Which player cost Leeds United £12 million from Inter Milan in May 2001?
4. What is the former name of the team now known as Milton Keynes Dons?
5. Which Premiership manager spent more than £100 million on transfers, but failed to win a single trophy by 2002 and was sacked?
6. Has there been a Premiership season when all three promoted teams have stayed up?
7. Which side was promoted to the Premiership in 2006, entering English football's top flight for the first time in their 135-year history?
8. Which Arsenal midfielder wore an electronic tag in the Premiership, and why?
9. In September 2004, which manager took over the reins at Newcastle United from Sir Bobby Robson?
10. Season 2004–5 saw a major 'rebranding exercise' by the Football League. What was it?
11. Name the only team to be relegated from the Premiership with more than 40 points.
12. In October 2004, a Chelsea player had his contract terminated after testing positive for cocaine. Who was he?
13. Who scored the 10,000th Premiership goal?
14. Which former Arsenal and England player died of cancer at the age of 33 in March 2001?
15. What is the name of the stadium Oxford United moved to in 2001?

1. Sunderland in the Championship 2. Kevin Campbell (Arsenal, Everton and Nottingham Forest), Les Ferdinand (QPR, Newcastle United and Spurs) 3. Robbie Keane 4. Wimbledon FC 5. David O'Leary of Leeds United 6. Yes. In 2001–2, Fulham, Blackburn and Bolton came up and Ipswich, Derby and Leicester went down 7. Reading 8. Jermaine Pennant served 30 days in jail for drink-driving (and reportedly giving his name as Ashley Cole), then was tagged before going back on loan with Birmingham 9. Graeme Souness 10. The First, Second and Third Divisions became The Championship and Leagues One and Two 11. West Ham in 2002–03 12. Adrian Mutu 13. Les Ferdinand for Spurs against Fulham on 15 December 2001 14. David Rocastle 15. The Kassam Stadium.

Quiz 2

1. Which Division One game was abandoned on 16 March 2002 because one team only had six players?
2. Which team was relegated from the Premiership in May 2003 with a record low of four wins, 19 points and a total of 21 goals?
3. Name the team who surrendered a 3–0 half-time lead over Manchester United to lose 5–3 at home in September 2001.
4. Who is Newcastle's all-time leading scorer?
5. Which club did Sven-Goran Eriksson manage before he came to England in 2001?
6. Who scored the equalizer against Greece at Old Trafford that sent England to the 2002 World Cup Finals?
7. Which club was David Seaman playing for when he hung up his gloves at the end of the 2003–4 season?
8. On 12 July 2001, Manchester United broke the British transfer record for a midfielder. Who was it?
9. Name five players who have each scored for five separate Premiership teams.
10. Who was nicknamed the 'Tinker Man' when he was the manager at Chelsea?
11. Who moved to Bolton Wanderers for a single day in 2006 before having 'a change of heart' and joining Manchester City?
12. Which player collapsed and died at the age of 28 playing for Cameroon in June 2003?
13. On 25 August 2004, which team beat Blackburn 3–0 to establish an all-time record of 43 games unbeaten in England's top flight?
14. Name the manager who clocked up 1000 competitive games on 20 November 2001.
15. Which team lost 3–2 at Villa in May 2001 to end 34 years in the top flight?

1. West Brom were leading Sheffield United 3–0 when the Blades lost two further players to injury after having three sent off 2. Sunderland 3. Spurs 4. Alan Shearer with 206 goals 5. Lazio 6. David Beckham 7. Manchester City 8. Juan Sebastian Veron cost £28.1 million from Lazio 9. Stan Collymore, Nick Barmby, Ashley Ward, Benito Carbone and Michael Hughes 10. Claudio Ranieri 11. Dietmar Hamann when he left Liverpool 12. Marc-Vivien Foe who was on loan at Manchester City and had an undetected heart condition 13. Arsenal's 'Invincibles' who went on to extend the record to 49 games 14. Dario Gradi for Crewe Alexandra 15. Coventry City.

Quiz 3

1. Name the two pairs of team-mates to be jointly made FA Premier League Player of the Month.
2. Which Newcastle team-mates were sent off for fighting each other on the pitch at St James's Park against Villa in April 2005?
3. Who reported his former club Chelsea for 'tapping up' three Leeds United youth players in 2006?
4. Which team set a UK record of 76 consecutive unbeaten league games at senior level when they drew 1–1 at Bromley in Rymans Division One in 2004?
5. Which team went unbeaten throughout the 2003–4 season?
6. The 'old' Wembley famously had 39 steps. How many does 'new' Wembley have?
7. Who were England playing in 2004 when Shaun Wright-Phillips and Ashley Cole were subjected to continual racist abuse?
8. Which four Premiership players have each been relegated with four separate teams?
9. Which Midlands striker was jailed for six years in 2004 for causing death by dangerous driving?
10. As of August 2007, who was the longest-serving manager in the Premiership?
11. Who scored the only goal in the last game at 'old' Wembley against England in October 2000?
12. Which rugby manager became director of football at Southampton in June 2005?
13. Which short-lived Tottenham manager did Martin Jol succeed in November 2004?
14. Name the team that set a dismal new record in 2006–7 for the fewest goals scored at home in a season in England's top division.
15. Why was a special meeting called by Hearts players on 8 February 2006?

1. Dennis Bergkamp and Edu (Arsenal), February 2004; Robbie Keane and Dimitar Berbatov (Spurs), April 2007 2. Lee Bowyer and Kieron Dyer 3. Ken Bates 4. AFC Wimbledon who eventually took the record to 78 5. Arsenal 6. 107 7. Spain at the Bernabeu, Madrid 8. Ashley Ward, Hermann Hreidarsson, Marcus Bent and Nigel Quashie 9. West Bromwich Albion's Lee Hughes 10. Sir Alex Ferguson who joined Manchester United in November 1986 11. Didi Hamann scored for Germany (and Kevin Keegan resigned as manager) 12. Sir Clive Woodward 13. Jacques Santini 14. Manchester City with ten, which beat Sunderland's 14 in 2002–3 and Woolwich Arsenal's 11 in 1912–3 15. To find out whether owner Vladimir Romanov was picking the team – coach Graham Rix refused to confirm or deny speculation.

Quiz 4

1. Which manager made history by winning his third successive Premiership league title in 2001?
2. Who won their first title in 50 years during their centenary season with a 2–0 win over Bolton in April 2005?
3. In August 2006, which Manchester City defender elbowed Portsmouth's Pedro Mendes in the head so hard that he had to spend the night in hospital?
4. Which player, on loan from West Ham to Bournemouth, scored in ten successive Division Two games in 2000–1?
5. Which three players were sent off for their part in a brawl at the end of the 2007 Carling Cup Final?
6. Which was the first FA Cup Final to go to penalties?
7. Which team ended their 33–year exile from the top flight in the 2000–1 season?
8. Who were the first team ever to survive in the Premiership after being bottom of the league at Christmas?
9. Which club did Petr Cech come from, and how much did he cost, when he joined Chelsea on 8 June 2004?
10. Which famous team promptly went into administration when they were relegated to the Third Division, League One, for the first time in their history?
11. Who did Liverpool beat 5–4 in May 2001 to win the UEFA Cup?
12. Who beat Arsenal 6–1 in February 2001?
13. Who was the surprise choice as Manager of the Year in 2001?
14. Who became the most expensive defender in the world, smashing the British transfer record in 2002?
15. Which goalkeeper received the Barclaycard Golden Gloves award in 2003 only to be dropped by his club the following season?

1. Sir Alex Ferguson with Manchester United 2. Chelsea 3. Ben Thatcher 4. Jermain Defoe 5. John Obi Mikel (Chelsea), Kolo Toure and Emmanuel Adebayor (both Arsenal) 6. Arsenal versus Manchester United in May 2005. Patrick Vieira converted the winning spot-kick 7. Fulham under Jean Tigana 8. West Bromwich Albion in 2004-5 9. Rennes for £7.2 million 10. Leeds United 11. Alaves of Spain 12. Manchester United 13. George Burley of Ipswich Town whose side finished fifth in the Premiership after being hotly tipped for relegation 14. Rio Ferdinand who left Leeds United for Manchester United for £29.1 million 15. Chelsea's Carlo Cudicini.

Quiz 5

1. Why did Francesco Totti win the European Golden Boot for 2006–7 with 26 goals when Eduardo Da Silva (now Arsenal) and Alfonso Alves scored 34 for Dinamo Zagreb and Heerenveen respectively?
2. Who replaced Fernando Torres at Atletico Madrid when he joined Liverpool?
3. Why did Jose Mourinho give Roman Abramovich a six-finger salute at Wembley after Chelsea had beaten Manchester United in the FA Cup Final in 2007?
4. Which controversial referee, aka 'the Thing from Tring', retired at the end of 2006–7?
5. Which goalkeeper did Paul Robinson beat when he scored a goal from 80 yards at White Hart Lane in 2007?
6. Which record did referee Mike Riley break in a game between Lyon and Roma in 2006–7?
7. Who scored the fastest-ever Champions League goal?
8. Which side won the European Under-21 championship in 2007?
9. What incident at the 2007 European Under-21 medal ceremony upset Dutch manager Foppe de Haan?
10. In the semi-finals of the 2007 Under-21 championships, there was a grand total of 32 penalties in the shoot-out after a 1–1 draw between England and Holland. Who missed for England?
11. How much did Thierry Henry cost Barcelona when he left Arsenal in June 2007?
12. Who returned to play for England's national side in 2007, setting up two goals in the 3–0 win against Estonia?
13. What was the first-ever match played at 'new' Wembley in March 2007?
14. Who was the top scorer in the European Under-21 Finals in 2007, and which English club did he join?
15. Who were the first Bulgarian team to make the Champions League group stages, and how many points did they get?

1. A special points system means you earn more points per goal in a 'top' league such as Serie A 2. Diego Forlan 3. To signify the six major trophies he had won since joining the club 4. Graham Poll 5. Ben Foster who was on loan to Watford from Manchester United 6. He awarded the highest number of yellow cards for a Champions League game – 11: eight to Roma, three to Lyon 7. Ron Makaay scored in 10.2 seconds for Bayern Munich against Real Madrid in 2006–7 8. Holland, who beat Serbia 4–1 in the final 9. Several Dutch players with Surinamese roots were carrying the flag of Surinam 10. Justin Hoyte, Nigel Reo-Coker, Matt Darbyshire and Anton Ferdinand 11. £16 million 12. David Beckham 13. England Under-21s drew 3–3 with Italy Under-21s in a friendly in front of a crowd of 60,000 14. Holland's Maceo Rigters (with four goals) who joined Blackburn Rovers 15. Levski Sofia in 2006–7, who became the sixth team to score *nul points* in their group.

World Cup 2006

Quiz 1

1. Which player won his 100th cap in the 2006 World Cup Final?
2. What was the official song of the 2006 World Cup?
3. Which city hosted the 2006 World Cup Final?
4. Which country conducted its 2006 World Cup campaign against the backdrop of a raging match-fixing scandal back home?
5. Which team has Brazil defeated the most times in the World Cup Finals?
6. How many World Cups had been contested before the 2006 tournament?
7. Who was top scorer at the 2006 World Cup?
8. Was the 2006 World Cup Final the first to be settled by penalties?
9. How many times have 2006 runners-up France failed to qualify for the World Cup Finals?
10. What was the name of the official Adidas match ball?
11. Who rounded off Argentina's 24-pass move by scoring against Serbia & Montenegro?
12. Where will the 2010 World Cup Finals be held?

1. Italy's Fabio Cannavaro 2. 'Time of Our Lives', sung by Il Divo and Toni Braxton 3. Berlin 4. Italy 5. Sweden 6. 17 7. Germany's Miroslav Klose 8. No, in 1994 Brazil beat Italy on penalties to take the trophy 9. Six 10. Teamgeist 11. Esteban Cambiasso 12. South Africa.

Quiz 2

1. Which player committed the most fouls at the 2006 World Cup Finals?
2. The top scorer at the 2006 World Cup scored five goals, nobody scored four, but how many players scored three?
3. Which was the only team to play in the 2006 semi-finals never to have won a World Cup?
4. Of the teams that failed to qualify for the World Cup, which two were highest in the FIFA rankings in May 2006?
5. How many goals did Trinidad & Tobago score during their World Cup campaign?
6. Which was the most poorly attended game at the 2006 World Cup?
7. Which team was the only former World Cup Winner not to qualify for the 2006 tournament?
8. Who was the oldest player to see action at the 2006 World Cup?
9. What was unusual about the 2006 World Cup's opening match between Germany and Costa Rica?
10. What were the official mascots for the World Cup?
11. Other than the final, which game pulled in the biggest live TV audience worldwide?
12. Which goalkeeper saved three penalties in a penalty shoot-out?

1. France's Thierry Henry, who committed a total of 20 fouls 2. Eight: Hernan Crespo (Argentina); Ronaldo (Brazil); Zinedine Zidane (France); David Villa (Spain); Fernando Torres (Spain); Maxi Rodriguez (Argentina); Thierry Henry (France); Lucas Podolsky (Germany) 3. Portugal 4. Nigeria and Denmark – both were ranked 11 5. None 6. Serbia & Montenegro v Holland with an attendance of 37,216 7. Uruguay. They lost to Australia in a play-off qualifier 8. 40-year-old Tunisian goalkeeper Ali Boumnijel 9. It was the first time the opening game was contested by the host nation instead of the holder 10. A lion called Goleo VI and his friend Pille, a talking football 11. Brazil v Croatia, 160 million 12. Ricardo for Portugal v England.

Quiz 3

1. 2006 was the first time the top ten FIFA-ranked teams all qualified for the World Cup. True or false?
2. Which two players shared the worst disciplinary record at the 2006 tournament?
3. Which player made his World Cup Final debut in 2006, having been left on the bench for the 1998 final after playing all six matches on the road to it?
4. Which team scored the most goals at this World Cup?
5. To which German town did England players' wives and girlfriends – or WAGs as they are infamously known – lay siege during the 2006 World Cup?
6. Which eight teams were seeded first at the 2006 World Cup?
7. Who scored the first goal of the 2006 World Cup?
8. Which coach established a record for 12 consecutive World Cup wins?
9. How many players retired from international football after the Portugal–Germany play-off for third place?
10. What was printed on the personalized match balls for each match in the 2006 tournament?
11. What World Cup landmark was reached when Brazil beat Ghana 3–0?
12. Which team has gone without defeat in 25 World Cup Final games played in Europe (excluding penalty shoot-outs)?

1. True 2. Portugal's Costinha and Ghana's Asamoah Gyan with four yellow cards and one red 3. France's Thierry Henry 4. Germany with 13 5. Baden-Baden 6. Argentina, Brazil, England, France, Germany, Italy, Mexico, Spain 7. Germany's Philipp Lahm 8. Luiz Felipe Scolari of Portugal, after Portugal scraped past England on penalties (Scolari won seven matches in charge of his own country, Brazil) 9. Three: Portugal's Luis Figo and Pauleta, and Germany's Oliver Kahn 10. The name of the stadium, the national teams, the date of the match and the kick-off time 11. Brazil set a new record of 11 consecutive wins in the World Cup, stretching back to 2002 12. Italy has not lost in Europe, except on penalties, since Germany 1974.

Quiz 4

1. Name the second highest-scoring team of the 2006 World Cup.
2. What landmark did David Beckham achieve during England's second-round game against Ecuador?
3. What was different about the match ball that was used in the 2006 final compared to the other games?
4. Which Italian player suffered injury setbacks in the three World Cup Finals, meaning that he never played beyond the second round?
5. What was fundamentally different about the qualifying stages of the 2006 World Cup?
6. Fans of which nation were forced to remove their *lederhosen* before entering the stadium for a first round match, and why?
7. Who was the youngest player to take to the pitch during the 2006 finals?
8. Hyundai Motor Company supplied what to each of the 32 finalists?
9. Which team at the 2006 World Cup boasted players called Goliath, Loco, Rats and Love?
10. How many former World Cup-winning nations were at the 2006 tournament and who were they?
11. Which illness caused Harry Kewell to miss games during the 2006 World Cup Finals?
12. Which country awarded medals to every player in the national squad for reaching the second round?

1. Argentina with 11 2. The first England player to score in three World Cup tournaments. He scored against Colombia in 1998 and Argentina in 2002 3. It was gold, whereas all the others were white 4. Alessandro Nesta 5. It was the first time ever that the defending champions (in this case Brazil) did not qualify automatically 6. Holland. The lederhosen bore the logo of Dutch brewery Bavaria, which FIFA accused of 'ambush marketing' at the expense of official beer sponsor, Budweiser 7. Togo's Assimou Toure who was born on January 1 1988 8. Team buses 9. Angola 10. Six: Brazil, Germany, Italy, France, Argentina, and England 11. Gout 12. Ecuador.

Quiz 5

1. Which team at the 2006 World Cup represented a country that no longer existed, playing under a redundant flag?
2. Australia made its second World Cup appearance in 2006, but when was its first?
3. How many participating teams in the 2006 tournament were coached by Brazilians?
4. How many nations made their World Cup debut in 2006, and who were they?
5. Who won the Lev Yashin award for the best goalkeeper at the 2006 finals?
6. Which team was the lowest in the FIFA rankings to qualify for the 2006 World Cup?
7. Who scored the fastest goal of the 2006 tournament?
8. Zinedine Zidane was sent off in the 2006 World Cup Final. Who else has been sent off in a World Cup Final?
9. What was unique about the goalscoring statistics of the 2006 World Cup?
10. Who said: 'I think there's every chance Wayne Rooney could go back to the Man United training ground and stick one on Cristiano Ronaldo', following the England striker's sending-off?
11. Which coach at the finals reads tarot cards to relax and allegedly refuses to pick players whose star sign is Scorpio?
12. Which England player was chosen for FIFA's all-star team in 2006?

1. Serbia & Montenegro which split into two countries, Serbia and Montenegro, on June 5, 2006 2. 1974, 32 years ago 3. Five. Brazil (Carlos Alberto Parreira), Costa Rica (Alexandre Guimarães), Japan (Zico), Portugal (Luiz Felipe Scolari) and Saudi Arabia (Marcos Paqueta) 4. Eight. They were Angola, Ivory Coast, the Czech Republic, Ghana, Serbia & Montenegro, Togo, Trinidad & Tobago and Ukraine 5. Italy's Gianluigi Buffon 6. Togo at 61 7. Asamoah Gyan of Ghana after one minute and 10 seconds against the Czech Republic 8. Three players: Argentines Pedro Monzon and Gustavo Abel Dezotti were both sent off in 1990, while France's Marcel Desailly saw red in 1998 9. No player scored a hat-trick 10. Former England international and BBC pundit Alan Shearer 11. Raymond Domenech of France 12. John Terry.

Quiz 6

1. Who received the first booking of the 2006 World Cup Finals?
2. Which team didn't concede a single goal during the 2006 tournament, but still went out?
3. Which top-seeded teams in 2006 didn't finish top of their groups?
4. Which team's World Cup preparations were thrown into disarray by a pay dispute?
5. Who scored more goals during the group stage, Argentina or Spain?
6. Who was the smallest player at the World Cup?
7. Who was Poland's leading scorer at this World Cup?
8. Which team's kit was manufactured by Joma?
9. Who was the only player who was not a defender to score an own-goal during the World Cup?
10. What is special about Gennaro Gattuso?
11. Which Italian was sent off for elbowing Brian McBride of the USA?
12. The current World Cup trophy was designed by Silvio Gazzaniga and replaced the Jules Rimet trophy in 1974. Which team kept the Jules Rimet after winning it three times?

1. Costa Rica's Danny Fonseca during the opening game against Germany 2. Switzerland 3. France and Mexico 4. Togo. Coach Otto Pfister resigned as coach of the team over the dispute, only to be reinstated the day before Togo's opening match against South Korea 5. Neither, they both scored eight 6. Ecuador's Christian Lara, at just 5ft 3in 7. Bartosz Bosacki 8. Costa Rica 9. Portugal's Emmanuel Petit 10. He is the first World Cup winner since 1982 to sport a beard 11. Daniele de Rossi 12. Brazil

Quiz 7

1. What did match officials have at the 2006 World Cup that they'd never had before?
2. In 2006 Brazil's Ronaldo beat Gerd Müller's total World Cup goals record, but how many goals did Müller score at World Cup Finals?
3. Which language was the principal tongue of more nations at the 2006 World Cup than any other?
4. What went wrong before the match between South Korea and Togo?
5. Which sports manufacturer supplied kit to more World Cup contestants than any other?
6. How many different players scored Italy's 12 goals during the tournament?
7. Which was the lowest FIFA-ranked team to make it to the quarter-finals?
8. Which 2006 finalist's nickname is 'the Black Stars'?
9. In 2006 which team became the first ever to fail to convert a single penalty during a shoot-out?
10. True or false: the opening match of the 2006 World Cup featured the most goals in an opening match in World Cup Finals.
11. In which language is the name of each winning team engraved on the current trophy?
12. Which teams have won the current trophy the most times?

1. Microphones and earpieces so they could communicate with each other 2. 14 3. Spanish. It is the principal tongue of six countries: Argentina, Costa Rica, Ecuador, Mexico, Paraguay and Spain 4. The organisers played the Korean national anthem twice, before playing the Togolese one 5. Puma, which supplied the kit to 12 of the 32 finalists 6. 10 7. Ukraine 8. Ghana 9. Switzerland 10. True. Germany beat Costa Rica 4–2 11. English 12. Germany (1974, 1990); Argentina (1978, 1986); Brazil (1994, 2002); Italy (1982, 2006). The trophy can no longer be won outright: winners keep it for four years and then receive a copy.

Quiz 8

1. How many cards were issued during the Portugal–Holland game?
2. Who said: 'It was really difficult for us playing in the midday sun with that 3 o'clock kick-off'?
3. Which African side progressed furthest in the 2006 World Cup?
4. How many stadia were used during the 2006 tournament in Germany?
5. Which national coach resigned three times on air during radio interviews prior to the 2006 World Cup, only to deny doing so the next day?
6. Who was named 'Best Young Player' at the 2006 tournament?
7. How did the 2006 World Cup Final differ from every final since 1978?
8. Which player had more shots during the 2006 tournament than anyone else, but still failed to score a goal?
9. Which player was awarded three yellow cards in a single match before being shown the red card?
10. Which team conceded the most goals at the 2006 World Cup?
11. Who won the FIFA Man of the Match award in the 2006 World Cup Final?
12. As early as the quarter-finals, in what respect had the 2006 World Cup Finals surpassed all previous tournaments?

1. 16 yellows and four reds, a World Cup record 2. David Beckham after England's win against Paraguay 3. Ghana, who reached the quarter-finals 4. 12 5. Mexico's Ricardo La Volpe. He resigned for real after Mexico were eliminated in the second round 6. Germany's Lukas Podolski 7. It didn't feature Brazil or Germany 8. Frank Lampard, who had 24 shots in five games 9. Croatia's Josip Simunic 10. Serbia & Montenegro, who let in 10 11. Andrea Pirlo of Italy 12. Red and yellow cards: there was a grand total of 345 yellow and 28 red by the end of the final in Berlin.

Quiz 9

1. Who was the most capped player at the 2006 finals?
2. True or false: Peter Crouch was the tallest player at the World Cup.
3. Which club had more representatives at the World Cup than any other?
4. Which team competing in the 2006 World Cup Finals beat both Brazil and Argentina during qualifying matches?
5. Who is the only person to have won the World Cup as both a player and manager?
6. France's Zinedine Zidane won the 2006 Golden Ball trophy for best player, but who came second?
7. The 2006 semi-finals exclusively featured European nations. When was the last time this happened, and who were the semi-finalists?
8. Who was the youngest player to travel to the World Cup?
9. Who refereed the World Cup Final?
10. Which team drew with holders Brazil and beat 2006 favourites Argentina in qualifying?
11. Which country topped the FIFA rankings released just after the finals had ended?
12. Who headed home the World Cup's 2,000th goal?

1. Saudi Arabia's Mohammed Al Deayea 2. False. The tallest player was Serbia & Montenegro's Nikola Zigic at 6ft 8in 3. Arsenal with 15 players 4. Ecuador 5. 2006 ambassador and organiser Franz Beckenbauer of Germany 6. Italy's Fabio Cannavaro 7. It was in 1982 and they were France, Italy, Poland and West Germany 8. England's 17-year-old Theo Walcott, born on the 16 March 1989 9. Argentina's Horacio Elizondo 10. Paraguay 11. Brazil 12. Sweden's Marcus Allback v England in their 2–2 draw.

Quiz 10

1. Which record did Brazilian defender Cafu set during the 2006 World Cup Finals?
2. Which international coach was widely criticized in his home country for commuting from California to games during qualifying?
3. What was unique about Argentina's victory over Serbia & Montenegro?
4. Who was the first player to be sent off during the 2006 tournament?
5. On what did Ukraine coach Oleg Blokhin blame his team's 4–0 defeat to Spain?
6. What does FIFA stand for?
7. Which team scored the most goals in World Cup qualifying?
8. True or false: when France beat Brazil in the quarter–finals, it was the third World Cup meeting in a row in which they had done so.
9. Of the 12 stadia used for the 2006 World Cup, how many were situated in the former East Germany?
10. Which teams were joint winners of the FIFA Fair Play award in 2006?
11. Which team had the best disciplinary record?
12. And which team had the worst disciplinary record?

1. He became the first footballer to play in four consecutive World Cup Finals 2. Jürgen Klinsmann 3. For the first time in a World Cup Finals, all three of a team's substitutes came on and scored. Esteban Cambiasso, Carlos Tévez and Lionel Messi all bagged goals 4. Avery John of Trinidad & Tobago, who received two yellow cards against Sweden 5. Noisy frogs outside their hotel keeping the players awake at night 6. Fédération Internationale de Football Association 7. Mexico, with 67 8. True. France beat Brazil in 1986, 1998 and 2006 9. One, the Zentralstadion in Leipzig 10. Spain and Brazil 11. Saudi Arabia, with just five yellow cards 12. Portugal, with 24 yellow and two red cards.

WORLD CUP 2002

Quiz 1

1. Which Irish footballer went home before the World Cup after a row with manager Mick McCarthy?
2. Which country failed in their bid to 'retire' the No 10 squad number?
3. How many goalless draws were there in the 2002 World Cup?
4. Which country beat France in the opening game of the 2002 World Cup?
5. Who scored a hat-trick of headers in Germany's 8–0 demolition of Saudi Arabia in the 2002 World Cup?
6. Which 2002 World Cup team was coached by Alexander Guimaraes?
7. Who was the youngest member of England's World Cup squad?
8. Which Brazilian footballer was fined for 'simulation' in Brazil's first match against Turkey in the 2002 World Cup?
9. How many Arsenal players were in France's 2002 World Cup squad?
10. Who was the only English-based player in Belgium's 2002 World Cup squad?
11. Which Italian Serie A team's players scored the most goals in the 2002 World Cup?
12. Who scored England's penalty in their 2002 World Cup victory over Argentina?
13. Which 2002 World Cup team was coached by Oleg Romantsev?
14. Who missed a penalty in normal time for the Republic of Ireland against Spain in the 2002 World Cup?
15. Which 2002 World Cup squad featured two Southampton players?

1. Roy Keane 2. Argentina 3. Three 4. Senegal 5. Miroslav Klose 6. Costa Rica 7. Joe Cole 8. Rivaldo 9. Three 10. Branko Strupar 11. Internazionale 12. David Beckham 13. Russia 14. Ian Harte 15. Ecuador.

Quiz 2

1. Who scored Germany's goals in the quarter-final and semi-final, but missed the final through suspension?
2. Which three teams failed to score in the 2002 World Cup?
3. Who scored Argentina's winning goal against Nigeria in the 2002 World Cup?
4. Which Premiership team had players on each team in the match between the Republic of Ireland and Cameroon?
5. Who won the Golden Boot as top scorer in the 2002 World Cup?
6. Which player, who signed for Arsenal, scored the only goal in Japan's historic 1–0 victory over Russia?
7. Who scored his first international goal for England against Sweden in the 2002 World Cup?
8. Which 2002 World Cup team was coached by Bora Milutinovic?
9. Who scored a penalty for Spain in their 3–1 win over Slovenia in the 2002 World Cup?
10. Which team knocked Sweden out of the 2002 World Cup?
11. Who scored the fastest goal in the 2002 World Cup?
12. Which team beat France 2–0 to knock them out of the 2002 World Cup?
13. Who refereed the 2002 World Cup Final?
14. Which 2002 World Cup team was coached by Hernan Dario Gomez?
15. Who scored South Korea's golden goal that knocked Italy out of the 2002 World Cup?

1. Michael Ballack 2. France, China and Saudi Arabia 3. Gabriel Batistuta 4. Sunderland (McAteer and Mboma) 5. Ronaldo, Brazil 6. Junichi Inamoto 7. Sol Campbell 8. China 9. Fernando Hierro 10. Senegal 11. Hakan Sükür (Turkey v South Korea) 12. Denmark 13. Pierluigi Collina 14. Ecuador 15. Ahn Jung-Hwan.

Quiz 3

1. Which Leeds United player scored for South Africa against Spain in the 2002 World Cup?
2. Who coached the Italian team at the 2002 World Cup?
3. Which team knocked Japan out of the 2002 World Cup?
4. Who was the only Premiership player in Poland's 2002 World Cup squad?
5. Which 2002 World Cup team was coached by Bruce Arena?
6. Who scored the Republic of Ireland's equaliser against Cameroon in the 2002 World Cup?
7. Which country was coached by former Italy boss Cesare Maldini in the 2002 World Cup?
8. Who scored two goals in Denmark's 2–1 victory over Uruguay?
9. Which team beat South Korea 3–2 in the third-place play-off at the 2002 World Cup?
10. Who captained Brazil at the 2002 World Cup?
11. Which 2002 World Cup team was coached by Guus Hiddink?
12. Who scored a last-minute penalty for the Republic of Ireland against Spain in the 2002 World Cup?
13. Which Croatian defender was sent off in their match against Mexico in the 2002 World Cup?
14. Who came off the bench to score Italy's equaliser against Mexico in the 2002 World Cup?
15. Against which team did Brazil score the most goals in the 2002 World Cup?

1. Lucas Radebe 2. Giovanni Trapattoni 3. Turkey 4. Jerzy Dudek 5. USA 6. Matt Holland 7. Paraguay 8. Jon Dahl Tomasson 9. Turkey 10. Cafu 11. South Korea 12. Robbie Keane 13. Boris Zivkovic 14. Alessandro Del Piero 15. Costa Rica (5).

Quiz 4

1. Who scored Brazil's winning goal against England before being sent off?
2. Which 2002 World Cup team was coached by Tommy Soderberg and Lars Lagerback?
3. Who scored both of Italy's goals in their 2–0 win over Ecuador?
4. Which two countries achieved maximum points in the group stages of the 2002 World Cup?
5. Who was the most-capped player in Italy's 2002 World Cup squad?
6. Which Manchester City striker scored for Costa Rica in the 2002 World Cup?
7. Who scored Sweden's equaliser against England in the 2002 World Cup?
8. Which 2002 World Cup team was coached by Jomo Sono?
9. Which Manchester United player scored for Uruguay against Senegal in the 2002 World Cup?
10. Which team knocked Mexico out of the 2002 World Cup?
11. Who was Paraguay's eccentric goalkeeper and captain?
12. Which two Turkey players were sent off in their first match against Brazil in the 2002 World Cup?
13. Who scored a penalty to give South Africa a 2–2 draw against Paraguay?
14. Which team won group F with only five points in the 2002 World Cup?
15. Who was credited with England's opening goal against Denmark in the 2002 World Cup?

1. Ronaldinho 2. Sweden 3. Christian Vieri 4. Brazil and Spain 5. Paolo Maldini 6. Paulo Wanchope 7. Niclas Alexandersson 8. South Africa 9. Diego Forlán 10. USA 11. Jose Luis Chilavert 12. Alpay and Hakan Unsal 13. Quinton Fortune 14. Sweden 15. Rio Ferdinand.

Quiz 5

1. Which goalkeeper won the Lev Yashin trophy in the 2002 World Cup?
2. Who was Brazil's coach at the 2002 World Cup?
3. Which team knocked Denmark out of the 2002 World Cup?
4. Which two teams beat Portugal in the group stages of the 2002 World Cup?
5. Which Celtic player scored both of Sweden's goals in their 2–1 victory over Nigeria in the 2002 World Cup?
6. Who were the two Premiership players in Germany's 2002 World Cup squad?
7. Which 2002 World Cup team was coached by Bruno Metsu?
8. Who scored Spain's opening goal in their 3–1 win over Slovenia in the 2002 World Cup?
9. Which Watford defender was a member of South Africa's 2002 World Cup squad?
10. Who scored the golden goal that took Turkey to the semi-finals of the 2002 World Cup?
11. Which country did the Nigerian-born striker Emmanuel Olisadebe play for in the 2002 World Cup?
12. Who was Belgium's top scorer with three goals in the 2002 World Cup?
13. Which 2002 World Cup team was coached by Javier Aguirre?
14. Who was the only Premiership player in Argentina's 2002 World Cup squad?
15. Which 2002 World Cup team had the youngest coach?

1. Oliver Kahn, Germany 2. Luiz Felipe Scolari 3. England 4. USA and South Korea 5. Henrik Larsson 6. Christian Ziege and Dietmar Hamann 7. Senegal 8. Raúl 9. Pierre Issa 10. Ilhan Mansiz 11. Poland 12. Marc Wilmots 13. Mexico 14. Juan Sebastián Veron 15. Slovenia.

World Cup Winners

Argentina

1. Who were Argentina's first-ever opponents in the World Cup Finals?
2. What was the score in that match?
3. Who did Argentina beat 6–1 in the 1930 semi-finals – USA or Yugoslavia?
4. Argentina were beaten in the first round in 1934. By whom?
5. Name one of the three other teams in Argentina's group for the first round of the 1958 finals.
6. Which team beat Argentina 6–1 in their third and final group match of 1958?
7. Argentina first faced England in the World Cup in 1962. Who won?
8. What was the score?
9. Name any of England's scorers.
10. Who was in goal for England against Argentina in 1962?
11. Where did Argentina play their group games in 1966?
12. Which other three teams were in their 1966 group?
13. Who scored England's goal in the 1966 quarter-final with Argentina at Wembley?
14. Was the attendance at Wembley that day more or less than 90,000?
15. Argentina suffered defeat in their first match of the 1974 finals. Who were their Eastern European conquerors?

1. France in 1930 2. 1–0 to Argentina 3. USA 4. Sweden 5. West Germany, Northern Ireland and Czechoslovakia 6. Czechoslovakia 7. England 8. 3–1 9. Ron Flowers, Bobby Charlton and Jimmy Greaves 10. Ron Springett 11. Villa Park and Hillsborough 12. Spain, West Germany and Switzerland 13. Geoff Hurst 14. More – 90, 584 15. Poland.

Argentina

1. Argentina's first win of 1974 came in their third game, against a team making their only finals appearance. Who were they?
2. Argentina had three opponents in the second stage. Name one of them.
3. What was the score in the Argentina–Holland game in 1974?
4. Who were the hosts of the 1978 finals?
5. Their first opponents in the 1978 finals were European. Name them.
6. Who defeated Argentina in the final group game – Italy or France?
7. Who did Argentina defeat to qualify for the final of 1978?
8. Who was Argentina's captain in 1978?
9. Who defeated Argentina in the opening game of 1982 – Belgium, Hungary or Italy?
10. Who scored twice in Argentina's 4–1 defeat of Hungary in 1982?
11. Which future Tottenham manager also scored in that game?
12. Who was sent off in Argentina's defeat by Brazil?
13. In 1986 Argentina faced and beat a country they had not played for 56 years in a World Cup Finals series. Who?
14. What was the score: 1–0, 2–0 or 3–0?
15. Who scored for Argentina in that game?

1. Haiti 2. Holland, Brazil and East Germany 3.Holland won 4–1 4. Argentina 5. Hungary 6. Italy 1–0 7. Peru 6–0 8. Daniel Passarella 9. Belgium 10. Diego Maradona 11. Ossie Ardiles 12. Diego Maradona 13. Uruguay 14. Argentina won 1–0 15. Pedro Pasculli

Argentina

1. Who were Argentina's opponents in the 1986 World Cup semi-finals?
2. What was the score?
3. Who scored the opening goal in the 1986 World Cup Final?
4. Who was Argentina's top goalscorer in 1986?
5. Which player scored the winning goal in the 1986 final?
6. Argentina lost 1–0 in the opening game of 1990. Who to?
7. Who scored in 1990 for Argentina in their 2–0 win over the USSR?
8. What was the score in Argentina's quarter-final after 120 minutes?
9. Who were their opponents?
10. Argentina went on to win on penalties. By what score?
11. Who scored Argentina's equaliser in the semi-final against Italy?
12. That game ended 1–1. What was the score after the penalty shoot-out?
13. Which Argentinian became the first player to be sent off in a World Cup Final?
14. Who was Argentina's goalkeeper in the 1990 final?
15. Who scored a hat-trick in Argentina's first game of 1994?

1. Belgium 2. 2–0 to Argentina 3. Jose-Luis Brown 4. Diego Maradona 5. Jorge Burruchaga 6. Cameroon 7. Troglio Burruchaga 8. 0–0 9. Yugoslavia 10. 3–2 11. Claudio Caniggia 12. 4–3 13. Pedro Monzon 14. Goicoechea 15. Gabriel Batistuta.

Argentina

1. Who were the opponents in Argentina's first game of 1994?
2. Argentina suffered defeat in their third game of 1994. Who to?
3. Which team beat Argentina in the second round?
4. Who scored Argentina's goals in that game?
5. How many goals did Argentina concede at the group stage in 1998?
6. How many games did they win at the group stage?
7. And how many goals did they score at the group stage?
8. Who did they score five of these goals against?
9. How many of these goals were scored after the dismissal of Darryl Powell in the 47th minute?
10. How many penalties, other than the shoot-out, were scored in the second round England–Argentina clash?
11. What was the score in the penalty shoot-out?
12. Who scored Argentina's goal in the quarter-final against Holland?
13. What was special about Lopez' goal?
14. When did Dennis Bergkamp score Holland's winner in that match?
15. Who is Argentina's top scorer in World Cup Finals?

1. Greece 2. Bulgaria 3. Romania 4. Gabriel Batistuta and Abel Balbo 5. None 6. Three 7. Seven 8. Jamaica 9. Four 10. Two, one for either side 11. 4–3 to Argentina 12. Claudio Lopez 13. It was the 100th goal scored by Argentina at World Cups 14. 89th minute 15. Gabriel Batistuta.

Brazil

1. Brazil's first–ever World Cup game was against whom?
2. What was the full–time score?
3. How many games did Brazil play in the 1934 World Cup tournament?
4. Who were their opponents?
5. In an amazing match, who did Brazil beat 6–5 after extra time in the first round of the 1938 finals?
6. Who then beat Brazil in the semi–finals?
7. Brazil hosted the 1950 finals. Name one of the three other countries in their first–round group.
8. Who held them to a 2–2 draw in the group stages?
9. How many games did Brazil play in the 1954 finals?
10. Who ended their tournament in the quarter–finals?
11. Brazil faced England for the first time in 1958. What was the score?
12. Pele scored his first World Cup goal in 1958. Against which country?
13. Who did Brazil beat 5–2 in the semi–finals?
14. How many goals did Pele score in the 1958 tournament altogether?
15. Which player scored in Brazil's first game of 1962 and later went on to manage them in the World Cup?

1. Yugoslavia 2. Yugoslavia 2–1 Brazil 3. One 4. Spain 5. Poland 6. Italy 7. Mexico, Switzerland and Yugoslavia 8. Switzerland 9. Three 10. Hungary 11. 0–0 12. Wales 13. France 14. Six 15. Mario Zagalo.

Brazil

1. Pele also scored in Brazil's first game of the 1962 finals. Who were their opponents?
2. England were Brazil's opponents in the quarter-finals. Who won?
3. Which fellow South American team did Brazil beat in the semi-finals?
4. Who did Brazil beat twice in the 1962 finals?
5. Which three players scored for Brazil in the final?
6. Brazil suffered two defeats to be knocked out in 1966. Who beat them?
7. Who scored in all of Brazil's 1970 World Cup Finals matches?
8. Who scored twice for Brazil against Peru in the quarter-final?
9. Who scored Brazil's 100th World Cup goal?
10. Who captained Brazil in 1970?
11. What did Brazil keep after their 1970 success?
12. Name one of Brazil's three opponents in their second-round group of 1974?
13. Who scored the only goal in Brazil's third group game against Austria?
14. Argentina were Brazil's next opponents. What was the score?
15. Who beat Brazil to make it to the 1974 final?

1. Mexico 2. Brazil 3–1 3. Chile 4. Czechoslovakia 5. Amarildo, Zito, Vava 6. Hungary and Portugal 7. Jairzinho 8. Tostao 9. Pele 10. Carlos Alberto 11. The Jules Rimet Trophy 12. East Germany, Argentina and Holland 13. Roberto 14. 0–0 15. Holland.

Brazil

1. Scotland were in Brazil's group in 1982. Which two other countries were their first-round opponents?
2. Four players scored for Brazil against Scotland in 1982. Name two.
3. What was the final score in the classic 1982 match between Brazil and Italy?
4. Which British country was beaten 3–0 by Brazil in the first round of the 1986 finals?
5. Who beat Brazil on penalties in the quarter-finals?
6. Who missed a penalty during that game before the shoot-out?
7. Scotland were beaten by Brazil in 1990. What was the score?
8. Who captained Brazil in their first game of USA 94?
9. Who, for Brazil, scored the goal that beat the hosts in 1994?
10. Who scored the winning goal in Brazil's quarter-final win over Holland?
11. Who did Brazil beat in the semi-finals?
12. Which Brazilian failed with his penalty in the shoot-out in the final?
13. Who was Brazil's captain for the final?
14. Who in the 1994 squad was a cousin of famous Brazilian player Socrates?
15. The youngest player in the Brazil squad, then aged 17, did not play a single game in 1994. He later went on to be the World Cup's top-scorer of all time with 15 goals. Who was he?

1. USSR and New Zealand 2. Zico, Oscar, Eder and Falcao 3. Italy 3 Brazil 2 4. Northern Ireland 5. France 6. Zico 7. 1–0 8. Rai 9. Bebeto 10. Branco 11. Sweden 12. Marcio Santos 13. Dunga 14. Rai 15. Ronaldo.

England

1. Who were England's first-ever opponents in the World Cup Finals?
2. Who in that match became England's first-ever goalscorer in the World Cup Finals?
3. In which year was that?
4. How many victories did England manage in their first finals?
5. Which European nation beat them 1–0 in their third and last match of the 1950 finals?
6. Who was England's first World Cup captain?
7. What was the result of England's high-scoring draw against Belgium in the 1954 finals?
8. Which two England players scored twice in that game?
9. Who did England beat in their second match in 1954?
10. Who did England then face in the quarter-finals?
11. Which two legendary England players scored in that match?
12. What was the final score?
13. England faced which country in their first match of the 1958 finals?
14. What was the final score in that match?
15. Who then eliminated England 1–0 in a play-off?

1. Chile 2. Stan Mortensen 3. 1950 4. One 5. Spain 6. Billy Wright 7. 4–4 8. Ivor Broadis, Nat Lofthouse 9. Switzerland 10. Uruguay 11. Nat Lofthouse, Tom Finney 12. 4–2 to Uruguay 13. USSR 14. 2–2 15. USSR.

England

1. Which future England manager played in the 1958 side?
2. One of his team-mates went on to become his assistant with England. Who was that?
3. Which country did England face first in Chile in 1962?
4. What was the score?
5. Which Manchester United player scored for England in their next match against Argentina?
6. Who knocked England out in the quarter-finals, 3–1?
7. England were the sole British representatives in the 1962 finals. True or false?
8. Who were England's first opponents in the 1966 finals?
9. What was the final score in that game?
10. Who scored England's first goal of the finals?
11. Who did England face in their last group match?
12. Which Tottenham striker suffered an injury against France and never regained his place?
13. Who replaced him for the quarter-finals and scored the winner against Argentina?
14. Who man-marked Eusebio in England's semi-final win over Portugal?
15. What was the date of the 1966 World Cup Final?

1. Bobby Robson 2. Don Howe 3. Hungary 4. England lost 2–1 5. Bobby Charlton 6. Brazil 7. True 8. Uruguay 9. 0–0 10. Bobby Charlton 11. France 12. Jimmy Greaves 13. Geoff Hurst 14. Nobby Stiles 15. 30 July.

England

1. Who scored England's 'other' goal in their 4–2 victory over West Germany in 1966, in addition to Geoff Hurst's hat-trick?
2. Against whom did England begin their defence of the trophy four years later in Mexico?
3. Who scored the winner for Brazil in England's next match of the 1970 finals?
4. Who scored West Germany's winning goal in the 1970 quarter-final against England?
5. Who replaced Gordon Banks in the England goal for that game?
6. Who came on as a second-half substitute in place of Bobby Charlton?
7. After 1970, how many years was it before England appeared in the World Cup Finals again?
8. When they did so, who were their first opponents in Spain?
9. Where were all of England's first-round group matches played in the 1982 finals?
10. Which two squad members appeared only in England's last match of the 1982 finals, and only then as substitutes?
11. Which country progressed from England's second-round group, knocking England out?
12. England failed to score in four consecutive World Cup Finals matches, against West Germany, Spain, Portugal and which other team?
13. Who ended the run with a hat-trick against Poland in 1986?
14. Where were England's group games played in Mexico that year?
15. Who was on-target against Paraguay in the second round along with Gary Lineker?

1. Martin Peters 2. Romania 3. Jairzinho 4. Gerd Mueller 5. Peter Bonetti 6. Colin Bell 7. Twelve 8. France 9. Bilbao 10. Trevor Brooking, Kevin Keegan 11. West Germany 12. Morocco 13. Gary Lineker 14. Monterrey 15. Peter Beardsley.

England

1. In the first game of Italia 90, who equalised for the Republic of Ireland against England?
2. Where were all of England's group matches played that year?
3. Who scored the winner for England in their last group match?
4. Who were their opponents?
5. Who did England then face in the second round?
6. Who scored England's winner in the last minute of extra-time?
7. Who saved England in the quarter-final against Cameroon with an equalizing penalty in normal time?
8. What was the final score in that match after extra-time?
9. Who scored for West Germany against England in the 1990 semi-final?
10. Who was the German goalkeeper who saved from Stuart Pearce in the penalty shoot-out to decide that match?
11. England were top scorers in their first-round group at France 1998. True or false?
12. Who were the only team not to lose to England at the group stage?
13. Where was the match played?
14. Southampton's Dan Petrescu, then with Chelsea, scored the winner in which minute?
15. Who had earlier equalized for England?

1. Kevin Sheedy 2. Cagliari 3. Mark Wright 4. Egypt 5. Belgium 6. David Platt 7. Gary Lineker 8. 3–2 to England 9. Andreas Brehme 10. Bodo Illgner 11. True, with five goals 12. Romania who won 2–0 13. Toulouse 14. 90th 15. Michael Owen.

France

1. France played in the first-ever World Cup game in 1930. True or false?
2. In the three group games in 1930, France played non-European nations. True or false?
3. Who was captain of France?
4. How many goals did France score in the 1930 finals?
5. How many games did France play in Italy in 1934?
6. Who did France beat in their first game as hosts in 1938?
7. Who scored twice for France in that game – Gino Colaussi, Jean Nicolas or Silvio Piola?
8. Who beat France in the second round in 1938?
9. How many World Cup games did France play in 1938?
10. How many goals did France score in their first World Cup match in 1958? Was it five, seven or nine?
11. Who were their opponents from South America?
12. Which British nation was the first to face France in World Cup Finals?
13. What was the score?
14. Just Fontaine scored in every French game in 1958. True or false?
15. How many World Cup goals did Fontaine score in that tournament?

1. True 2. True 3. Alex Villaplane 4. Four 5. One 6. Belgium 7. Jean Nicolas 8. Italy 9. Two 10. Seven 11. Paraguay 12. Scotland 13. France won 2–1 14. True 15. Thirteen.

France

1. How many points did France finish with at the 1966 finals?
2. Who were their first, non-European opponents?
3. What was the score?
4. A 2–0 defeat ended France's 1966 tournament. Who beat them?
5. When was the next time France qualified?
6. France suffered two 2–1 defeats in Argentina in 1978. By whom?
7. Who were France's opening opponents in 1982?
8. What was the score in the France–England match in 1982?
9. Who were France's opponents in the second-round group?
10. What was France's winning score against Austria?
11. In what peculiar circumstances was Alain Giresse's goal ruled out against minnows Kuwait?
12. Who were France's 1982 semi-final opponents?
13. Who in extra-time scored France's third goal?
14. What was the score after extra-time?
15. What was the score in the penalty shoot-out?

1. One 2. Mexico 3. 1–1 4. England 5. 1978 6. Italy and Argentina 7. England 8. France lost 3–1 9. Austria and Northern Ireland 10. 1–0 11. A member of the Kuwaiti royal family ran on to the pitch protesting that the Kuwait team had stopped playing after hearing a whistle from the crowd and told his players to leave the pitch. The Soviet referee then disallowed the goal, an action for which he was later suspended. France won 4–1 12. West Germany 13. Alain Giresse 14. 3–3 15. West Germany won 5–4.

France

1. Who were France's first opponents from across the Atlantic in 1986?
2. What was the score?
3. Who were beaten 3–0 by France in the group stages?
4. Which country, previous World Cup winners, were beaten by France in the second round?
5. Who were France's semi-final opponents?
6. What was the score?
7. What was the score in France's first and last matches of the 1998 tournament?
8. Which French player was sent off against Saudi Arabia?
9. Who scored the golden goal that beat Paraguay in the second round?
10. Which team did France beat on penalties?
11. Which team playing in their first World Cup did France beat in the semi-finals?
12. Which French player was sent off in the semi-finals thus missing the final?
13. Which French player scored two goals in the final?
14. Who was the unlikely scorer of the other?
15. Which French player was sent off in the final?

1. Canada 2. France won 1–0 3. Hungary 4. Italy 5. West Germany 6. France lost 2–0 7. 3–0 8. Zinedine Zidane 9. Laurent Blanc 10. Italy in the quarter-finals 11. Croatia 12. Laurent Blanc 13. Zinedine Zidane 14. Defender Emmanuel Petit 15. Marcel Desailly.

Germany

1. Who were West Germany's first World Cup opponents?
2. Who defeated West Germany in the second game of the 1954 finals?
3. What was the score?
4. At which stage of the 1954 finals did West Germany meet Hungary for the second time?
5. Who were West Germany's semi-final opponents in 1954?
6. West Germany faced Northern Ireland in 1958. Who scored twice for the Irish?
7. Which legendary German scored his first World Cup goal against Ireland?
8. Who beat West Germany in the 1958 semi-finals?
9. West Germany's first game in the 1962 tournament was goalless. Who were their opponents?
10. Who beat West Germany in the quarter-finals?
11. Who were beaten 5–0 in West Germany's first game in England 1966?
12. Which South Americans were beaten 4–0 in the quarter-finals?
13. Who scored West Germany's equalizer in the last minute of normal time in the final?
14. How many goals did Gerd Müller score in the 1970 finals?
15. Who scored in their quarter-final defeat of England?

1. Turkey 2. Hungary 3. 8–3 4. Final 5. Austria 6. Peter McParland 7. Uwe Seeler 8. Sweden 9. Italy 10. Yugoslavia 11. Switzerland 12. Uruguay 13. Weber 14. Ten 15. Franz Beckenbauer, Uwe Seeler and Gerd Müller.

Germany

1. Who scored the first German goal in the 1974 finals?
2. Who beat West Germany in the first round in 1974?
3. This was West Germany's first World Cup meeting with that team. True or false?
4. Which side was beaten 1–0 to guarantee West Germany their place in the final?
5. Who equalised for West Germany in the final?
6. Who did West Germany beat 6–0 in the 1978 tournament?
7. Who scored an own-goal in West Germany's last match of 1978?
8. Which country beat them in that game?
9. What was the score?
10. West Germany suffered defeat by an African nation in their first game of 1982. Who was it?
11. Who did they meet in the semi-finals?
12. What was unusual about this semi?
13. Who was the German goalkeeper guilty of perhaps the worst foul in World Cup history?
14. What was the score after extra time: 1–1, 2–2 or 3–3?
15. Who scored the winning penalty in the shoot-out?

1. Paul Breitner 2. East Germany 3. True 4. Poland 5. Paul Breitner 6. Mexico 7. Berti Vogts 8. Austria 9. 3–2 10. Algeria 11. France 12. It was the first to be settled on penalties 13. Harald Schumacher 14. 3–3 15. Horst Hrubesch.

Germany

1. Which team did Germany meet in the 1982 World Cup Final?
2. How did Antonio Cabrini achieve notoriety in this game?
3. What was the score in the 1982 final?
4. Who scored in West Germany's first two group games in 1986?
5. What was the Germany–Scotland score?
6. Who scored for Scotland?
7. Who did West Germany beat in a penalty shoot-out in the quarter-final?
8. What was the score after extra-time?
9. Who scored in the 1986 semi-final and final for West Germany?
10. Whom did West Germany beat in the semi-final?
11. Who scored Argentina's late winner in the final?
12. How many finals had the Germans now lost?
13. What does the German word *Schadenfreude* mean?
14. Who scored twice for West Germany against Yugoslavia in 1990?
15. West Germany played the group games in Milan's San Siro Stadium. Which three of their players played their club football there?

1. Italy 2. He was the first player to miss a penalty in a World Cup Final 3. Italy 3 West Germany 1 4. Klaus Allofs 5. 2–1 6. Gordon Strachan 7. Mexico 8. 0–0 9. Rudi Voeller 10. France 11. Burrachaga 12. Three 13. Taking pleasure in another's misfortune, which was what the rest of the world now did at Germany's expense. They had seemed unbeatable before the competition began 14. Lothar Matthaeus 15. Lothar Matthaeus, Andreas Brehme, Jurgen Klinsmann.

Germany

1. What was the Germany–Holland score in 1990?
2. Which two players were sent off in that game?
3. Who did the Germans beat in the quarter-final?
4. Who scored for England in normal time in the semi?
5. How did Pedro Monzon bring himself to the world's attention in the 1990 final?
6. How many red cards were there in that game?
7. Who scored for Germany?
8. In France 1998 Germany scored more goals than anyone else in their group. True or false?
9. Germany scored twice in each game and won them all. True or false?
10. Who did Germany play in the second round?
11. Who took the lead in that game?
12. What was the final score?
13. By what score did Germany lose to Croatia in the quarter-finals?
14. All the goals came after the Germans had been reduced to ten men, but who was sent off?
15. Who scored Croatia's first goal?

1. 2–1 2. Frank Rijkaard and Rudi Voeller 3. Czechoslovakia 4. Gary Lineker 5. He was the first to receive a red card in a World Cup Final 6. Two 7. Andy Brehme (penalty) 8. True with six 9. False; drew 2–2 with Yugoslavia 10. Mexico 11. Mexico 12. 2–1 to Germany 13. 3–0 14. Christian Woerns 15. Robert Jarni.

Italy

1. Who were Italy's first–ever World Cup opponents?
2. What year was it?
3. What was the score?
4. Who did Italy meet in the semi–final?
5. Who scored the only goal?
6. Who were their opponents in the final?
7. Who scored the winning goal in extra–time of the final?
8. Who was Italy's captain?
9. Which two Italian players scored in both the 1934 and 1938 tournaments?
10. Who did Italy beat in the second round in 1938?
11. Who were Italy's 1938 semi–final opponents?
12. Who did Italy beat in their second game in 1950?
13. Did Italy qualify for the second round?
14. Who did Italy face twice in 1954?
15. Who knocked Italy out of the 1954 finals?

1. USA 2. 1934 3. Italy won 7–1 4. Austria 5. Enrique Guaita 6. Czechoslovakia 7. Angelo Schiavio 8. Gianpiero Combi 9. Giovanni Ferrari and Guiseppe Meazza 10. France 11. Brazil 12. Paraguay 13. No 14. Switzerland 15. Switzerland.

Italy

1. Who were in Italy's group in 1962?
2. Which team beat Italy in the 1962 group stage?
3. Who were Italy's 2–0 opening victims in England in 1966?
4. How many more goals did Italy score in that tournament?
5. Who produced the shock of 1966 by beating Italy in the last group game?
6. What was the score in that match?
7. Who scored Italy's first goal in 1970?
8. Who were their opponents?
9. Who held Italy to a shock 0–0 draw in 1970?
10. Who were beaten 4–1 by Italy in the quarter-final?
11. Who were Italy's opponents in a classic semi-final?
12. Who scored the winning goal?
13. Who scored Italy's goal in the 4–1 defeat by Brazil in the final?
14. Who were Italy's opening victims in 1974?
15. Which legendary player scored Italy's opening goal in the 1978 finals?

1. West Germany, Chile and Switzerland 2. Chile 3. Chile 4. None 5. North Korea 6. 1-0 7. Angelo Domenghini 8. Sweden 9. Israel 10. Mexico 11. West Germany 12. Gianni Rivera 13. Roberto Boninsegna 14 Haiti 15. Paolo Rossi

Italy

1. Who were beaten 3–1 by Italy in the 1978 group stage – Hungary or Argentina?
2. Who was the only Italian player to score in the second stage?
3. Who were Italy's opponents in the third-place play-off?
4. Who won?
5. How many group games did Italy win in España 82?
6. Who did Italy beat 2–1 in the second-round group stage?
7. Who scored a hat-trick for Italy against Brazil at the same stage?
8. Who were Italy's 1982 semi-final opponents?
9. What was the score?
10. Who scored Italy's final goal against West Germany in the final?
11. What was Italy's winning score?
12. Who scored Italy's first goal in Mexico 86?
13. Who scored Italy's third goal in the game against South Korea?
14. Who knocked out Italy in the second round?
15. How many goals did Italy concede in the first five games of 1990?

1. Hungary 2. Paolo Rossi 3. Brazil 4. Brazil 2–1 5. None 6. Argentina 7. Paolo Rossi 8. Poland 9. 2–0 10. Alessandro Altobelli 11. 3–1 12. Alessandro Altobelli 13. Kwang-rae of South Korea (own goal) 14. France 15. None.

Italy

1. Who beat Italy on penalties in the 1990 semi-final?
2. Who scored a goal each for Italy in the 1990 third-place play-off?
3. Who were Italy's first opponents in 1994?
4. Who were Italy's second-round opponents?
5. Who scored twice for Italy against them?
6. Who was sent off against Nigeria after coming on as a sub?
7. Both Baggios scored in Italy's quarter-final win over Spain. Who scored first?
8. Which team did Italy beat in the semi-finals?
9. Who missed penalties for Italy in the final shoot-out?
10. Why did 'third time lucky' not ring true for the Italians in France 98?
11. Who did Italy lose to on penalties in 1998?
12. What was the score in the match after extra-time?
13. At the group stage, what did Italy manage that no other team in their group did?
14. Who were these wins against?
15. Which team, who beat Brazil at the group stage, then lost to Italy in the second round?

1. Argentina 2. Roberto Baggio, Toto Schillaci 3. Republic of Ireland 4. Nigeria 5. Roberto Baggio 6. Gianfranco Zola 7. Dino 8. Bulgaria 9. Franco Baresi, Daniele Massaro and Roberto Baggio 10. They also lost on penalties in 1990 and 1994 11. France 12. 0–0 13. They won! All the other games were draws 14. Austria and Cameroon 15. Norway.

Uruguay

1. In which country did Uruguay play their first World Cup match?
2. Uruguay's first match was against another South American nation. Who was it?
3. Uruguay won that first match. Was the score 1–0, 2–0 or 2–1?
4. Their first World Cup goalscorer was definitely not a Cuban. What was his name?
5. Uruguay won the 1930 World Cup after playing how many games?
6. How many of those matches did they win?
7. How many goals did Uruguay score in that first series – 10, 12 or 15?
8. Which South American country did Uruguay beat in the final of 1930?
9. Six goals were scored in that final. What was the scoreline?
10. Who scored a hat-trick for Uruguay against Yugoslavia in the 1930 semi-finals?
11. Uruguay beat Yugoslavia in that match by what score?
12. When did Uruguay next appear in the World Cup Finals?
13. Their first match of the 1950 World Cup Finals was against another South American team. Who was it?
14. Uruguay won that match by a runaway score. Was it 7–0, 8–0 or 9–0?
15. Uruguay beat Brazil 2–1 in the final pool in 1950 to win the World Cup again. Who scored their goals?

1. Uruguay 2. Peru 3. 1–0 4. Hector Castro 5. Four 6. All of them 7. 15 8. Argentina 9. 4–2 10. Pedro Cea 11. 6–1 12. 1950 13. Bolivia 14. 8–0 15. Juan Schiaffino and Alcides Ghiggia.

Uruguay

1. How many of their four matches in the 1950 finals in Brazil did Uruguay lose?
2. They drew 2–2 with one European country in 1950. Who was it?
3. In how many World Cup Finals series have Uruguay participated?
4. When was their last appearance in the tournament?
5. How many spectators were at their 1950 'final' against Brazil – to the nearest 1,000?
6. Where did Uruguay finish in the 1954 finals in Switzerland?
7. Who beat them in the third-place play-off?
8. What was the score?
9. Who did Uruguay beat 7–0 in the 1954 finals?
10. Uruguay failed to qualify for the 1958 finals. Who headed their South American group – Paraguay or Colombia?
11. Paraguay beat Uruguay 5–0 in their first group match. What was the score in the return game?
12. How many games did Uruguay play in the 1962 finals in Chile – two, three or five?
13. Uruguay were beaten by two Eastern European nations in 1962. Who were they?
14. They defeated a South American team in those finals. Who?
15. How many games did Uruguay play in the 1966 series in England?

1. None 2. Spain 3. Ten 4. 2002 5. 200,000 6. Fourth 7. Austria 8. 3–1 9. Scotland 10. Paraguay 11. Uruguay won 2–0 12. Three 13. Yugoslavia and USSR 14. Colombia 15. Four.

Uruguay

1. Uruguay's only victory of the 1966 finals was by 2–1 against whom?
2. They were beaten 4–0 in the quarter-finals by whom?
3. Two Uruguayans were sent off in the 1966 finals. Who were they?
4. How many games did Uruguay play in the 1970 finals in Mexico?
5. How many times were they beaten?
6. Who beat them in the 1970 semi-finals?
7. Uruguay scored only once in West Germany in the 1974 finals. Who got their goal?
8. Uruguay finished with ten men against Holland in their first finals match of 1974. Who was ordered off?
9. They qualified for the 1974 finals with a superior goals return over which team in their South American group?
10. What was the result of Uruguay's home group match against that team?
11. After 1974, how many years elapsed before Uruguay's next appearance in the finals?
12. They failed to qualify in 1978, finishing second in their group to whom?
13. Who beat Uruguay to the qualifying spot in 1982?
14. How many of their four matches in the 1986 finals did Uruguay win?
15. How many did they lose?

1. France 2. West Germany 3. Horacio Troche and Hector Silva 4. Six 5. Three 6. Brazil 7. Ricardo Pavoni 8. Julio Montero-Castillo 9. Colombia 10. Colombia won 1–0 11. Twelve 12. Bolivia 13. Peru 14. None 15. Two.

World Cup History

Quiz 1

1. In which year did Croatia make their first appearance in the finals?
2. For which Italian club was Dan Petrescu playing at the time of USA 94?
3. To date, how many times have the Dutch East Indies played in the finals?
4. For which Dutch side was Belgium's Luc Nilis playing at the time of France 98?
5. By what score did England beat Kuwait in the first round of the 1982 finals?
6. For which English club was Scotland's David Speedie playing at the time of the 1986 finals?
7. Who lost all three games in Group A of Italia 90?
8. Who did Yugoslavia beat to qualify for the 1962 finals?
9. Who lost all three games in Group F of USA 94?
10. How many goals did Italy concede in Group 2 of the 1970 finals?
11. Which teams drew 0–0 in the opening game of the 1970 finals?
12. Which team placed third in the 1978 finals?
13. For which Spanish side was West Germany's Bernd Schuster playing at the time of the 1982 finals?
14. Which Asian team finished bottom of Group A in the 1986 finals?
15. What birthday was Pat Jennings celebrating when Northern Ireland lost 3–0 to Brazil in the 1986 finals?

1. 1998 2. Genoa 3. Once 4. PSV Eindhoven 5. 1-0 6. Chelsea 7. USA 8. South Korea 9. Morocco 10. None 11. Russia and Mexico 12. Brazil 13. Barcelona 14. South Korea 15. 41st.

Quiz 2

1. Who did Mexico beat to qualify for the 1962 finals?
2. For which French club side was Sweden's Anders Linderoth playing at the time of the 1978 finals?
3. Up to 2002, in their six games in the finals, how many goals had El Salvador conceded?
4. For which Italian team was Gheorghe Hagi playing at the time of USA 94?
5. Who headed Group 5 of the 1982 finals?
6. Who scored two for England against France in the 1966 finals?
7. For which club side were Bruce Rioch and Don Masson playing at the time of the 1978 finals?
8. How many of their group games did Iraq lose in the 1986 finals?
9. Who beat Argentina in the opening game of Italia 90?
10. Who did Ireland beat in their opening game of USA 94?
11. Which national side did Ali Parvin and Ghafour Djahani represent at the 1978 finals?
12. By what score did Argentina beat Peru in the second phase of the 1978 finals?
13. Which teams opened the 1986 finals on 31 May with a 1–1 draw?
14. Which team finished bottom of England and Italy's qualifying group for the 1978 finals?
15. For which Spanish team was goalkeeper Zubizarreta playing at the time of the 1986 finals?

1. Paraguay 2. Marseille 3. 22 4. Brescia 5. Northern Ireland 6. Roger Hunt 7. Derby County 8. Three 9. Cameroon 10. Italy 11. Iran 12. 6–0 13. Italy and Bulgaria 14. Luxembourg 15. Athletic Bilbao.

Quiz 3

1. How many English club players were in Holland's France 98 squad?
2. Who scored the Republic of Ireland's goal in their 2–1 defeat against Mexico in USA 94?
3. How many goals did the UAE concede in Group D of Italia 90?
4. For which club was Pele playing at the time of the 1970 finals?
5. Which African side did Northern Ireland play in the 1986 finals?
6. Which Spanish club was Romario playing for at the time of USA 94?
7. Who coached Saudi Arabia in France 98?
8. Of Denmark's 22-man squad at the 1998 finals, how many played for English clubs?
9. Who did Brazil beat to qualify for the 1958 finals?
10. Which team did Luis Hernandez represent in France 98?
11. Who lost all three of their games in Group 6 of the 1982 finals?
12. How many goals did Canada score in the 1986 finals?
13. Who lost all three of their Group C games in Italia 90?
14. Which two teams won all three second-phase group games in the 1974 finals?
15. How many of the 12 teams won both their games in phase two of the 1982 finals?

1. Five 2. John Aldridge 3. Eleven 4. Santos 5. Algeria 6. Barcelona 7. Carlos Alberto Parreira 8. Four 9. Peru 10. Mexico 11. New Zealand 12. None 13. Sweden 14. Holland and Germany 15. None.

Quiz 4

1. Who beat Costa Rica in the second round of Italia 90?
2. For which Italian side was Germany's Christian Ziege playing at the time of France 98?
3. Who did Wales beat to qualify for the 1958 finals?
4. What was the aggregate score between Iran and Australia in the 1998 Asia-Oceania play-off for France 98?
5. How many times have Cuba played in the World Cup Finals?
6. How many times have Algeria played in the finals?
7. Which were the only two sides with maximum points after round 1 of the 1986 finals?
8. How many times have Canada played in the finals?
9. Who coached Scotland at France 98?
10. Of France's 22 team members at France 98, how many were playing for English league clubs?
11. By what score did West Germany beat France on penalties in the 1982 semi-finals?
12. Which Asian team lost all three games in Group E of Italia 90?
13. For which club was Gordon Banks playing at the time of the 1970 finals?
14. Who did Mexico beat to qualify for the 1958 finals?
15. Which team did Hans Krankl and Kurt Welzl represent in the 1982 finals?

1. Czechoslovakia 2. AC Milan 3. Israel 4. 3–3 5. Once 6. Twice 7. Brazil and Denmark 8. Once 9. Craig Brown 10. Four 11. 5–4 12. South Korea 13. Stoke City 14. Costa Rica 15. Austria.

Quiz 5

1. Who was West Germany's trainer in the 1974 finals?
2. Which two of the home countries qualified for the 1954 finals?
3. For which German team was Tony Woodcock playing at the time of the 1982 finals?
4. Who scored Scotland's goal in their 1986 2–1 defeat against West Germany?
5. Who lost all eight games in the 1982 World Cup qualifying group headed by Belgium?
6. Who coached Spain in France 98?
7. Who did Italy beat to qualify for the 1962 finals?
8. Which team did Jerzy Gorgon and Robert Gadocha represent in the 1974 finals?
9. How many goals did Mexico concede in Group 1 of the 1970 finals?
10. Who did Germany beat in the opening game of USA 94?
11. For which Italian club was Dino Zoff playing at the time of the 1970 finals?
12. With which side did Scotland draw 0–0 in Group E of the 1986 finals?
13. For which Italian club was Brazil's Falcão playing at the time of the 1982 finals?
14. Who headed Group F after the first phase of Italia 90?
15. Which Spanish side was Bebeto playing for at the time of USA 94?

1. Helmut Schön 2. England and Scotland 3. Cologne 4. Gordon Strachan 5. Cyprus 6. Javier Clemente 7. Israel 8. Poland 9. None 10. Bolivia 11. Napoli 12. Uruguay 13. Roma 14. England 15. Deportivo La Coruña.

Quiz 6

1. To date, how many times have New Zealand appeared in the finals?
2. For which English club was Ray Houghton playing at the time of USA 94?
3. Which German club side was Sweden's Roland Sandberg with at the time of the 1974 finals?
4. Who was Kevin Keegan playing for at the time of the 1982 finals?
5. How many goals did El Salvador score in the 1970 finals?
6. Who scored Scotland's goal in their 1998 2–1 defeat against Brazil?
7. For which French club side was Colombia's Carlos Valderrama playing at the time of Italia 90?
8. In which year did Morocco first appear in the finals?
9. For which English team was Ludek Miklosko playing at the time of Italia 90?
10. For which English club was Peter Shilton playing at the time of Italia 90?
11. Which club was Scotland's David Hay with at the time of the 1974 finals?
12. How many goals did Cameroon concede in Group B in USA 94?
13. For which French club side was Michel Platini playing at the time of the 1978 finals?
14. Who did Austria beat to qualify for the 1954 finals?
15. With which two teams did Morocco draw 0–0 in the 1986 finals?

1. Once 2. Aston Villa 3. Kaiserslautern 4. Southampton 5. None 6. John Collins 7. Montpellier 8. 1970 9. West Ham 10. Derby County 11. Celtic 12. Eleven 13. Nantes 14. Portugal 15. England and Poland

Quiz 7

1. Which team did Augustine Okocha play for in the 1998 finals?
2. For which English club was Kevin Moran playing at the time of Italia 90?
3. Which team did Vicente Pereda and Aaron Padilla represent in the 1970 finals?
4. For which Italian club side was Gianluca Vialli playing at the time of Italia 90?
5. Who knocked Romania out of USA 94 on penalties?
6. Who did Portugal defeat in the 1966 World Cup quarter-finals?
7. For which team was Terry Butcher playing at the time of Italia 90?
8. In which year did Portugal make their second appearance in the finals?
9. For which Italian team was Ruud Gullit playing at the time of Italia 90?
10. In which year did England first compete in the World Cup finals?
11. For which Spanish club was West Germany's Günther Netzer playing at the time of the 1974 finals?
12. By what score did Belgium defeat the USSR in the 1986 finals?
13. Who lost all three games of Group D in USA 94?
14. Who did Turkey beat to qualify for the 1954 finals?
15. For which French club was Holland's Johnny Rep playing at the time of the 1978 finals?

1. Nigeria 2. Sheffield Wednesday 3. Mexico 4. Sampdoria 5. Sweden 6. North Korea 7. Rangers 8. 1986 9. AC Milan 10. 1950 11. Real Madrid 12. 4–3 13. Greece 14. Spain 15. Bastia

Quiz 8

1. For which German club side was Austria's Anton Polster playing at the time of France 98?
2. Which Italian side was Argentina's Batistuta playing for at the time of USA 94?
3. Who scored Jamaica's first goal in the 1998 finals?
4. At the time of France 98, which Italian club was South Africa's Phil Masinga playing for?
5. For which French club side was Mick McCarthy playing at the time of USA 94?
6. For which club side were Paolo Rossi and Marco Tardelli playing at the time of the 1982 finals?
7. Which country did Taher El Khalej represent in France 98?
8. By what score did England beat Paraguay in the 1986 finals?
9. Who did Italy beat to qualify for the 1954 finals?
10. For which English club side was Scotland's Stuart McCall playing during Italia 90?
11. Who coached Italy in France 98?
12. How many goals did Zaire concede in Group 2 of the 1974 finals?
13. For which Spanish side was Brazil's Rivaldo playing at the time of France 98?
14. How many goals did Haiti concede in Group 4 of the 1974 finals?
15. Of Norway's 22 players at the 1998 finals, how many were playing club football in England at the time?

1. Cologne 2. Fiorentina 3. Robbie Earle 4. Bari 5. Lyon 6. Juventus 7. Morocco 8. 3-0 9. Egypt 10. Everton 11. Cesare Maldini 12. Fourteen 13. Barcelona 14. Fourteen 15. Eleven.

Quiz 9

1. For which Italian side was Rudi Völler playing at the time of Italia 90?
2. French striker Just Fontaine notched 13 goals in six games in 1958, still a record for a single tournament. Where was he born and what was the first club he played for?
3. Which team finished second to Argentina in the South American qualifying group for France 98?
4. Who scored Scotland's goal against Norway in the 1998 finals?
5. For which English side was Andy Townsend playing at the time of Italia 90?
6. Who lost all eight of their qualifying games for the 1982 finals in the group headed by Yugoslavia?
7. Of Scotland's 22 players at the 1998 finals, how many played for English clubs at the time?
8. Who did South Korea beat to qualify for the 1954 finals?
9. Who ended his career with a red card in a World Cup final, but still received the Golden Ball award for being the outstanding performer in the competition?
10. By what score did West Germany beat Mexico on penalties in a 1986 World Cup quarter-final?
11. Which South American side finished bottom of Group 3 in the 1974 finals?
12. For which German side was Brazil's Dunga playing at the time of USA 94?
13. Who coached Norway in France 98?
14. Which team did goalkeeper Luis Rubiños represent in the 1970 finals?
15. Which country did Rigobert Song represent in France 98?

1. Roma 2. Marakesh, Morocco. His first club was USM Casablanca 3. Paraguay 4. Craig Burley 5. Norwich City 6. Luxembourg 7. Eight 8. Japan 9. Zinedine Zidane, who was sent off for headbutting Marco Materazzi in 2006 10. 4-1 11. Uruguay 12. VfB Stuttgart 13. Egil Olsen 14. Peru 15. Cameroon.

Quiz 10

1. For which Spanish club was West Germany's Ulrich Stielike playing at the time of the 1982 finals?
2. In which year did Turkey make their first appearance in the finals?
3. For which English club was Eddie McGoldrick playing at the time of USA 94?
4. Which team did Jean-Claude Desir and Philippe Vorbe represent in the 1974 finals?
5. For which French team was Argentinian Jorge Luis Burruchaga playing at the time of the 1986 finals?
6. Who coached France at France 98?
7. For which Belgian team was Poland's Grzegorz Lato playing at the time of the 1982 finals?
8. Which Italian club was Chile's Ivan Zamorano playing for at the time of España 82?
9. How old was Alan Hansen when Scotland's 1982 finals were over?
10. Which country did the USA beat to qualify for the 1934 finals?
11. Who lost all three games in Group 3 of the 1970 finals?
12. Who did the Republic of Ireland beat on penalties in Round 2 of Italia 90?
13. For which Spanish club was Ruben Ayala playing at the time of the German World Cup Finals of 1974?
14. How many teams won all three of their group games in USA 94?
15. Which two teams drew 0–0 in the opening game of the 1978 finals?

1. Real Madrid 2. 1954 3. Arsenal 4. Haiti 5. Nantes 6. Aime Jacquet 7. Lokeren 8. Internazionale 9. 27 10. Mexico 11. Czechoslovakia 12. Romania 13. Atletico Madrid 14. None 15. West Germany and Poland.

Quiz 11

1. Which Italian club was Brazil's Junior playing for at the time of Mexico 86?
2. In which year did Tunisia first appear in the finals?
3. Which Italian side was West Germany's Hans-Peter Briegel playing for at the time of Mexico 86?
4. Who coached Germany in France 98?
5. Which Spanish club was Johann Cruyff playing for at the time of the 1974 finals?
6. Who did Scotland draw 1-1 with in the 1978 finals?
7. Of Italy's 22 players at the 1998 finals, how many were playing with English clubs at the time?
8. For which club was Asa Hartford playing at the time of the 1982 finals?
9. Which country did Egypt beat to qualify for the 1934 finals?
10. What were the scores of both semi-finals in Italia 90?
11. How many goals did Mexico concede in Group 2 of the 1978 finals?
12. Who won all three games in Group 3 of the 1970 finals?
13. By what score did Argentina beat Yugoslavia on penalties in the quarter-final of Italia 90?
14. Which club side did East Germany's Peter Ducke and Bernd Bransch represent at the time of the 1974 finals?
15. Who knocked the Republic of Ireland out of USA 94?

1. Torino 2. 1978 3. Verona 4. Berti Vogts 5. Barcelona 6. Iran 7. One 8. Everton 9. Palestine 10. 1-1
11. 12 12. Brazil 13. 3-2 14. Carl Zeiss Jena 15. Holland.

Quiz 12

1. Which country did Sami al Jaber represent at USA 94?
2. Who headed Group 1 of the 1974 World Cup Finals?
3. Who scored Scotland's goal in their 1974 1–1 draw with Yugoslavia?
4. For which Italian side was Swede Tomas Brolin playing at the time of USA 94?
5. Who scored Wales' first goal in the 1958 finals?
6. Which World Cup hosts played the fewest games in a tournament?
7. Who was Uruguay's first-choice goalkeeper at Mexico 70 – to many the world's No 1 keeper at the time?
8. Who coached Argentina at France 98?
9. For which Spanish side was Hristo Stoichkov playing at the time of USA 94?
10. Which country did Spain beat to qualify for the 1934 finals?
11. Which European side headed Group 3 of the 1978 finals?
12. Which Italian club was Brazil's Edinho playing for at the time of the 1986 finals?
13. For which Italian club was Ray Wilkins playing at the time of the 1986 finals?
14. For which Spanish side was Argentina's Jorge da Silva playing at the time of the 1986 finals?
15. Who drew 0–0 in Group A in Phase 2 of the 1978 finals?

1. Saudi Arabia 2. East Germany 3. Joe Jordan 4. Parma 5. John Charles 6. France (two matches in 1938) 7. Ladislao Mazurkiewicz 8. Daniel Passarella 9. Barcelona 10. Portugal 11. Austria 12. Udinese 13. AC Milan 14. Atletico Madrid 15. Italy and West Germany.

Quiz 13

1. For which Italian side was Jürgen Kohler playing at the time of USA 94?
2. Who scored Scotland's goal in their 3–1 defeat by Peru in 1978?
3. Name the only US player to score in the 2006 World Cup finals.
4. By what score did Brazil beat Wales in the 1958 finals?
5. For which Italian team was Joe Jordan playing at the time of the 1982 finals?
6. Who coached Brazil at France 98?
7. Of the six games in Group 1 of España 82, how many finished goalless?
8. For which Portuguese side was Brazil's Aldair playing at the time of Italia 90?
9. Who beat El Salvador 10–1 in the 1982 finals but still didn't qualify for Phase 2?
10. Which country did Hungary beat to qualify for the 1938 finals?
11. Who lost 1–0 in the opening game of the 1982 finals?
12. For which Italian side was Maradona playing at the time of Italia 90?
13. Which teams drew 0–0 in the opening game of the 1974 finals?
14. In 2006, who became the first English player to score at three World Cup finals?
15. Which country did Daniel Amokachi represent at USA 94?

1. Juventus 2. Joe Jordan 3. Clint Dempsey 4. 1–0 5. AC Milan 6. Mario Zagallo 7. Three 8. Benfica 9. Hungary 10. Greece 11. Argentina 12. Napoli 13. Brazil and Yugoslavia 14. David Beckham 15. Nigeria.

Quiz 14

1. Who won all three of their Group 1 games in the 1978 finals?
2. How many players with the first name Andriy were in the Ukraine squad in 2006?
3. Who scored the first goal of the 2006 World Cup finals?
4. Up to 2002, how many times had Australia played in the World Cup Finals?
5. For which Spanish club was Mexican Hugo Sanchez playing at the time of the 1986 finals?
6. For which Italian side was Stefan Effenberg playing at the time of USA 94?
7. Which country has won the World Cup the most times?
8. For which Spanish club was goalkeeper Andoni Zubizarreta playing at the time of France 98?
9. Which four European teams took part in the first World Cup in Uruguay in 1930?
10. Who knocked Nigeria out of USA 94?
11. How many goals did Australia score in the 1974 World Cup Finals?
12. For which Dutch side was Romario playing at the time of Italia 90?
13. What happened to the original Jules Rimet trophy?
14. Which country's squad featured goalkeeper Joseph-Antoine Bell at Italia 90?
15. Of which national team was Bo Johansson the coach at France 98?

1. Italy 2. Seven 3. Philip Lahm 4. Once 5. Real Madrid 6. Fiorentina 7. Brazil: they had won five times up to 2006 8. Valencia 9. France, Belgium, Romania and Yugoslavia; 13 teams took part in all 10. Italy 11. None 12. PSV Eindhoven 13. In 1970 Brazil's third victory allowed them to keep the trophy, but it was stolen in 1983 and disappeared for ever 14. Cameroon 15. Denmark.

Quiz 15

1. Up to 2002, in their six games in the World Cup Finals, against which team did Bolivia achieve their best result – a 0–0 draw?
2. Of South Africa's 22 players at the 1998 finals, how many were playing for English clubs?
3. Up to 2002, how many times had Greece appeared in the finals?
4. For which French team was Jürgen Klinsmann playing at the time of USA 94?
5. Who scored both of Haiti's goals in the 1974 finals?
6. Who knocked Argentina out of USA 94?
7. Which country did Switzerland beat to qualify for the 1950 finals?
8. Which country did Italy beat 4–1 in the quarter-finals of Mexico 70?
9. Which country did Roland Hattenberger and Kurt Jara represent in the 1978 finals?
10. For which English club was Sammy McIlroy playing at the time of the 1986 finals?
11. For which Spanish club was Mario Kempes playing at the time of the 1978 finals?
12. For which country did Cyrille Makanaky play at Italia 90?
13. For which club side was Northern Ireland's Sammy McIlroy playing at the time of the 1982 finals?
14. What was the score in both of the 1986 World Cup semi-finals?
15. For which Italian club was Mark Hateley playing at the time of the 1986 finals?

1. South Korea 2. Three 3. Once 4. Monaco 5. Emmanuel Sanon 6. Romania 7. Luxembourg 8. Mexico 9. Austria 10. Manchester City 11. Valencia 12. Cameroon 13. Stoke City 14. 2–0 15. AC Milan.

True or False?

Quiz 1

1. Liverpool legend Ian Rush later played for Newcastle United.
2. Patrick Mboma's squad number at Sunderland in 2001–2 was 70.
3. Goalkeeper Ian Walker is the son of the former Everton manager Mike Walker.
4. The attendance at the Molesey–Arundel FA Cup preliminary-round tie in 2001–2 was 16.
5. The Japanese game of *kemari* is also called courtier's football.
6. All Arsenal's Boxing Day league fixtures from 1991 to 1999 finished goalless.
7. Manchester United's Gary Neville's nickname at school was 'Ziggy'.
8. Goalkeeper Alan Fettis was born in South Africa.
9. Scotland manager George Burley collected rare beer-bottle tops as a boy.
10. Cameroon goalkeeping coach Thomas Nkono was arrested before their game with Mali in the 2002 African Nations Cup for allegedly using 'black magic' on the pitch.
11. Former Chelsea man Marcel Desailly was nicknamed 'the Lion'.
12. Tottenham Hotspur's mascot is called Chirpy the Cockerel.
13. Peter Crouch is shorter than Chelsea striker Gianfranco Zola.
14. Nigel Clough was born in Nottingham.
15. The Sir Stanley Matthews West Stand at Blackpool's home ground Bloomfield Road has been sponsored by Pricebusters.

1. True 2. False. He wanted it to be 70 (he was born in 1970) but wasn't allowed it. He played in the No 7 shirt 3. True 4. False. It was 17 5. True 6. False 7. False 8. False 9. False 10. True 11. False. He's nicknamed 'the Rock' 12. True 13. False 14. False, he was born in Sunderland. 15. True.

Quiz 2

1. Jimmy Greaves played for England in the 1966 World Cup Final.
2. Witton Albion have played home games at the Bargain Booze Stadium.
3. Arsene Wenger has a degree in Economics.
4. Ledley King's middle name is Renton.
5. Alan Shearer broke his nose in April 2002 following a clash with former teammate and close friend Robert Lee.
6. Former Chelsea player Thomas Harmer was nicknamed 'Harmer the Alarmer'.
7. German side Cottbus play their home games in the Stadium of Friendship.
8. Alessandro Pistone played for AC Milan prior to joining Newcastle United.
9. Paul Gascoigne won 57 international caps for England.
10. Stuart Pearce won 57 international caps for England.
11. In 2002, Halifax Town became the first team to drop out of the Football League twice.
12. Golfer Paul Lawrie is a supporter of Aberdeen Football Club.
13. TV chef Jamie Oliver had a trial for Oxford United.
14. Former Liverpool man Vegard Heggem was born in Rio de Janeiro.
15. Dion Dublin only scored one league goal during his spell at Manchester United.

1. False 2. True 3. True 4. False. It's Brenton 5. True 6. False. He went by the nickname of 'Harmer the Charmer' 7. True 8. False. He played for Inter Milan 9. True 10. False. He won 78 caps 11. False. Newport County were the first to do this 12. True 13. False 14. False 15. False. He scored two league goals.

Quiz 3

1. Former Chelsea goalkeeper Peter Borota was a direct descendant of the Ethiopian leader Haile Selassie.
2. Former England manager Graham Taylor was awarded the Freedom of the Borough of Watford in November 2001.
3. Michael and Shane Duff, formerly of Cheltenham Town, are not related.
4. Barnsley's Carl Barrowclough's favourite food is tripe.
5. Scientists from three ice-breakers, the *Oden*, *Healy* and *Polarstern*, played a round-robin football tournament in the Arctic.
6. Manchester United manager Alex Ferguson is part-owner of a racehorse named Humility.
7. Roland Nilsson was in charge at Coventry City for nine months in the 2001–2 season.
8. Former Crewe manager Dario Gradi was once punched by a PG Tips TV monkey.
9. Yeading FC are nicknamed 'the Ding'.
10. Dutch defender Mario Melchiot's favourite after-dinner treats are a cigar and brandy.
11. Chelsea player Damien Duff's nickname at school was 'Santa's Little Helper'.
12. Bruno Marioni of Tenerife was sent off in the first minute of their 2–0 away defeat at Sevilla in October 2001.
13. Molesey FC are nicknamed 'the Moles'.
14. Pelé was the youngest player to appear in a World Cup Final.
15. Hamilton Academical play at the Ballast Stadium.

1. False 2. True 3. False. They are brothers 4. False 5. True 6. False 7. False. He was in charge for only seven months 8. False 9. True 10. False. He neither smokes nor drinks 11. False 12. True 13. True 14. True 15. True.

Quiz 4

1. The official programme for the 1930 FA Cup Final cost 2d.
2. Brighton & Hove Albion have a player called Clare Kildare.
3. Meals available at Bradford City's Up Front Café include a McCallburger and a Hallebutty Fishwich.
4. Stand-up comedian Terry Alderton played in goal for Harrow Borough in their 5–0 away defeat at Chesham United in October 2001.
5. Ex-England boss Sven-Goran Eriksson released a CD of his favourite classical tunes in 2002.
6. The FA announced in April 2002 that 61,667 women and girls play competitive football.
7. Former Middlesbrough player Bernie Slaven announced in 2002 that he was standing as a mayoral candidate for the town.
8. Dorking FC are nicknamed 'the Chicks'.
9. Southampton's St Mary's Stadium had a curse on it removed by Cerri 'Dragonoak' Connelly.
10. 1960s and 1970s footballer Bob Earnshaw played 252 games for Barnsley while remaining a school teacher.
11. Tottenham's Robbie Keane is a distant cousin of television presenter Ant McPartlin.
12. Former FA Cup Final hero Andy Linighan of Arsenal played for non-league side St Albans City in 2001–2.
13. Fulham were sponsored by Pizza Hut in 2001–2.
14. Tooting & Mitcham United are nicknamed 'the Terribles'.
15. Wolverhampton Wanderers were relegated three years in succession in the 1980s.

1. False. It cost 6d 2. False. They do however have a player called Kerry Mayo 3. False 4. True 5. True 6. True 7. True 8. True 9. True 10. True 11. False 12. True 13. True 14. False. They're nicknamed 'the Terrors' 15. True.

Quiz 5

1. Liverpool's sponsors over the years have included Crown Paints.
2. Notts County director Albert Scardino is a former Pulitzer prize-winning journalist.
3. Bristol City were promoted three years in succession in the 1980s.
4. Free cigarettes were distributed to the crowd before the 1939 FA Cup Final.
5. Hull City goalkeeper Paul Musselwhite is a keen accordion player.
6. Jermain Defoe's nickname at West Ham United was 'Wrighty'.
7. David Beckham had a spell on loan to Preston North End.
8. Carl Cort was born in Little Dunmow.
9. Ex-Bolton Wanderers manager Sam Allardyce won a competition at school for a poem about rock guitarist Jimi Hendrix.
10. Ex-Charlton Athletic striker John Robinson was born in Bulawayo.
11. Chelsea and Arsenal played each other in the 1950 and 1952 FA Cup semi-finals.
12. Juan Veron is the brother-in-law of pop singer Julio Iglesias.
13. Wick played Bashley in the FA Cup preliminary round in 2001–2.
14. The unusual kick-off time for the League Cup Final between Chelsea and Stoke City on Saturday, 4 March 1972 was 2.30 pm.
15. Geoff Hurst is the only player to have scored a hat-trick in a World Cup Final.

1. True 2. True 3. False. They were relegated three years in succession in the 1980s 4. False 5. False 6. True 7. True 8. False 9. False 10. True 11. True 12. False 13. True 14. False. It was 3.30 pm 15. True.

THE BRITISH FOOTBALL TEST

Quiz 1

1. Who in October 1936 became the youngest player to score a hat-trick in the English football league?
2. Who was manager of Plymouth Argyle in 1978–9?
3. In which year did Bobby Moore sign as a pro with West Ham?
4. What was the name of Swansea City's ground before 2005?
5. From which club did Dele Adebola join Birmingham?
6. At which club did Francis Benali spend the majority of his career?
7. Who was Rangers manager from 1978 to 1983?
8. Which was Micky Adams' first league club?
9. Which club did Denis Law join from Huddersfield in 1960?
10. Which prodigy joined Spurs from Barcelona in June, 2008 and what nationality is he?
11. At which club was George Best when he won his last cap for Northern Ireland?
12. In which season did Gary Ablett score his first league goal for Liverpool?
13. What age was Jack Charlton when he won his first cap for England?
14. How many league appearances did Joey Beauchamp make for West Ham following his move from Oxford in 1994?
15. For which league team did Northern Ireland defender Mal Donaghy play from 1992 to 1994?

1. Tommy Lawton 2. Malcolm Allison 3. 1958 4. Vetch Field 5. Crewe Alexandra 6. Southampton 7. John Greig 8. Gillingham 9. Manchester City 10. Giovani dos Santos, who is half-Mexican, half-Brazilian but has Spanish citizenship; his father is the Brazilian international Zizinho 11. Fulham 12. 1986-7 13. 29 14. None 15. Chelsea.

Quiz 2

1. For which league club did Francis Lee make his debut at the age of 16?
2. Which team won the 1997–8 Football Conference?
3. From which club did Liverpool sign Alan Hansen in 1977?
4. Which Premier League team had the lowest average gate in 1997–8?
5. From which Northern Ireland club did Portsmouth sign Derek Dougan in 1957?
6. Which club did Frank Worthington boss from 1985 to 1987?
7. Who scored four goals for England against Portugal on his debut in 1947?
8. Which club did Alan Buckley manage from 1982 t0 1986?
9. Who was captain of Ipswich in their 1978 FA Cup victory?
10. Who was West Bromwich Albion manager from 1978 to 1981?
11. In which year did Glenn Hoddle take over as Swindon boss?
12. To which club did John Beresford move from Newcastle United?
13. In which year were Portsmouth formed?
14. Where did Torquay United play their home games in 2008?
15. Who was Tottenham Hotspur's manager from 1984 to 1986?

1. Bolton Wanderers 2. Halifax Town 3. Partick Thistle 4. Southampton 5. Distillery 6. Tranmere Rovers 7. Stan Mortensen 8. Walsall 9. Mick Mills 10. Ron Atkinson 11. 1991 12. Southampton 13. 1898 14. Plainmoor 15. Peter Shreeves

Quiz 3

1. For which league club did Ron Flowers play from 1951 to 1966?
2. Which former Leeds United player was manager of Scunthorpe from 1983 to 1984?
3. Who in 1967 became the first substitute to win an FA Cup winner's medal?
4. Which team won the 1997–8 Unibond League?
5. How many full England caps did Howard Kendall win?
6. From which club did Sunderland sign Kevin Ball?
7. In which year did Sir Matt Busby die?
8. What are the first names of the Brightwells who played for Manchester City in the 1980s and 1990s?
9. From which club did Manchester United sign Pat Crerand in 1963?
10. In which year was ex-Evertonian Michael Branch born?
11. Which was Steve Perryman's first league club as a manager?
12. What is Martin Chivers' middle name?
13. In which year was ex-Arsenal hero Lee Dixon born?
14. Which two national sides did Billy Bingham manage?
15. How many caps did Gordon Banks win for England?

1. Wolves 2. Allan Clarke 3. Cliff Jones 4. Barrow 5. None 6. Portsmouth 7. 1994 8. Ian and David 9. Celtic 10. 1978 11. Brentford 12. Harcourt 13. 1964 14. Northern Ireland and Greece 15. 73.

Quiz 4

1. Which club plays at Portman Road?
2. From which club did Leeds United buy David Hopkin?
3. For which Scottish club did Danny McGrain play his entire career?
4. To which club did Southampton sell Nicky Banger?
5. To which club did Joey Jones move from Chelsea in 1985?
6. Which team won the 1997–8 League of Wales?
7. Which Premier League side had the lowest attendance in 1997–8 – specifically 7,688?
8. How many league games did Nick Barmby play for Middlesbrough from 1995–7?
9. In which year was Dwight Yorke born?
10. From which Welsh non-league side did Port Vale sign Mark Bright?
11. Which league club plays at Bramall Lane?
12. For which English team did David McCreery play after his spell with Tulsa Roughnecks?
13. Which team won the 1997–8 FA Umbro Trophy?
14. Which club did Paul McGrath join from Manchester United in 1989?
15. Which team won the 1997–8 FA Youth Cup?

1. Ipswich Town 2. Crystal Palace 3. Celtic 4. Oldham Athletic 5. Huddersfield 6. Barry Town 7. Wimbledon 8. 42 9. 1971 10. Leek Town 11. Sheffield United 12. Newcastle United 13. Cheltenham Town 14. Aston Villa 15. Everton.

Quiz 5

1. How many caps did John Charles – the 'Gentle Giant' – win for Wales?
2. From which club did Southampton buy Mark Wright in 1982?
3. With which club did Tommy Docherty begin his playing career?
4. Which club did Mark Lawrenson manage from 1989 to 1990?
5. With which club did George Graham sign as a pro in 1961?
6. With which two English clubs was Terry Butcher player-manager after leaving Rangers?
7. From which club did Leicester buy Robbie Savage?
8. For which English club did Belfast-born Joe Bambrick sign in 1934?
9. How many caps did Peter Beardsley win for England?
10. From which club did Gillingham sign Ade Akinbiyi?
11. Which team won the FA Carlsberg Vase in 1997–8?
12. Which former Welsh international became manager of Wrexham in 1989?
13. Which Division One team had the lowest average gate in 1997–8?
14. Whose record of 41 England caps was beaten by Billy Wright in 1952?
15. In which year was Ashley Ward born?

1. 38 2. Oxford United 3. Celtic 4. Peterborough 5. Aston Villa 6. Coventry and Sunderland 7. Crewe Alexandra 8. Chelsea 9. 59 10. Norwich City 11. Tiverton Town 12. Brian Flynn 13. Crewe Alexandra 14. Bob Crompton 15. 1970.

Quiz 6

1. Which club did Alan Durban manage from 1978 to 1981?
2. For which club did Wilf Mannion play in 1955 after leaving Middlesbrough?
3. From which club did Oxford United sign John Aldridge?
4. Which England international led Blackpool to three FA Cup Finals between 1948 and 1953?
5. From which club did Birmingham buy Paul Furlong?
6. In which year was ex-Evertonian Michael Ball born?
7. How many points clear were Celtic when they beat Rangers to the 1997–8 league title?
8. In which Scottish town do St Mirren play?
9. Which team had the highest average gate in Division One in 1997–8?
10. Which former England caretaker manager died on his birthday in 1990?
11. Who was manager of Sheffield United from 1981 to 1986?
12. Who scored a hat-trick for Scotland's 'Wembley Wizards' in their 5–1 victory over England in 1928?
13. Name the two Devon league teams.
14. In which year was John Aloisi born?
15. Which league club plays at Edgeley Park?

1. Stoke City 2. Hull City 3. Newport County 4. Harry Johnston 5. Chelsea 6. 1979 7. Two 8. Paisley 9. Sunderland 10. Joe Mercer 11. Ian Porterfield 12. Alec Jackson 13. Plymouth and Exeter 14. 1976 15. Stockport.

Quiz 7

1. From which club did Liverpool buy David James?
2. From which club did Manchester City sign Colin Bell in 1966?
3. For which club did Alan Ball sign as an amateur in 1961?
4. From which league club did Leeds United sign Lee Bowyer?
5. Which club side was Ron Burgess with when he won 32 caps for Wales?
6. In which Scottish city do St Johnstone play?
7. From which club did Blackburn buy Jeff Kenna?
8. For which club did Jimmy Dickinson make 764 league appearances between 1943 and 1965?
9. Which club plays at Sincil Bank?
10. Which club did Bobby Charlton manage after leaving Manchester United?
11. From which club did Tottenham Hotspur sign Pat Jennings?
12. Before joining Sunderland as boss in 1987, which club had Denis Smith previously managed?
13. Which club did Jimmy Greaves join on leaving Spurs in 1970?
14. Which team won the 1997–8 Smirnoff Irish League?
15. In which country was Scotland international Richard Gough born?

1. Watford 2. Bury 3. Blackpool 4. Charlton Athletic 5. Tottenham Hotspur 6. Perth 7. Southampton 8. Portsmouth 9. Lincoln 10. Preston North End 11. Watford 12. York City 13. West Ham 14. Cliftonville 15. Sweden.

Quiz 8

1. Which London club did Paul Bracewell join from Sunderland in 1997–8?
2. Which Liverpool manager won an FA Amateur Cup winner's medal with Bishop Auckland in 1939?
3. Which club plays at Kenilworth Road?
4. From which club did Everton sign Earl Barrett in the 1994–5 season?
5. Who was Manchester City's top league goalscorer in 1997–8?
6. In which year did Paul Ince move from West Ham United to Manchester United?
7. Who was Tottenham Hotspur manager from 1987 to 1991?
8. Which player was the first five-figure signing in British football?
9. From which club did Bradford City buy Jamie Lawrence?
10. Against which team did Nat Lofthouse score twice on his England debut in 1950?
11. Which club did Terry Venables manage from 1980 to 1984?
12. How old was Leslie Compton when he made his England debut in 1950?
13. Which player–manager replaced Ian Porterfield as manager of Reading in 1991?
14. Which football club did Alex Ferguson join in 1957?
15. Which former Leeds United player managed Rochdale from 1986 to 1988?

1. Fulham 2. Bob Paisley 3. Luton Town 4. Aston Villa 5. Paul Dickov 6. 1989 7. Terry Venables 8. David Jack 9. Leicester City 10. Yugoslavia 11. QPR 12. 38 13. Mark McGhee 14. Queen's Park 15. Eddie Gray.

Quiz 9

1. What is the name of Sunderland's stadium?
2. How old was Steve Coppell when he became Crystal Palace manager in 1984?
3. From which team did Spurs buy Portuguese winger Jose Dominguez?
4. How many league clubs did Trevor Brooking play for in his career?
5. Who was West Bromwich Albion's highest league goalscorer in 1997–8?
6. With which English club did Ally McCoist play from 1981 to 1983?
7. In which year was England international Gareth Barry born?
8. With which league club did Northern Ireland international Sam Irving end his career?
9. Who replaced Dave Jones as manager of Southampton?
10. How many goals did Tom Finney score for England?
11. Which team have recently moved stadiums away from Millmoor?
12. What is the nickname of Norwich City?
13. Which club plays at Carrow Road?
14. From which club did Stuart Pearce join Nottingham Forest in 1985?
15. Who was Sheffield United's top league goalscorer in 1997–8?

1. Stadium of Light 2. 29 3. Birmingham City 4. One 5. Lee Hughes 6. Sunderland 7. 1981 8. Bristol Rovers 9. Glenn Hoddle 10. 30 11. Rotherham United 12. 'The Canaries' 13. Norwich City 14. Coventry City 15. Brian Deane.

Quiz 10

1. What was Tottenham Hotspur's worst final league position under Bill Nicholson?
2. Against which country did Geoff Hurst make his international debut?
3. Who was manager of Norwich City from 1973 to 1980?
4. Which Scot captained the 'Wembley Wizards' in 1928?
5. In which Scottish town do Raith Rovers play?
6. For which club did Scotland and Manchester United player Jimmy Delaney end his career?
7. Which club did Pat Crerand manage from 1976 to 1977?
8. Who in 1991 became the youngest ever player to play for Wales?
9. In which year did Notts County form?
10. Who held the Liverpool league scoring record of 245 goals until surpassed by Ian Rush?
11. From which Northern Ireland club did Tottenham Hotspur sign Gerry Armstrong?
12. Who in 1930 became the youngest ever FA Cup finalist at Wembley?
13. From which club did Oxford sign midfielder Mark Angel?
14. For which club did Herbert Chapman sign as a professional in 1901?
15. At which league club did Coventry player David Burrows begin his career?

1. 11th 2. West Germany 3. John Bond 4. Jimmy McMullan 5. Kirkcaldy 6. Elgin City 7. Northampton Town 8. Ryan Giggs 9. 1862 10. Roger Hunt 11. Bangor 12. Cliff Bastin 13. Sunderland 14. Northampton Town 15. West Bromwich Albion.

Quiz 11

1. In which season did Neil Ardley make his first appearance for Wimbledon?
2. From which club did Frank McLintock join Arsenal in 1964?
3. At which London club did Kevin Campbell begin his career?
4. Who captained Newcastle in their 1985 FA Youth Cup win?
5. In which year was Sol Campbell born?
6. In which city was Everton's Danny Cadamarteri born?
7. From which club did Chelsea buy Dan Petrescu?
8. Which club did Jimmy Frizell manage from 1970 to 1982?
9. Who was Sheffield Wednesday's top league goalscorer in 1997–8?
10. Which club did Martin O'Neill join from Norwich in 1983?
11. In which city was Leeds United manager David O'Leary born?
12. Which Scottish side plays at Dens Park?
13. How many league goals did Brett Angell score in his Everton career?
14. From which club did Derby County sign Deon Burton?
15. From which club did Bradford City buy goalkeeper Gary Walsh?

1. 1990–1 2. Leicester City 3. Arsenal 4. Paul Gascoigne 5. 1974 6. Bradford 7. Sheffield Wednesday 8. Oldham 9. Paolo Di Canio 10. Notts County 11. London 12. Dundee 13. One 14. Portsmouth 15. Middlesbrough.

Quiz 12

1. With which Welsh club did Nathan Blake first play league football?
2. For which club did Emlyn Hughes win a League Cup winner's medal in 1980?
3. How many league games did Mark Bosnich play for Manchester United in his first spell there?
4. Billy Liddell signed for Liverpool in 1939. In which year did he make his league debut?
5. How many league goals did Matt Carbon score while at Derby?
6. For which club did Jimmy Armfield sign as an amateur in 1951?
7. From which club did Nottingham Forest buy Chris Bart-Williams?
8. Which Manchester City player scored two goals in six minutes for England against Italy at Highbury in 1934?
9. Which club did Kingsley Black join from Nottingham Forest?
10. Which English Third Division club did Bobby Collins join in 1967?
11. From which club did Dixie Dean join Everton in 1925?
12. In which Scottish town do Queen of the South play?
13. With which club did Mick Channon end his career?
14. In which year was Dennis Wise born?
15. With which club did midfielder Jim Baxter end his career?

1. Cardiff 2. Wolves 3. Three 4. 1946 5. None 6. Blackpool 7. Sheffield Wednesday 8. Eric Brook 9. Grimsby 10. Bury 11. Tranmere Rovers 12. Dumfries 13. Portsmouth 14. 1966 15. Rangers.

Quiz 13

1. From which club did Arsenal sign goalkeeper Vince Bartram?
2. Which Arsenal and Huddersfield player appeared in a then record five Wembley FA Cup Finals between 1927 and 1938?
3. Which club did Clayton Blackmore join from Manchester United?
4. For which two teams did Mark Hughes play on the same day – 11 November 1987?
5. At which league club did Steve Bould begin his league career?
6. For how much did Millwall sell Tony Cascarino to Aston Villa in 1990?
7. How many league goals did David Batty score in his first spell at Leeds United?
8. From which club did Andy Booth join Sheffield Wednesday?
9. Of which club was Gordon Lee manager from 1975 to 1977?
10. In which year was Gary Lineker awarded the OBE?
11. Peter Nicholas earned the last of his 73 caps for Wales while playing for which club?
12. At which league club did Franz Carr begin as an apprentice?
13. How many caps did Jimmy Nicholl win for Northern Ireland?
14. To which club did Arsenal sell Jimmy Carter in 1995?
15. At which former league club did Warren Barton begin his career?

1. Bournemouth 2. Joe Hulme 3. Middlesbrough 4. Wales and Bayern Munich 5. Stoke City 6. £1 million 7. Four 8. Huddersfield Town 9. Newcastle United 10. 1992 11. Watford 12. Blackburn 13. 73 14. Portsmouth 15. Maidstone United.

Quiz 14

1. At which Welsh club did former Tottenham Hotspur striker Chris Armstrong start his career?
2. Which former Sunderland captain was manager of Middlesbrough from 1963 to 1966?
3. At which London club did Phil Babb start his career?
4. Which three managers have won the English League with more than one club?
5. In which year was Manchester United's Wes Brown born?
6. From whom did West Ham buy Paul Kitson?
7. In which year did Billy Bremner make his debut for Leeds United?
8. In which year was Wimbledon's Robbie Earle born?
9. Which Spanish club did John Aldridge join after leaving Liverpool?
10. On which island was John Barnes born?
11. Which club did Scotland international Bobby Evans join as player-manager after leaving Chelsea in 1961?
12. At which Midlands club did Gary Charles start as a trainee?
13. Who scored the winning goal for Stoke City in the 1972 League Cup Final?
14. What is the name of the home ground that Coventry City vacated in 2005 for the Ricoh Arena?
15. Who moved from Sunderland to Middlesbrough for £1,000 in 1905?

1. Wrexham 2. Raich Carter 3. Millwall 4. Herbert Chapman, Brian Clough and Kenny Dalglish 5. 1979 6. Newcastle United 7. 1960 8. 1965 9. Real Sociedad 10. Jamaica 11. Newport County 12. Nottingham Forest 13. George Eastham 14. Highfield Road 15. Alf Common.

Quiz 15

1. At which league club did Wolverhampton Wanderer's Steve Bull begin his career?
2. At which two clubs was Dave Bassett manager before joining Sheffield United in 1988?
3. How many full international caps did Trevor Francis win for England?
4. Which club played their 2006 home games at Roots Hall?
5. At which ground did Derby County play their 2008 home games?
6. Which team won promotion to the Premiership via the play-offs at the end of the 2001-2 season?
7. Who was manager of Coventry City from 1993 to 1995?
8. Which former Everton manager was boss at Preston North End from 1975 to 1977?
9. Which club did Neil Aspin join from Leeds?
10. Which QPR player made 514 league appearances for the club between 1950 and 1963?
11. What age was Gerry Francis when he took over the England captaincy in 1975?
12. At which league club did Steve Bruce begin his career?
13. From which club did Liverpool sign Ray Houghton in 1987?
14. Who was manager of Manchester United from 1971 to 1972?
15. Which Northern Ireland international was Oldham manager from 1966 to 1968?

1. West Bromwich Albion 2. Wimbledon and Watford 3. 52 4. Southend 5. Pride Park Stadium 6. Birmingham City 7. Phil Neal 8. Harry Catterick 9. Port Vale 10. Tony Ingham 11. 25 12. Gillingham 13. Oxford United 14. Frank O'Farrell 15. Jimmy McIlroy.

Quiz 16

1. From which club did Middlesbrough sign George Camsell in 1925?
2. From which club did Sunderland buy Lee Clark?
3. Which Arsenal player was out of the game for a year following injury in the 1952 FA Cup Final?
4. From which Irish club did Danny Blanchflower join Barnsley in 1948?
5. Which football team plays at Dean Court (although sponsorship deals can mean that its official name varies)?
6. From which club did Sheffield Wednesday sign Peter Atherton?
7. In which city was Trevor Francis born?
8. In which year was John Oster born?
9. For which club did Stan Cullis play his entire career?
10. Which league club plays at a home ground that was originally called the Alfred McAlpine Stadium?
11. Against which country in was England player Alan Mullery sent off in 1968 ?
12. Who was Middlesbrough manager from 1973 to 1977?
13. For which team did Dave Mackay become player-manager in 1971?
14. In which year was Ian Branfoot appointed manager of Southampton?
15. Who earned 25 caps as a goalkeeper for England between 1929 and 1936, then a record for the position?

1. Durham City 2. Newcastle United 3. Walley Barnes 4. Glentoran 5. AFC Bournemouth 6. Coventry City 7. Plymouth 8. 1978 9. Wolverhampton Wanderers 10. Huddersfield Town 11. Yugoslavia 12. Jack Charlton 13. Swindon Town 14. 1991 15. Harry Hibbs.

Quiz 17

1. Which was Ray Clemence's first professional club?
2. From which club did Bolton Wanderers sign Gudni Bergsson?
3. Which Yorkshire club is nicknamed 'the Owls'?
4. Which was Peter Beardsley's first league club?
5. Who was voted PFA Young Footballer of the Year in 1987?
6. For which Scottish club did Craig Burley sign on leaving Chelsea?
7. With which club did Johnny Haynes turn pro in 1952?
8. Who was manager of Portsmouth from 1974 to 1977?
9. Who managed Chelsea in their 1955 league championship year?
10. In which year did John Rudge take over as manager of Port Vale?
11. How many full caps did Billy Bonds win for England?
12. From which club did West Ham sign Eyal Berkovic?
13. In which year did Nigel Clough join Liverpool from Nottingham Forest?
14. How many league goals did midfielder Ian Bishop score for West Ham in his nine-season career there?
15. With which league team did England player Bryan Douglas spend his entire career?

1. Scunthorpe United 2. Tottenham Hotspur 3. Sheffield Wednesday 4. Carlisle 5. Tony Adams 6. Celtic 7. Fulham 8. Ian St John 9. Ted Drake 10. 1983 11. None 12. Southampton 13. 1993 14. 12 15. Blackburn Rovers.

Quiz 18

1. With which Irish club did ex-Liverpool and Ireland defender Jim Beglin begin his career?
2. Which Northern Ireland and Manchester United striker broke Pelé's record as the youngest player to play in the World Cup Finals when he came on in Spain 82?
3. From which club did Everton purchase Everton legend Graeme Sharp?
4. Which team did former Everton star Adrian Heath manage on retiring as a player?
5. For how many years did Glenn Hoddle ply his trade with Monaco?
6. Peter Beardsley started his career with Carlisle but which country did he go to for a few years before settling with Newcastle United?
7. Which manager gave John Barnes his England debut against Northern Ireland at Windsor Park?
8. Who was John Barnes' manager at Watford at that time?
9. Which club did Joe Jordan join on leaving Manchester United?
10. With which side did Ally McCoist finish his playing career?
11. With which club did controversial RTE pundit Eamonn Dunphy spend the best part of his playing career?
12. Which club did Dunphy's RTE companion John Giles join on leaving Manchester United in 1963?
13. How many goals in 29 appearances did Ian Rush score for Juventus?
14. Which club did Kerry Dixon join when he left Chelsea?
15. With which German club did legend Tony Woodcock spend two stints?

1. Shamrock Rovers 2. Norman Whiteside 3. Dumbarton 4. Burnley 5. Four 6. Canada - he had two spells with the Vancouver Whitecaps 7. Bobby Robson 8. Graham Taylor 9. AC Milan 10. Kilmarnock 11. Millwall 12. Leeds United 13. 12 14. Southampton 15. FC Köln

High Scores & Top Scorers

Quiz 1

1. Who was the Premiership's top scorer in the 2006–7 season?
2. How many goals did he get?
3. Who finished top scorer in the 2007–8 season with 31 goals?
4. Which two players shared second spot with 24 goals?
5. Which other Manchester United player finished in the top ten?
6. True or false: none of the top-ten scorers in the 2007–8 season was English?
7. True or false: the top-ten scorers in 2007–8 were all from different countries?
8. True or false: Robbie Keane was the smallest of the strikers to finish in the top-ten scorers in the 2007–8 Premiership?
9. The biggest win in the 2006–7 Premiership season was 6–0. Which teams were involved?
10. The most goals in a game was eight. Who played in that game?
11. True or false: Robbie Keane was the only Irishman in the top-ten scorers in the 2006–7 Premiership season?
12. Name the only Liverpool player in the top-ten goalscorers in the 2006–7 Premiership season.
13. Name three of the four Englishmen in the top-ten Premiership scorers of 2005–6.
14. Name the two Welsh and Irish players in the top-ten scorers of 2005–6.
15. True or false: with 21 league goals Ruud van Nistelrooy was the top scorer in 2005–6?

1. Didier Drogba 2. 20 3. Cristiano Ronaldo 4. Emanuel Adebayor and Fernando Torres 5. Carlos Tevez 6. True 7. True 8. False. Carlos Tevez is smaller 9. Reading 6 West Ham United 0 10. Arsenal 6 Blackburn 2 11. False. Kevin Doyle (Reading) was 12. Dirk Kuyt 13. Darren Bent, Frank Lampard, Wayne Rooney, Marlon Harewood 14. Robbie Keane and Craig Bellamy 15. False. Thierry Henry scored 27.

Quiz 2

1. Who lost 6–1 at Leeds United on 13 May, 2001?
2. Who beat Coventry City 6–1 on 21 October, 2000?
3. Who did England beat 6–0 on 17 February, 1993 at Wembley in a World Cup qualifier?
4. By what score did Rangers beat St Mirren on 4 November, 2000?
5. By what score did Arsenal beat Manchester City on 28 October, 2000?
6. Who lost 4–0 at home to Liverpool on 15 October, 2000?
7. Chris Sutton scored 25 Premiership goals in 1993–4. For which side was he playing?
8. Which former Division One, London-based side lost 4–0 at Swansea City on 16 September 2000?
9. By what score did Celtic beat Hearts on 18 November 2000?
10. Who won the PFA Player of the Year award after scoring 25 goals in the 1993–4 Premiership?
11. Who lost 5–0 to Arsenal on 9 December, 2000?
12. Who beat Leicester City 6–1 on 26 December, 2000?
13. By what score did Wimbledon beat QPR on 24 February 2001?
14. Which player in the 1993–4 runners-up side scored a total of 31 Premiership goals?
15. Who was voted PFA Young Player of the Year, scoring 41 goals in all competitions in 1993–4?

1. Bradford City 2. Chelsea 3. San Marino 4. 7-1 5. 5-0 6. Derby County 7. Norwich City 8. Luton Town 9. 6-1 10. Eric Cantona 11. Newcastle United 12. Arsenal 13. 5-0 14. Alan Shearer 15. Andy Cole.

Quiz 3

1. By what score did Celtic beat Aberdeen on 16 December 2000?
2. In 1993–4, which player returned to Newcastle to score 25 goals and share an incredible year with strike partner Andy Cole?
3. Who beat Hibernian 4–0 on 20 May, 2001?
4. Who lost 4–0 at home to Celtic on 26 December, 2000?
5. By what score did Manchester United beat Arsenal on 25 February 2001?
6. Veteran striker Jimmy Quinn was the English League's top scorer with 34 goals in 1993–4. For which club did he play?
7. Who beat QPR 5–0 on 10 February, 2001?
8. Who beat Dunfermline Athletic 7–1 on 24 February 2001?
9. How many goals did Stan Collymore score for Premiership side Nottingham Forest in 1994–5?
10. By what score did Celtic beat Kilmarnock on 2 January 2001?
11. Alan Shearer finished as the Premiership's top scorer with 25 goals in 31 games in 1996–7. For which club did he play?
12. Which 36-year-old was Division One's leading goalscorer with 24 league goals in 1994–5?
13. Who beat Dundee 5–1 on 12 August 2000?
14. By what score did West Ham United beat Charlton Athletic on 26 December 2000?
15. How many goals did Wrexham striker Gary Bennett amass during the 1994–5 season?

1. 6–0 2. Peter Beardsley 3. Rangers 4. Dundee United 5. 6–1 6. Division Two champions Reading 7. Preston North End 8. Heart of Midlothian 9. 22 10. 6–0 11. Newcastle United 12. Tranmere Rovers striker John Aldridge 13. Hibernian 14. 5–0 15. 39 goals in all competitions.

Quiz 4

1. In which season did Kevin Phillips open his Premiership goalscoring account at Sunderland with 30 goals? It made him the highest-scoring footballer in the whole league at the time.
2. By what score did Manchester United beat Southampton on 28 October 2000?
3. Which Dutchman finished the Premiership as top scorer in 2000–1 with 23 goals?
4. Who won 4–0 at Manchester City on 13 January 2001?
5. By what score did Hibernian beat Heart of Midlothian on 22 October 2000?
6. Who lost 7–3 at Inverness Caledonian Thistle on 2 December, 2000?
7. Dion Dublin's 18 Premiership goals almost single-handedly saved which club from relegation in 1996–7?
8. Who lost 5–0 at home to Wimbledon on 9 September, 2000?
9. By what score did Manchester United beat Bradford City on 5 September 2000?
10. Who was the unlikely second-highest scorer in the Premiership in 2000–1 with 19 goals?
11. Who lost 5–0 at Blackburn Rovers on 1 April 2001?
12. Who lost 5–0 at Manchester City on 9 December 2000?
13. Who did Everton beat 7–1 in the Premiership in 2007–8?
14. Who beat Derby 6–2 at the start of the 2007–8 season?
15. How many goals did Villa put past Blackburn in November 2007?

1. 1999–2000 2. 5–0 3. Jimmy Floyd Hasselbaink 4. Leeds United 5. 6–2 6. Ayr United 7. Coventry City 8. Sheffield Wednesday 9. 6–0 10. Marcus Stewart (Ipswich Town) 11. Burnley 12. Everton 13. Sunderland 14. Arsenal 15. Four.

Quiz 5

1. Who did Chelsea draw 4–4 with on 26 December 2007?
2. After beating which side 4–0, in 2007–8, did Wayne Rooney say, 'Growing up, I used to love watching Brazil and I think the football we play is similar to the way Brazil play'?
3. Which team, then a surprising third in the league, were put in their place by a 6–0 drubbing at the hands of Chelsea during the 2007–8 season?
4. Which team were beaten 6–0 by Aston Villa in 2007–8?
5. Which London side hammered Derby 5–0 in November 2007–8?
6. Who beat Derby 6–0 on 1 September 2007?
7. Who scored his first hat-trick for Manchester United in a 6–0 win over Newcastle in the 2007–8 season?
8. Who was the unlikely scorer of a great volley in the same game?
9. Who scored a hat-trick in Wigan's 5–3 win over Blackburn in December 2007?
10. What score did Arsenal beat Blackburn by on 23 December 2006?
11. Who was the Premier League's new top scorer with 22 goals in 1992–3?
12. In the same year which player set a club record for Portsmouth by scoring 42 league goals?
13. Before injury ended Shearer's 1992–3 season, how many goals had he scored in 21 Premier League games for Blackburn Rovers?
14. Who in 1992–3 scored 25 Division One goals to help Newcastle win promotion to the Premier League (he then spurned the chance of Premier League football by signing for Wolves)?
15. How many goals did Andy Cole score in his first 12 games for Division One champions Newcastle in the 1992–3 season?

1. Aston Villa 2. Aston Villa 3. Manchester City 4. Derby County 5. West Ham United 6. Liverpool 7. Cristiano Ronaldo 8. Rio Ferdinand 9. Marcus Bent 10. 6–2 11. Teddy Sheringham 12. Guy Whittingham 13. 16 14. David Kelly 15. 12

International Football

Quiz 1

1. Which Preston legend won 76 caps for England and scored 30 goals between 1946 and 1958?
2. Which player, nicknamed 'the Maestro', did the ever-generous Pele describe as the 'best passer of the ball I've ever seen'?
3. Which midfield player scored five goals for Peru in the 1978 World Cup Finals?
4. By what surprising scoreline did the Republic of Ireland beat Turkey in October, 1990 in a qualifier for the 1992 European Championships?
5. Against whom did Simone Inzaghi make his international debut for Italy in 2000?
6. Which former Brazilian international's full name is Marcos Evangelista de Moraes?
7. Who scored two goals for England against Portugal in the 1966 World Cup semi-final?
8. Which former Dutch legend was the assistant coach to Guus Hiddink for the Netherlands' 1998 World Cup campaign?
9. Who became Wales' most-capped outfield player in a World Cup qualifier against Armenia in March 2001?
10. Which record did David Healy break on 17 November 2007?
11. Who is reported to have said this about Lothar Matthaus in his biography: 'He is the best rival I've ever had. I guess that's enough to define him'?
12. Who succeeded Gerard Houllier as manager of France in 1994?
13. In which country was ex-French international Claude Makelele born?
14. What nationality is the central defender Ozalan Alpay?
15. In which decade was German international Pierre Littbarski born?

1. Tom Finney 2. Johnny Haynes 3. Teofilo Cubillas 4. 5-0 5. Spain 6. Cafu 7. Bobby Charlton 8. Johan Neeskens 9. Dean Saunders 10. He scored his 13th goal in a Euro 2008 qualifier which made him the highest-ever goalscorer in a UEFA European Championship qualifying campaign 11. Diego Maradona 12. Aime Jacquet 13. The Democratic Republic of the Congo 14. Turkish 15. The 1960s.

Quiz 2

1. Who won FIFA's World Best Female Player award in 2001–2 and again in 2002–3?
2. How many times has Thierry Henry picked up the FIFA award for World's Best Player?
3. Who kept goal for England in the 1992 European Championship Finals?
4. In which decade was the former Italy coach Arrigo Sacchi born?
5. Under what name does Spanish international Oliveira Jesus Alvarez Gonzalez play?
6. Which former AC Milan star ran for President in Liberia?
7. In the correct order, name the top three players of the 2007–8 season as chosen by FIFA.
8. In which country was former Polish striker Emmanuel Olisadebe born?
9. Where was the England–Greece World Cup qualifier played in October 2001?
10. How many caps did Peter Shilton win for England?
11. Which English player earned the nickname 'Lion of Vienna' by scoring twice in England's 3–2 victory over Austria on 25 May 1952?
12. Who scored Wales' goal which led to Brazil's 1–0 defeat at Cardiff Arms Park in a friendly in September 1991?
13. For which country was Aleksander Chidvadze the coach from 1994–6?
14. In which decade was former Dutch international Jan Wouters born?
15. How did England remain unbeaten in the 1960 European Championships, but still fail to win it?

1. Mia Hamm (USA) 2. None. He has been second twice 3. Chris Woods 4. The 1940s 5. Oli 6. George Weah 7. Kaká, Lionel Messi and Cristiano Ronaldo 8. Nigeria 9. Old Trafford 10. 125 11. Nat Lofthouse 12. Dean Saunders 13. Georgia 14. The 1960s 15. By not entering in the first place.

Quiz 3

1. Who held the record for the most goals scored in Euro qualifiers before David Healy broke it in 2007?
2. At the start of the 2008–9 season who was the only African to have won the World's Best Player award?
3. At which club did Geoff Hurst play 411 of his professional games?
4. Which two Gordons scored in Scotland's 2–0 away win against San Marino in May 1991 in a qualifier for the 1992 European Championships?
5. In which decade was former German international Olaf Thon born?
6. Which Uruguayan's fluidity and grace on the ball won him the nickname 'El Principe' (the Prince)?
7. What was Franky Vercauteren's nickname?
8. How many goals did Nobby Stiles score for England?
9. At the start of the 2008–9 season who were the only players to have won the World's Best Player award three times?
10. For which country did Rene Orlando Houseman play in the 1978 World Cup Finals?
11. Against which country did Gabriel Batistuta make his international debut for Argentina in 1991?
12. Who saved David Batty's penalty, eliminating England from the 1998 World Cup?
13. Did former AC Milan star George Weah win the 2005 Liberian presidential election?
14. Which two strikers did Alf Ramsey choose in the group stages of the 1966 World Cup?
15. Against which team did Jimmy Greaves receive the injury that put him out of the 1966 World Cup Final reckoning?

1. Davor Suker (12 goals in 10 games) 2. George Weah 3. West Ham United 4. Gordon Strachan and Gordon Durie 5. The 1960s 6. Enzo Francescoli 7. The Little Prince 8. One 9. Zinedine Zidane and Ronaldo 10. Argentina 11. Brazil 12. Carlos Roa 13. No, he lost to Ellen Johnson-Sirleaf in the second round of voting 14. Jimmy Greaves and Roger 'Ernie' Hunt 15. France.

Quiz 4

1. Finish this famous quote: 'Maggie Thatcher, can you hear me? Maggie Thatcher ...'
2. Which legendary hard man captained the Scottish national side at the World Cup in West Germany in 1974?
3. Against which country did Dietmar Hamann make his debut for Germany in 1997?
4. In which decade was German international Andreas Moller born?
5. True or false: Colin Bell won 48 caps for England?
6. Which former ballboy at Napoli made his international debut for Italy against Northern Ireland in 1997?
7. In which decade was former Dutch international Aron Winter born?
8. Who were the first two Italian players to gain more than 100 international caps?
9. Which international side has Marius Maldarasanu played for?
10. Who won FIFA's World's Best Female Player award in 2003–4, 2004–5 and 2005–6?
11. Finish the name of this distinguished former England player: Robert Frederick Chelsea _____.
12. Which former Norwegian international had a Manchester United testimonial in 2008?
13. True or false: former Italy goalkeeper Walter Zenga was born in South Africa?
14. How many goals did David O'Leary score for the Republic of Ireland in his 68 appearances for the country?
15. Which midfield enforcer got a rare goal for England in their 1–0 win over Turkey in Izmir in May 1991 in a qualifier for the 1992 European Championships?

1. '... your boys took a hell of a beating! Your boys took a hell of a beating!' – Bjørge Lillelien, Norwegian commentator after his country had beaten England 2-1 in 1981 2. Billy Bremner 3. South Africa 4. The 1960s 5. True 6. Fabio Cannavaro 7. The 1960s 8. Dino Zoff and Paolo Maldini 9. Romania 10. Birgit Prinz (Germany) 11. Robert Frederick Chelsea 'Bobby' Moore 12. Ole Gunnar Solskjaer 13. False 14. One 15. Dennis Wise.

Quiz 5

1. Which Tottenham hero made his England debut on 2 July 1950 against Spain in the World Cup Finals in Brazil and went on to score five goals in nine internationals in his short England career?
2. Which prolific former Marseille striker scored both of France's goals in their 2–1 win over Czechoslovakia in Paris in October 1990 in a qualifier for the 1992 European Championships?
3. What is the nickname of former Italian international Filippo Inzaghi?
4. For which African country has midfielder Ndjitap Geremi played international football?
5. Who knocked Denmark out of Euro 84 and Mexico 86?
6. Which German footballing legend was voted the 1980–1 European Footballer of the Year?
7. In which decade was former German international Andreas Brehme born?
8. Who scored the opening goal for Brazil in the 1978 World Cup Finals?
9. In which country was French international Ibrahim Ba born?
10. Who was voted Asian Footballer of the Year in 1999?
11. With which club did Swiss legend Stephane Chapuisat win a Champions League medal?
12. Which German was named European Footballer of the Year and World Soccer Player of the Year in 1990?
13. In which decade was Japanese midfielder Hidetoshi Nakata born?
14. Which prolific midfielder scored England's equaliser in their 1–1 draw with Brazil in a friendly at Wembley in May 1992?
15. What nationality is the striker Rune Lange?

1. Eddie Baily 2. Jean-Pierre Papin 3. Pippo 4. Cameroon 5. Spain 6. Karl-Heinz Rummenigge 7. The 1960s 8. Reinaldo 9. Senegal 10. Ali Daei 11. Borussia Dortmund 12. Lothar Matthaus 13. The 1970s 14. David Platt 15. Norwegian

Quiz 6

1. Who coached the Dutch national side from 1992 to 1994?
2. True or false: Stan Bowles won five caps for England?
3. Which footballer, who was 25 at the time, scored both goals on his England debut in a 2–2 draw against Yugoslavia at Highbury on 22 November 1950?
4. Name the three West Ham players to feature in the 1966 World Cup side against Argentina.
5. Which commentator said this: 'We are best in the world! We have beaten England! England, birthplace of giants'?
6. Which football legend worked as a switchboard technician at the Liberia Telecommunications Corporation before becoming a footballer?
7. In which country was Edgar Davids born?
8. Which international side has Marinko Galic played for?
9. Against which country did Roy Keane make his 50th international appearance for the Republic of Ireland?
10. In which year did Thomas Hassler win his 100th cap for Germany?
11. True or false: when Bobby Moore retired from international football, his 108 caps made him the most-capped player for England?
12. Which famous Turkish forward scored the only goal in the World Cup qualifier which ended Azerbaijan 0–1 Turkey in October 2000?
13. True or false: Alan Ball reached 100 caps for England?
14. In which decade was former Dutch international Johan Neeskens born?
15. For which country has Idan Tal played international football?

1. Dick Advocaat 2. True 3. Nat Lofthouse 4. Bobby Moore, Martin Peters and Geoff Hurst 5. Bjørge Lillelien – after Norway beat England in a World Cup qualifier 6. George Weah 7. Surinam 8. Slovenia 9. Cyprus 10. 2000 11. True. Shilton was the next person to break the record 12. Hakan Sukur 13. False. He only won 72 caps 14. The 1950s 15. Israel.

Quiz 7

1. Which former England international played only for Bolton at club level and scored 30 goals in 33 appearances for England?
2. Which former Manchester United player scored the only goal in the World Cup qualifier which ended Bulgaria 0–1 Czech Republic in September 2000?
3. Who scored Italy's goal in their third-place play-off game with Brazil in the 1978 World Cup Finals?
4. For which country did Leopoldo Luque score four goals in the 1978 World Cup Finals?
5. How many goals did Bobby Moore score for England?
6. True or false: Dino Baggio made his full international debut in 1991?
7. In which decade was former Italian international Nicola Berti born?
8. When David Healy scored a hat-trick for Northern Ireland in September 2006 he was the first player to do so since whom?
9. Who captained Northern Ireland when they reached the 1958 quarter-finals of the World Cup?
10. True or false: Franky Vercauteren won five European trophies with Anderlecht?
11. For which country did Hassan Rowshan appear in the 1978 World Cup Finals?
12. To within ten, how many caps did Morten Olsen win for Denmark?
13. Which Brazilian defender has the nickname 'Pluto'?
14. In which decade was former Italian international Gianluca Vialli born?
15. Which Fulham player became the first player to be paid £100 a week following the abolition of the £20 maximum wage in 1961?

1. Nat Lofthouse 2. Karel Poborsky 3. Franco Causio 4. Argentina 5. Two 6. True 7. The 1960s 8. Colin Clarke 9. Danny Blanchflower 10. True. He won two Cup Winners' Cup, one UEFA Cup and two Supercups 11. Iran 12. 102 13. Aldair 14. The 1960s 15. Johnny Haynes.

Quiz 8

1. Finish the commentary: 'And here comes Hurst, he's got ...'
2. Which footballer famously danced with the Jules Rimet Trophy in his hand while holding his false teeth in the other, after playing a storming game in the World Cup Final?
3. Which former Notts County legend scored 22 goals in 23 games for England between 1938 and 1948?
4. Who was the 2006–7 FIFA World's Best Player?
5. Against which country did Arsenal's Tony Adams make his England debut in 1987?
6. For which country has Hany Ramzy been a full international?
7. For which country did Ed de Goey played make his full international debut in 1992?
8. For which country has Ofer Talker played international football?
9. In which year did Ronald De Boer make his international debut for the Netherlands?
10. True or false: Karl-Heinz Rummenigge had a scoring rate of more than one goal every second game for Germany?
11. In how many World Cups did Belgian Enzo Scifo play?
12. Which country qualified as host nation for the 1978 World Cup Finals?
13. What is the nickname of Turkey international Oguz Cetin?
14. True or false: former Wimbledon coach Egil Olsen never played for the Norwegian national side.
15. For which German side did Hans-Peter Briegel play most of his professional career?

1. '...some people are on the pitch, they think it's all over! (Hurst shoots and scores)... It is now!' 2. Nobby Stiles 3. Tommy Lawton 4. Fabio Cannavaro 5. Spain 6. Egypt 7. Netherlands 8. Israel 9. 1993 10. False. It was just under that. He scored 45 goals in 95 games 11. Four - 1986, 1990, 1994 and 1998 12. Argentina 13. The Emperor 14. False. He played 16 games for Norway 15. FC Kaiserslautern.

Quiz 9

1. Who was Spain's top scorer at the 1994 World Cup Finals?
2. In which country was Jimmy Floyd Hasselbaink born?
3. Against which team did Preben Elkjaer score a hat-trick at Mexico 86?
4. When he retired in 1997, which Uruguayan was the most-capped outfield player in Uruguayan international football history?
5. Which international team did Danny Blanchflower play for?
6. Only three Englishmen have won both World and European Cups. Name them.
7. Who in 1995 was named FIFA World Player of the Year, European Footballer of the Year, and African Footballer of the Year?
8. Which player, infamous for his tan, gold chain and headers, scored Germany's goal which beat England 1-0 at Wembley in a friendly in September 1991?
9. In which decade was former German international Klaus Augenthaler born?
10. In which country was former Belgian international Luis Oliveira born?
11. Which country has Poland-born forward Tomasz Radzinski represented?
12. What nationality is the striker Alberto Acosta?
13. Who scored the goal that put England past Argentina and into the semi-finals of the 1966 World Cup?
14. Which former Fulham man made 56 appearances for England, including 22 as captain, many while playing for Fulham in the Second Division?
15. Which Irish legend is reported to have turned down the invitation to appear live on *This Is Your Life* in 1961, saying to Eamonn Andrews: 'I consider this programme to be an invasion of privacy ... Nobody is going to press-gang me into anything'?

1. Jose Luis Caminero 2. Surinam 3. Uruguay 4. Enzo Francescoli 5. Northern Ireland 6. Nobby Stiles, Bobby Charlton and Ian Callaghan 7. George Weah 8. Karlheinz Riedle 9. The 1950s 10. Brazil 11. Canada 12. Argentine 13. Geoff Hurst 14. Johnny Haynes 15. Danny Blanchflower.

Quiz 10

1. Against which team were the Czech Republic playing when Karel Poborsky famously chipped the keeper in Euro 96?
2. Which Danish player, a star of the Mexico 86 team, also helped Verona win a rare Serie A title in 1985?
3. Which former Belgian star was coaching Marseille at the start of the 2007–8 season?
4. What was the furthest Franky Vercauteren's Belgium went in the World Cup while he was a player?
5. True or false: Liam Brady never got the chance to play in a major tournament with Ireland?
6. How many World Cups has Lothar Matthaus played in?
7. Which African country has goalkeeper Kemoko Camara represented as a full international?
8. Who scored both goals for Wales against Armenia in a World Cup qualifier in March 2001?
9. Why did Don Hutchison withdraw from the Scotland squad to play the Faroe Islands and the Czech Republic in 1999?
10. True or false: Jeff Astle won 20 caps for England?
11. Which two players, who played for opposing teams in Liverpool, scored the goals for England that beat Poland 2–0 at Wembley in October 1990 in a qualifier for the 1992 European Championships?
12. In which decade was former German international goalkeeper Bodo Illgner born?
13. Against which Eastern European country did Sol Campbell make his international debut in 1996?
14. In which country was former Evertonian and Portugal player Abel Xavier born?
15. Who won FIFA World's Best Female Player award in 2006–7 and 2007–8?

1. Portugal 2. Preben Elkjaer (Larsen) 3. Eric Gerets 4. They got a fourth-place finish in Mexico 86 5. True 6. Five – 1982, 1986, 1990, 1994, 1998 7. Guinea 8. John Hartson 9. To go on honeymoon 10. False. He won five 11. Gary Lineker and Peter Beardsley 12. The 1960s 13. Hungary 14. Mozambique 15. Marta (Brazil)

Quiz 11

1. Against which Premiership side did Cristiano Ronaldo score with a cheeky back-flick in the 2007-8 season?
2. Against which team did Zinedine Zidane score arguably the best goal ever in a Champions League Final? It was a left-footed volley from the edge of the area from a high lob.
3. For which national side did Franky Vercauteren play?
4. When Lothar Matthaus retired from international football he was the most-capped German player of all time. How many caps did he win?
5. In which year did Frank Lampard come second in the FIFA voting for World's Best Player?
6. Which international side did coach Vasilis Daniil take charge of in March, 1999?
7. For which international side did Fernando Caceres play in the 1994 World Cup Finals?
8. Against which side did Colin Hendry make his international debut for Scotland in 1993?
9. For which international side has defender Emre Asik played?
10. Who was voted Romanian Player of the Century in 1999?
11. For which international side has Sasa Gajser played?
12. Under what name is former Spanish international Antonio Alvarez Perez better known?
13. Under what name did Spanish international Francisco Jemez Martin play?
14. Which country has defender Kakha Kaladze represented?
15. In which decade was former Italian international Carlo Ancelotti born?

1. Aston Villa 2. Bayer Leverkusen 3. Belgium 4. 150 5. 2005-6 6. Greece 7. Argentina 8. Estonia 9. Turkey 10. Gheorghe Hagi 11. Slovenia 12. Ito 13. Paco 14. Georgia 15. The 1950s.

Hat-Trick Heroes

Quiz 1

1. Who scored the first hat-trick of the 2007–8 Premiership season?
2. Which two players scored hat-tricks in Wigan's 5–3 home win over Blackburn on 15 December 2007?
3. Against which two sides did Benjani get his two hat-tricks in 2007–8?
4. Fernando Torres also struck two hat-tricks. Against who?
5. One other player got two hat-tricks in 2007–8. Who?
6. Who holds the record for most hat-tricks in the English game?
7. Dimitar Berbatov scored the most goals in one game. How many?
8. Against who did he score them?
9. Who else scored four goals in one game in the 2007–8 season?
10. Who did he score his four against?
11. True or false: the game in which Roque Cruz and Marcus Bent scored a hat-trick each was only the second time that a player from both sides had scored a hat-trick in the Premiership?
12. Who scored the last hat-trick of the 2005–6 season?
13. What was significant about it?
14. How did he celebrate the goal?
15. Who scored the first hat-trick of the 2005–6 season?

1. Emmanuel Adebayor (Arsenal) 2. Roque Santa Cruz (Blackburn Rovers) and Marcus Bent (Wigan Athletic) 3. Reading and Derby County 4. Middlesbrough and West Ham United 5. Emmanuel Adebayor (Arsenal) 6. Dixie Dean (Everton), 37 hat-tricks 7. Four 8. Reading 9. Frank Lampard 10. Derby 11. False. It was the first time 12. Thierry Henry 13. It was the last game to be played at Highbury 14. He kissed the grass at Highbury 15. Marlon Harewood, in West Ham United's 4–0 victory over Aston Villa.

Quiz 2

1. Mark Walters scored Liverpool's first Permiership hat-trick against which side?
2. Against whom did Robbie Fowler get his first Liverpool hat-trick?
3. Robbie Fowler amazingly hit hat-tricks for Liverpool in 1993, 1994, 1995, 1996, 1998, 1999, and 2001. He scored hat-tricks twice against which two clubs?
4. Against which club did Michael Owen score two hat-tricks while playing for Liverpool?
5. Who did Owen get his last hat-trick against in a Liverpool jersey?
6. Which Southampton player hit a hat-trick against Liverpool in 1994?
7. Which Leeds player got a memorable four goals against Liverpool at Elland Road in November 2000?
8. In what year did Thierry Henry knock three past Liverpool at Highbury?
9. Which Coventry player had one of the best footballng days in his career when he knocked three past Liverpool in 1995?
10. Which Newcastle United player scored a hat-trick against Liverpool in November 1993?
11. Who holds the World Record for the fastest hat-trick?
12. Who holds the record for the fastest English Football League hat-trick?
13. Who set the record for the fastest hat-trick in Premiership history when he scored three goals in four minutes and 33 seconds for Liverpool against Arsenal in 1994?
14. Who had set a better record in the old Division One?
15. Against whom and how fast was that Division One record set by him?

1. Coventry City, April 1995 2. Southampton, October 1993 3. Arsenal and Southampton 4. Newcastle United 5. West Bromwich Albion, April 2003. He actually scored four goals 6. Matt Le Tissier 7. Mark Viduka 8. 2004 9. Peter Ndlovu 10. Andy Cole 11. Ross County player Tommy Ross. He scored three goals in 90 seconds, versus Nairn County FC in Victoria Park in 1964 12. James Hayter who came on as an 84th-minute substitute for Bournemouth against Wrexham. He scored three goals in less than 140 seconds 13. Robbie Fowler 14. Nigel Clough 15. Clough took four minutes to score three for Nottingham Forest against Queens Park Rangers in 1987-8.

Quiz 3

1. Who set the record for the fastest hat-trick in the history of Major League Soccer in June 1998 against the Dallas Burn?
2. Which three players have scored two hat-tricks in the same World Cup competition?
3. Which Argentinian player scored hat-tricks in two different World Cup Finals tournaments?
4. Who scored the first World Cup Final hat-trick?
5. How many hat-tricks were scored in the 2006 World Cup Finals?
6. Who is the only player to have scored two hat-tricks in the UEFA European Football Championship?
7. Against whom did Dennis Bergkamp score an amazing hat-trick in September 1997?
8. Which footballing legend, who died in 2007, once held the record for the fastest goal in league football, which he held between 1943 and 1993?
9. Which Arsenal flyer hit a hat-trick in a 5–1 win over Boro in 1999?
10. Against whom did 'Romford' Ray Parlour hit three in December 2000?
11. Which Brighton player caught the attention of the big guns by hitting three against Torquay in 2000?
12. Which Burnley player hit hat-tricks in 1999 against Oxford and Colchester?
13. Which hitman scored three during Sunderland's 5–0 win over Derby in 1999?
14. Which player continued his success in Scotland by helping himself to three in a 7–1 drubbing of Dundee by Rangers in February 2000?
15. Geoff Horsfield scored a hat-trick against Northampton in 1999. At which club was he playing at the time?

1. Harut Karapetyan of Los Angeles Galaxy. It took him five minutes 2. Sandor Kocsis (1954), Just Fontaine (1958) and Gerd Müller (1970) 3. Gabriel Batistuta in the 1994 and 1998 World Cups 4. Geoff Hurst, 1966 5. None 6. Michel Platini 7. Leicester City 8. Jock Dodds. He smashed three goals in just two and a half minutes for Blackpool against Tranmere 9. Marc Overmars 10. Newcastle 11. Bobby Zamora 12. Andy Payton 13. Kevin Phillips 14. Rod Wallace 15. Fulham.

Quiz 4

1. Who scored Hearts' three goals in a 3–0 win over Aberdeen in August 1999?
2. When Leicester drubbed Sunderland 5–2 in 2000, who was the surprise scorer of a hat-trick?
3. Which Manchester City player kept up his great scoring record with three against Fulham in January 2000?
4. Who scored three for Manchester United in a 3–1 win against Derby in November 2000?
5. And which Manchester United player scored a rare hat-trick in a 7–1 win over West Ham in April 2000?
6. In October 1999 two players, one from each side, scored hat-tricks in a Scottish league game. Which teams were playing?
7. Which two players scored the hat-tricks?
8. Against who did Rod Wallace score a hat-trick for Rangers in March 2000?
9. Which former Manchester United player scored the hat-trick that saw Rotherham United clinch victory over Swindon Town in March 2001?
10. Who scored Rotherham's hat-trick against Carlisle in February 2000?
11. Which player got four for Sheffield United in a 6–0 win over West Brom in Febraury 2000?
12. Which former Leeds star scored three against Southampton in August 1999?
13. Which Norwegian player scored a hat-trick for Tottenham in a 7–2 win over Southampton in March 2000?
14. Which Irishman scored three against Coventry while on a short stint with Tranmere (one of his many clubs) in September 1999?
15. Which team was Nicky Barmby playing for when he put three past West Ham in February 2000?

1. Gary McSwegan 2. Stan Collymore 3. Shaun Goater 4. Dwight Yorke 5. Paul Scholes 6. Motherwell 5–6 Aberdeen 7. Robert Winters (Aberdeen) and John Spencer (Motherwell) 8. Motherwell 9. Mark Robins 10. Leo Fortune-West 11. Marcus Bent 12. Michael Bridges 13. Steffen Iversen 14. David Kelly 15. Everton.

Quiz 5

1. When Wimbledon beat Sunderland 3–2 at home in October 1999, who scored three times for the Dons?
2. Which English-born Nigerian footballer scored three for Wolves against Grimsby in November 1999?
3. Who scored a hat-trick for Wycombe against Bury in February 2000?
4. Whose hat-trick helped Milwall defeat Reading 5–0 in November 1999?
5. Against which club did Yossi Benayoun score a treble for Liverpool in an 8–0 slaughter in the Champions League in 2007?
6. Which West Ham defender managed to pull off an unlikely hat-trick against Newcastle in 1986?
7. What was unusual about the Newcastle goalkeeper that day?
8. Which rookie Liverpool defender came on for Ian Rush against Wigan to score an unlikely hat-trick in a League Cup tie?
9. In 2005–6, who scored three of his five goals that season in a 4–3 win for Blackburn over Manchester United?
10. Who scored three in his 2003 debut for Arsenal in a 6–1 win over Southampton?
11. Who else got a hat-trick that day?
12. What was most unusual about Jose Luis Chilavert's hat-trick when his side Velez Sarsfield hammered Ferro Carril Oeste?
13. Who got a penalty-spot treble during the 1986 Liverpool–Coventry game?
14. Who scored an unlikely hat-trick with his head in Newcastle's UEFA Cup tie win over Royal Antwerp in 1994?
15. Who scored a hat-trick for Manchester United (with the head, left foot and right foot) in United's 6–2 win over Arsenal in the 1990 League Cup?

1. Carl Cort 2. Ade Akinbiyi 3. Sean Divine 4. Paul Moody 5. Besiktas 6. Alvin Martin 7. There were three different keepers: Martin Thomas, Chris Hedworth and Peter Beardsley. Beardsley was in goal when Martin hit his hat-trick in the 8–1 victory for West Ham 8. Steve Staunton 9. David Bentley 10. Jermaine Pennant 11. Robert Pires 12. He was a goalkeeper and all three were penalties 13. Jan Molby 14. Rob Lee 15. Lee Sharpe

MISCELLANY

Quiz 1

1. Name the two teams, prior to 2008–9, to have won the Charity Shield without having won the League or FA Cup.
2. What was the first Italian club Liam Brady played for after he left Arsenal?
3. Who was the second player to score a hat-trick in a European Cup Final?
4. Prior to the 2008–9 Commnity Shield game, what was the highest score ever in the fixture?
5. For which Serie A side did Hans-Peter Briegel play a key part in winning a surprise Serie A title?
6. Who were the losing semi-finalists in the 1971 League Cup?
7. Which club has had the second most players win the FIFA Player of the Year Awards?
8. True or false: Swindon let in 100 goals in their first year in the Premiership?
9. In which year or years was David Beckham voted FIFA's second best player in the world?
10. Which small club won the 1884 Scottish FA Cup?
11. Which team did Danny Blanchflower turn out for before moving to Spurs?
12. Which Northern Irishman is best remembered as the man who crossed the ball for Gerry Armstrong to score for Northern Ireland in their famous win against Spain, in Spain 1982?
13. Which Scottish club are nicknamed 'The Diamonds' or 'The Waysiders'?
14. Which former footballer's second job earned him the nickname the 'Preston Plumber'?
15. Who were the opposition when Pat Jennings scored a goal for Tottenham in the 1967 Charity Shield?

1. Leicester City and Brighton & Hove Albion 2. Juventus 3. Alfredo Di Stefano 4. Manchester United 8-4 Swindon Town (1911) 5. Hellas Verona 6. Bristol City and Manchester United 7. Real Madrid 8. True 9. 1999 and 2001 10. Queen's Park 11. Aston Villa 12. Billy Hamilton 13. Airdrieonians 14. Tom Finney 15. Manchester United.

Quiz 2

1. At the start of the 2008–9 season, which team had won the most Charity/Community Shield titles?
2. If one were to rank players by their top three finishes in the FIFA Player of the Year Awards, which player would be the world's second best since the introduction of the awards in 1991?
3. List five Scottish teams whose names start with the same letter that they end with.
4. For which two English clubs did George Weah play?
5. In which country was ex-Chelsea player Marcel Desailly born?
6. Danny Blanchflower's younger brother, Jackie Blanchflower, played for which side?
7. Northern Irishman, Gerry Armstrong, is known for his goals in the 1982 World Cup, but for which club did he play at the time?
8. In which two years did Trevor Brooking win the FA Cup with West Ham?
9. Which Scottish club plays at Cliftonhill Stadium?
10. True or false: Trevor Brooking played two games for St Pat's Athletic in the Republic of Ireland?
11. Which player joined Barcelona from Arsenal in July, 2008??
12. Who captained the Borussia Dortmund side that won the Champions League?
13. Which unusually named team were the first to win the Pro League in the USA?
14. Which German side did West Ham beat in the 1965 European Cup Winners Cup?
15. In which historic seaside town was Aston Villa's Gareth Barry born?

1. Manchester United 2. Ronaldo 3. Kilmarnock, Celtic, Dundee United, East Fife, East Stirlingshire 4. Chelsea and Manchester City 5. Ghana 6. Manchester United 7. Watford 8. 1975 and 1980 9. Albion Rovers 10. False. He played for Cork City 11. Alexander Hleb 12. Matthias Sammer 13. Long Island Rough Riders 14. 1860 Munich 15. Hastings.

Quiz 3

1. Did Pat Jennings play longer for Arsenal or Tottenham?
2. Which German side won the Champions League in 1996–7?
3. How old was Paolo Futre when he made his international debut for Portugal?
4. Who scored the last-minute winner in West Ham's 1964 FA Cup win?
5. With which team did Martin O'Neill finish his playing career?
6. With which Irish side did Danny Blanchflower start his career?
7. Which club won the 1887 Scottish FA Cup?
8. Which player captained the West Ham side to the FA Cup over Preston North End in 1964?
9. At the start of the 2008–9 season, which player held the record for most goals scored for Northern Ireland?
10. How many goals did Bobby Moore score for West Ham?
11. Which Scottish club is famed for playing home games at Gayfield Park?
12. With which club did Nobby Stiles finish his playing career?
13. Which club did Brechin City beat 12–1 in the 1928 Scottish FA Cup?
14. Which Chelsea player, despite being at the peak of his talents, chose to move to Third Division Notts County for a record transfer fee of £20,000 in 1947?
15. From which club did Manchester United buy Jesper Olsen in 1984?

1. Tottenham 2. Borussia Dortmund 3. 17 4. Ronnie Boyce 5. Notts County 6. Glentoran 7. Hibernian 8. Bobby Moore 9. David Healy 10. He scored 24 goals in 544 games 11. Arbroath 12. Preston North End 13. Thornhill 14. Tommy Lawton 15. Ajax Amsterdam.

Quiz 4

1. How old was Norman Whiteside when his promising career was cut short?
2. Which club did Glenn Hoddle manage after his move from Swindon?
3. Which understated player performed well for Manchester United in central midfield against Juventus and in central defence against Bayern Munich in United's 1999 Champions League win?
4. Who was captain of Spurs when they did the domestic double in 1961?
5. Who is older – Joe Cole or Ashley Cole?
6. Which club, famed for its attacking ethos, scored most goals in Division One in 1950–1?
7. When Lian Brady returned to England from Italy, who did he play for?
8. Which former powerhouse in Scottish football won the 1885 Scottish FA Cup?
9. What is former South Africa striker Shaun Bartlett's first name?
10. When Trevor Brooking scored the winner in the 1980 FA Cup Final, which team was defeated?
11. Which side did Karel Poborsky go to when he left Manchester United?
12. True or false: Hristo Stoichkov won FIFA Player of the Year in 1992?
13. Which Scottish club is nicknamed 'Blue Toon'?
14. From which non–league club did Aston Villa sign Noel Blake in 1979?
15. One Manchester United player missed a penalty in the 2007–8 Champions League Final penalty shoot–out. Who was it?

1. 26 2. Chelsea 3. Ronny Johnsen 4. Danny Blanchflower 5. Ashley Cole 6. Tottenham Hotspur 7. West Ham United 8. Renton 9. Thurston 10. Arsenal 11. Benfica 12. False, he was second in 1992 and 1994 13. Peterhead 14. Sutton Coldfield Town 15. Ronaldo.

Quiz 5

1. Which highly esteemed former player helped earn promotion for Swindon into the Premiership as a manager in 1992–3?
2. True or false: despite his form Chris Waddle never earned more than five England caps under Graham Taylor?
3. Which manager brought Chris Waddle to Sheffield Wednesday?
4. Who scored both goals for West Ham in their 1965 European Cup Winners Cup?
5. What is Sol Campbell's middle name?
6. What did the Belize team Juventus Caribbean rename themselves in 1998–9?
7. In which country was former Charlton Athletic defender Chris Bart-Williams born?
8. Which Scottish team is nicknamed 'The Wasps'?
9. Who was the first player to be sent off in a Scottish FA Cup Final?
10. What is the name of the trophy awarded by the Spanish newspaper *Marca* to the best goalkeeper in La Liga?
11. Which Scottish club plays at Shielfield Park?
12. Which two teams whose names begin with S were the losing semi-finalists in the 1986 FA Cup?
13. Which club won the Cup in the Netherlands in 1944 and now have a team named after them in the Middlesex League (Tilburg Regent)?
14. How many times did Mario Zagallo win the World Cup as coach of Brazil?
15. Which team remained undefeated in the first football league in 1888–9?

1. Glenn Hoddle 2. True 3. Trevor Francis 4. Alan Sealey 5. Jeremiah 6. Juventus Pepsi 7. Sierra Leone 8. Alloa Athletic 9. Jock Buchanan 10. The Ricardo Zamora Trophy (Trofeo Ricardo Zamora) 11. Berwick Rangers 12. Sheffield Wednesday and Southampton 13. Willem II Tilburg 14. Two 15. Preston North End.

Quiz 6

1. For which Scottish club did Chris Waddle play?
2. What is the name of the trophy awarded by Spanish sports newspaper *Marca* to the top goalscorer for each league season?
3. After which famous player is the trophy named?
4. Against which European side did Manuel Negrete famously score with a left-footed scissors kick at the 1986 Mexico World Cup?
5. From which club did Manchester United sign Ole Gunnar Solskjaer?
6. Apart from doing the Double, which other record did Spurs set in 1960–61?
7. Which former England international played all 433 of his professional games between 1946 and 1960 for Preston North End?
8. What nationality is the former Cambridge United player Jonas Axeldal?
9. CD Libertas and CD Alacranes merged in 1950 to form which club in El Salvador?
10. In which year did the 200th derby between Dundee and Dundee United take place?
11. In which city was Irish international Stephen Carr born?
12. True or false: Tony Cottee didn't manage to score any goals for Norwich?
13. Which Scottish club is nicknamed 'The Binos'?
14. Which Scottish club's home ground is called Somerset Park?
15. In which country is there a team called Excelsior Mouscron?

1. Falkirk 2. The Pichichi Trophy 3. Athletic Bilbao player, Rafael Moreno 'Pichichi' 4. Bulgaria 5. Molde 6. They won 11 games in a row at the start of the season 7. Tom Finney 8. Swedish 9. Atletico Marte 10. 1998 11. Dublin 12. False. He scored one 13. Stirling Albion 14. Ayr United 15. Belgium.

Quiz 7

1. Which Liverpool manager signed Jan Molby?
2. Which South American former Marseille player is widely viewed to have been an inspiration to Zinedine Zidane?
3. True or false: Liam Brady played two seasons with Juventus and won two league titles in 1981 and 1982?
4. With which Italian side did Andreas Möller spend two seasons before returning to Germany?
5. Which footballer was successfully treated for testicular cancer and was named the Football Writers' Association Footballer of the Year in 1964?
6. What was the nickname of the former Scottish League club Third Lanark?
7. Which country, part of the former Soviet Bloc, beat Sri Lanka 12–1 in a friendly in January 1964?
8. Which club, a powerful force in the 1880s, won the 1882 Scottish FA Cup?
9. In which decade was Portsmouth's Eyal Berkovic born?
10. Which club won the League in the Netherlands in 1951?
11. Which South Coast side were Division One champions in 1948–9?
12. What nationality is goalkeeper John Filan?
13. Which two London sides were the losing semi-finalists in the 1972 League Cup?
14. Which Scottish club's home ground is called Borough Briggs?
15. Which coastal Scottish team play at Stair Park?

1. Joe Fagan 2. Enzo Francescoli 3. True 4. Juventus 5. Bobby Moore 6. The Hi-Hi's 7. East Germany 8. Queen's Park 9. 1970s 10. PSV Eindhoven 11. Portsmouth 12. Australian 13. Tottenham Hotspur and West Ham United 14. Elgin City 15. Stranraer.

Quiz 8

1. Which Danish footballer played for Liverpool between 1984 and 1996 and became famed for picking up the Scouse accent, as well as his great control of a game?
2. Which two Chelsea men missed their penalties in the 2007–8 Champions League Final penalty shoot-out?
3. Which club did Lothar Matthäus manage at the start of the 2008–9 season?
4. Who scored the winner for Liverpool in the 1977–8 European Cup Final?
5. Which two teams, whose names begin with L, were the losing semi-finalists in the 1985 FA Cup?
6. For which Italian team did ex-Bradford player Benito Carbone play most of his games in Italy?
7. Which two clubs, one from either side of the Pennines, were the losing semi-finalists in the 1977 FA Cup?
8. For which club did Lauren Charvet sign in 1998?
9. What is the middle name of ex-Newcastle United player Titus Bramble?
10. Which two teams from the South Coast were the losing semi-finalists in the 1984 FA Cup?
11. Which team threatened Queen Park's cup domination by winning the 1883 Scottish FA Cup?
12. Which former England international played a club-record 658 games and scored 158 goals for Fulham between 1952 and 1970?
13. With which US club did Bobby Moore finish his professional career?
14. When Bobby Moore pulled on the Number 6 shirt for his debut against Manchester United, who was he replacing that day?
15. True or false: Once Bobby Moore replaced him, that player never played for the side again?

1. Jan Molby 2. John Terry and Nicholas Anelka 3. Maccabi Netanya 4. Kenny Dalglish 5. Liverpool and Luton Town 6. Inter Milan 7. Leeds United and Everton 8. Newcastle United 9. Malachi 10. Southampton and Plymouth Argyle 11. Dumbarton 12. Johnny Haynes 13. Seattle Sounders 14. Malcolm Allison 15. True. He never played top-flight football again.

Quiz 9

1. Which club did Ronny Johnsen go to when he left Manchester United?
2. Which club did Jan Molby play for before he moved to Liverpool?
3. Which Israeli managed the losing Chelsea side in the 2007–8 Champions League Final?
4. How many Englishmen were in the starting line up in the 2007–8 Champions League Final between Chelsea and Man United?
5. Name one of only a handful of players to have been awarded the title of English Footballer of the Year on two occasions, when he won it in both 1958 and 1961?
6. With which club did Nobby Stiles play the majority of his club career?
7. Which player has been immortalised in a water-feature sculpture called 'The Splash', which stands outside The National Football Museum?
8. Who reportedly stated: 'Tom Finney would have been great in any team, in any match and in any age … even if he had been wearing an overcoat'?
9. Which London and Yorkshire sides were the losing semi-finalists in the 1983 FA Cup?
10. Who was the first player to score a hat-trick in a European Cup Final?
11. In which decade did Darren Ferguson join Wolverhampton Wanderers from Manchester United?
12. Which small London club managed to reach the semi-finals of the 1978 FA Cup?
13. Which two 'Citys' lost in the semi-finals of the 1981 League Cup?
14. For which country did Harry Hibbs play international football?
15. Which Scottish team's home ground is McDiarmid Park?

1. Aston Villa 2. Ajax 3. Avram Grant 4. Ten (six for United and four for Chelsea) 5. Danny Blanchflower 6. Manchester United 7. Tom Finney. It was inspired by the 1956 Sports Photograph of the Year and shows Finney beating two defenders at a waterlogged Stamford Bridge 8. Bill Shankly 9. Arsenal and Sheffield Wednesday 10. Ferenc Puskas 11. The 1990s 12. Leyton Orient 13. Manchester City and Coventry City 14. England 15. St. Johnstone.

Quiz 10

1. Name the very highly regarded Portuguese player in the Borussia Dortmund side that won the 1996–7 Champions League?
2. Which German player scored a brace to sink Juventus in the 1997 Champions League Final?
3. Who scored Nottingham Forest's winner in the 1978–9 European Cup Final?
4. Which English club did Bobby Moore join after leaving West Ham?
5. For which Italian club did Giovanni Trapattoni make more than 270 appearances as a player?
6. Who did Spurs beat in their 1963 European Cup Winners' Cup Final?
7. How many English clubs have had players selected for any of the top three awards in the FIFA Player of the Year Awards?
8. Who scored the winner for Manchester United in the 1999 Champions League Final?
9. Which club continued their excellent form in the cup by winning the 1886 Scottish FA Cup?
10. Which two teams, whose names begin with N, were the losing semi-finalists in the 1989 FA Cup?
11. Which team, now a Premiership giant, finished bottom of the 1894–5 football league?
12. If one were to rank players by their top three finishes in the FIFA Player of the Year Awards, which player would be the world's best since the introduction of the awards in 1991?
13. Which club has had the most players win the FIFA Player of the Year Awards?
14. Which Arsenal outfield maestro won the PFA Player of the Year in 1979?
15. Name the influential Scotsman who played for the Borussia Dortmund side that won the 1996–7 Champions League?

1. Paulo Sousa 2. Karl-Heinz Riedle 3. Trevor Francis 4. Fulham 5. AC Milan 6. Atlético Madrid 7. Six – Arsenal, Manchester United, Blackburn (Shearer 1996), Newcastle (Shearer 1996), Chelsea, Tottenham 8. Ole Gunnar Solskjaer 9. Queen's Park 10. Nottingham Forest and Norwich City 11. Liverpool 12. Zinedine Zidane 13. Barcelona 14. Liam Brady 15. Paul Lambert.

Disappearing, Defunct Teams & Former Giants

Quiz 1

1. Which club was founded in 1911 by Croatian students following a game they attended in Prague, which was then part of the Austro-Hungarian Empire?
2. From 1954 to 1966, workers from which organization were represented in the East German team, Dynamo Berlin (BFC Dynamo)?
3. In 1991, Dynamo Berlin was officially renamed FC Berlin. What events prompted this move?
4. Despite returning to the name BFC Dynamo (Dynamo Berlin), the side have struggled. In which league do they now play?
5. What was the longest run of consecutive East German league titles won by Dynamo Berlin in the 1970s and 1980s?
6. In 1983–4, Dynamo Berlin reached the quarter-final of the European Cup. Which Italian side knocked them out?
7. Name one of Hajduk Split's nicknames.
8. Which Hajduk youth academy player went on to become a top striker at Juventus, Lazio, and Middlesbrough?
9. In 1954, Dynamo Dresden lost the majority of its top-flight players. What happened?
10. Which former Dynamo Dresden player won European Footballer of the Year in 1996?
11. In 1989, Dresden defeated Aberdeen and Roma in the UEFA Cup. Who knocked them out in the semis?
12. Which Yugoslavian club knocked Dresden out of the quarter-final of the European Cup in 1990–1?
13. Records show that Dresden lost that two-legged affair 6–0. What was unusual about the scoreline?
14. Only one Serbian team has ever won the European Cup. Who?
15. In the 1991 final, which French star missed his penalty in the shoot-out to lose Marseille the trophy?

1. HNK Hajduk Split 2. It was the sports club of the Ministry of Police and the Ministry for Public Security of East Germany (or Stasi, the Secret Police) 3. The reunification of Germany and resultant administrative changes 4. NOFV-Oberliga Nord (the fifth tier of German football) 5. Ten (1979–88) 6. AS Roma 7. Bili (The Whites) or Majstor s mora (Master from the Sea) 8. Alen Boksic 9. Erich Mielke, head of the Stasi (secret police), demanded that the team be moved to Berlin. It did move to become Dynamo Berlin (see above) 10. Matthias Sammer 11. VfB Stuttgart 12. Red Star Belgrade 13. Red Star won 3–0 at home. However, in the return leg when Dresden were leading 2–1, fans rioted and Red Star were awarded a 3–0 victory 14. Red Star Belgrade 15. Manuel Amoros. Red Star Belgrade took the trophy.

Quiz 2

1. Which Scottish side were thumped 4–1 on aggregate in 1990–1 by Red Star Belgrade in the second round of the European Cup?
2. Despite winning the European Cup in 1991, Red Star were denied the European Super Cup by which English side?
3. Red Star's opponents had just three non-British players in the starting XI that day. Name them.
4. Which side beat Hamburg 4–0 in the 1981–2 final of the UEFA Cup?
5. The same side went on to win it again by beating Dundee United in the 1986–7 final. What was the score on aggregate?
6. What is Gothenburg's nickname (other than the Blue Whites)?
7. True or false: Gothenburg are the only Scandinavian team to have won a pan-European competition?
8. Which Yugoslavian side did Real Madrid defeat in the 1966 European Cup Final?
9. Who are the losing side's main rivals in their home league?
10. What was Partizan's stadium called for most of the 1940s and 1950s?
11. Partizan took part in the first-ever European Cup game, which ended 3–3. Who did they play?
12. Which English team did Partizan knock out at the 1965–6 European Cup semi-final stage?
13. Which English side did Partizan knock out of the 2003–4 European Champions League at the final stage of qualifying?
14. Partizan fans' nickname is 'Grobari'. What does it mean in English?
15. Which German World Cup star coached Partizan briefly in 2003?

1. Rangers 2. Manchester United 3. Peter Schmeichel, Denis Irwin and Andrei Kanchelskis 4. IFK Göteborg 5. 2-1 6. Änglarna (The Angels), Kamraterna (The Comrades) 7. True 8. FK Partizan 9. Red Star Belgrade (they're both Belgrade-based sides) 10. Stadium of the Yugoslav People's Army 11. Sporting Lisbon 12. Manchester United 13. Newcastle United 14. The Gravediggers (believed to be derived from their black kit, the colour of undertakers in Yugoslavia) 15. Lothar Matthaus.

Quiz 3

1. At the start of the 2008–9 season, which Warsaw-based club was the most successful Polish team in history?
2. Prior to 2008–9, when had they last won the league?
3. What is the furthest they have ever been in the European Cup?
4. Who knocked them out of the European Cup that year?
5. Which British side did they defeat in the group stages of the 1995–6 Champions League?
6. Who knocked them out at the quarter-final stages?
7. Which Englishman went to play briefly for them in 2004?
8. True or false: Anderlecht have won all four major European trophies – European Cup, UEFA Cup, Cup Winners' Cup and SuperCup?
9. How many times did Anderlecht make the Cup Winners' Cup Final in the 1970s?
10. Which London-based side did Anderlecht beat in the 1976 Cup Winners' Cup?
11. In 1955, Anderlecht played in the first-ever European Cup (then called the Champions Cup). Who knocked them out?
12. Which team were hammered by Anderlecht in the 1976 European Super Cup?
13. Which British side lost the Super Cup to Anderlecht in 1978?
14. Who did Liverpool beat in the 1977–8 final to clinch the European Cup?
15. In which year did Liverpool also deny Brugge the UEFA Cup?

1. Legia Warsaw 2. 2006–7. Runners-up in 2007–8 3. The semi-finals 4. Feyenoord (2–0 away from home, after a 0–0 draw in Poland) 5. Blackburn Rovers 6. Panathinaikos 7. Eddie Stanford 8. False. They still haven't won the European Cup 9. Three: in consecutive years from 1976 to 1978 10. West Ham United 11. MTK Budapest 12. Bayern Munich. Anderlecht won 5–3 on aggregate 13. Liverpool 14. Club Brugge KV 15. 1976.

Quiz 4

1. Under which name did the Republic of Ireland play between 1922 and 1937?
2. In which year did the unified Korea team divide into the two independent nations of South Korea and North Korea?
3. In 1992, 12 former USSR member states played together as a new team. Under what name did they go before splitting into separate national teams?
4. In what year did the USSR first play under that name?
5. What name did it play under prior to that?
6. Name the three national sides that had already seceded from the USSR prior to 1992.
7. In which year did North Vietnam and South Vietnam unite as a national side?
8. Name three of the five national sides that came about after Yugoslavia disintegrated in 1992.
9. What did Yugoslavia later change their name to?
10. And in which year did Serbia & Montenegro split to form two new national sides?
11. The team known as Israel came about after renaming an old side in 1948. What was the original name?
12. In 1957, a national side called Gold Coast was renamed. What was the name of the new and now fairly successful country/national side?
13. Under which name was national side Kampuchea playing in 1979?
14. Burkino Faso started playing under that name in 1984. What was it known as in the decades beforehand?
15. Which national side is officially recognized as the successors to the Dutch East Indies national side?

1. The Irish Free State 2. 1945 3. CIS – the Commonwealth of Independent States 4. 1917 5. Russia 6. Estonia, Latvia and Lithuania 7. 1976 8. Bosnia & Herzegovina, Croatia, FYR Macedonia, Slovenia, Yugoslavia 9. Serbia & Montenegro 10. 2006 11. Palestine/Eretz Israel 12. Ghana 13. Cambodia 14. Upper Volta 15. Indonesia, since 1949.

Quiz 5

1. In what year did Gretna FC go into administration and then go bust?
2. How much did the club owe when it went into administration?
3. Until which year did Gretna play in the English league?
4. In which year did Gretna win Scottish League Division One?
5. Who beat Gretna on penalties in the 2006 Scottish Cup Final?
6. True or false: with serious financial backing Gretna managed to rise from the bottom Scottish division to the Premier League in three consecutive years?
7. In which year did Wimbledon FC cease to exist?
8. Which club officially took over the mantle, and what is the name of the club that was started by disappointed supporters?
9. In which year was Wimbledon FC founded in the London Borough of Wimbledon?
10. What was the name of the ground where Wimbledon played the majority of their home games?
11. In which year did Wimbledon defeat Liverpool in the FA Cup Final?
12. Which manager took Wimbledon to their highest position in the Premiership?
13. By what name were Wimbledon's FA Cup-winning side often referred to?
14. Which former Don captained and scored for Jamaica in their 1998 World Cup campaign?
15. Which legendary Wimbledon goalkeeper played in all four Football League divisions with the club?

1. 2008 2. £4m 3. 2002 4. 2006–07 5. Hearts 6. True 7. 2004 8. Milton Keynes Dons and AFC Wimbledon 9. 1911 10. Plough Lane 11. 1988 12. Joe Kinnear (1992 to 1999) 13. The Crazy Gang 14. Robbie Earle 15. Dave Beasant.

Quiz 6

1. Which west London club, formed in 1839, was a founding member of the FA in 1863 and played one of the first association rules games against Richmond? (The club is now a rugby union club.)
2. Which Irish club, now a rugby club, is the oldest well-documented club to have continually existed since its foundation in 1854?
3. Which team do the English FA and FIFA officially recognize as the oldest club still playing association football?
4. Which now-defunct football club was founded in 1861 by the groundkeepers of the Great Exhibition in London?
5. Name three of the founding members of the English FA.
6. In which year did Aldershot FC go bust?
7. Which former England striker played for Aldershot six times while on loan from Millwall in 1985?
8. When Aldershot became the first winners of a play-off final, in 1987, who did they beat?
9. Which national side ceased to exist when its country was integrated into the People's Republic of China in 1945?
10. Which national side ceased to exist when its country was integrated into the People's Republic of China in 1948?
11. In what year did the Czechoslovakia national side become the independent nations of the Czech Republic and Slovakia?
12. In 1960, French Equatorial Africa and, consequently, its national football team mutated into four countries. Name two.
13. In the same year, French West Africa transformed into nine countries. Name four.
14. In what year did East and West Germany cease playing as separate sides?
15. In which year did Ireland cease playing as a unified national side and split into Northern Ireland and the Republic of Ireland?

1. Barnes Club 2. Dublin University Football Club 3. Sheffield Football Club, founded in October 24, 1857. They currently play in the Northern Premier League Division One South 4. Crystal Palace FC - the modern club of that name was founded in 1905 5. Barnes, Blackheath, Blackheath Proprietary School, Civil Service, Crusaders, Crystal Palace, Kensington School, Leytonstone Forest, No Names Club/NN Kilburn, Percival House, Surbiton 6. 1992 7. Teddy Sheringham 8. Wolverhampton Wanderers 9. Manchuria 10. Shanghai 11. 1993 12. Republic of the Congo, Gabon, Central African Republic, Chad 13. Mali, Senegal, Mauritania, Guinea, Burkina Faso, Benin, Togo, Côte d'Ivoire, Niger 14. 1990 15. 1922.

Quiz 7

1. Which Hungarian team had its golden age in the 1950s when it was also the army team?
2. Players from that era included Ferenc Puskas, Sandor Kocsis, Jozsef Bozsik and Zoltan Czibor, who all formed the nucleus of the famous Hungarian team of the 1950s. What were they nicknamed?
3. Between 1991 and 2003 Budapest Honved went under a different name. What was it?
4. Which legendary coach managed the team in 1947–8?
5. How many times did Honved win the domestic league in their golden era in the 1950s?
6. In the second European Cup ever held, Honved's first, which side defeated Honved under extenuating circumstances?
7. When the Soviet Union invaded Hungary, what unusual actions did Honved take?
8. Puskas famously joined Real Madrid. Which club did Czibor and Kocsis sign for?
9. Honved's second golden era was in the 1980s. How many domestic titles did they win during that decade?
10. Which shirt number has been retired at Honved? Whose shirt was it?
11. True or false: Ferenc Puskas' dad was also called Ferenc and played for the same club?
12. Which group had a song called 'I Was A Teenage Armchair Honved Fan'?
13. Which side won the Hungarian League in 1986–7, preventing Budapest from making it six in a row?
14. In which two years did Honved do the domestic double?
15. In what league do Honved now play?

1. Budapest Honved SE 2. The Mighty Magyars 3. Kispest Honved FC. When the team was originally formed Kispest was still a village, distinct from the city of Budapest 4. Béla Guttman 5. Four - 1950, 1952, 1954, 1955 6. Atlético Bilbao. The Hungarians didn't have a home leg due to civil war 7. They refused to go home and instead went on a world tour round Europe and Brazil. Eventually, the team split up and individual players dispersed among the prestigious clubs that they had played against 8. Barcelona 9. Six - 1980, 1984, 1985, 1986, 1988, 1989 10. Ferenc Puskas wore the No.10 shirt at Honved 11. True 12. Half Man Half Biscuit 13. MTK Hungária FC 14. 1985 and 1989 15. Nemzeti Bajnokság I/the National Championship/Soproni Liga (under sponsorship rules).

Quiz 8

1. Which French side have won the French league every decade since the 1960s but have recently only been restored to Ligue 1 after promotion from Ligue 2 in 2007–8?
2. What is the club's nickname?
3. Which former French captain and World Cup–winner began his career with Nantes in 1985?
4. During which five–year period did Claude Makelele begin his career there?
5. Which Argentinian legend played some of his best football at Nantes between 1985 and 1992?
6. Who knocked Nantes out of the 1979–80 UEFA Cup at the semi–final stage?
7. Which giant club knocked them out of the 1995–6 European Cup at the semi–final stage?
8. Which US team had the honour of signing Pele towards the end of his career and to this day his jersey is the only one that has been retired by the club?
9. True or false: at the height of US footballing fever in the 1970s, this club's attendances regularly topped 50,000?
10. Which Dutch legend played for the side between 1979 and 1984?
11. Name the feature–length film released about the side in 2006.
12. Which German 'giant' played alongside the Brazilian star?
13. Name the Northern Irishman who played in the same team as Pele.
14. Name the relatively unknown Scotsman, and former Villa man, who played in the same team as Pele.
15. True or false: despite their fame, the side won no US trophies or titles?

1. FC Nantes 2. Les Canaris (The Canaries) 3. Didier Deschamps 4. 1992–97 5. Jorge Luis Burruchaga 6. Valencia 7. Juventus 8. The New York Cosmos 9. False. They had a top attendance of 47,856 in 1978 10. Johan Neeskens 11. *Once In A Lifetime* 12. Franz Beckenbauer 13. Dave Clements, who also played for Coventry, Wednesday and Everton 14. Charlie Aitken 15. False. They won the Eastern Division title six years in a row between 1978 and 1983.

LEGENDS

Pele

1. What is Pele's real name?
2. Which group awarded Pele the title of Athlete of the Century?
3. For which Brazilian club did Pele play just over 600 games, before moving to the New York Cosmos?
4. True or false: Pele is the all-time top scorer for Brazil?
5. True or false: Pele made 105 appearances for Brazil?
6. Against which club side did Pele make a scoring debut?
7. How old was Pele when he first became top scorer in the Brazilian league?
8. Pele also scored on his international debut at the age of 16. But who beat Brazil that day?
9. Who did Pele's first World Cup goal come against in the 1958 World Cup?
10. Against which team did Pele score a hat-trick in the 1958 World Cup?
11. How many goals did he score in the 1958 final?
12. Against which side did Pele injure himself in the 1962 World Cup, which forced him to miss most of the tournament?
13. Why did Pele temporarily retire after the 1966 World Cup?
14. Against which side did Pele almost score a header, but in not doing so played a part in what is widely believed to be the best save ever?
15. Who is reported to have said this about Pele after the 1970 World Cup Final: 'I told myself before the game, he's made of skin and bones just like everyone else – but I was wrong'?

1. Edison Arantes do Nascimento 2. The International Olympic Committee 3. Santos 4. True 5. False. He made 92 appearances 6. Corinthians (1956) 7. 16 8. Argentina 9. Wales 10. France 11. Two 12. Czechoslovakia 13. He felt the tournament was overly physical 14. England – Gordon Banks' save 15. Italian defender Tarcisio Burgnich.

Diego Maradona

1. What is Maradona's middle name?
2. Which award did Maradona share with Pele in 2000?
3. How old was Maradona when he made his professional debut?
4. From which club did Barcelona sign Maradona?
5. At the time Barcelona paid a record fee for Maradona. How much was it?
6. Maradona guided Napoli to their only Serie A titles in which seasons?
7. And in which year did he guide Napoli to a UEFA Cup Final victory?
8. Which team did they beat in the UEFA Cup Final?
9. Against which team was Maradona sent off in the 1982 World Cup Finals?
10. Against which team did Maradona captain Argentina to victory in the 1986 final?
11. About which goal was Maradona talking when he said it was scored 'a little with the head of Maradona'?
12. Name three of the five players Maradona dribbled round to score his amazing second goal in that match.
13. Despite being double-marked, who did Maradona set up for the winning goal in the 1986 final?
14. Against which team did Maradona captain Argentina to defeat in the 1990 World Cup Final?
15. Why didn't Maradona play any further part in the 1994 World Cup after his game against Greece?

1. Armando 2. FIFA Player of the Century 3. 15 4. Boca Juniors 5. £5 million 6. 1986-7 and 1989-90 7. 1989 8. VfB Stuttgart 9. Brazil 10. West Germany 11. The goal in 1986 against England. His full quote was 'a little with the head of Maradona and a little with the hand of God.' 12. Glenn Hoddle, Peter Reid, Kenny Sansom, Terry Butcher and Terry Fenwick 13. Jorge Burruchaga 14. West Germany 15. He failed a drug test for ephedrine doping.

Michel Platini

1. How many World Cup Final tournaments did Platini play in?
2. Platini holds the record for the most goals scored in a European Championship. How many?
3. Which national award did Platini gain in 1988?
4. Why did Metz turn a young Platini down during a trial with the club?
5. For which club did Platini play between 1972 and 1979?
6. With which side did Platini win the French league in 1981?
7. Platini reached the European Cup Final in his first year with Juventus. What year was it?
8. In which two years did he help Juve to domestic league titles?
9. Against which side did Platini score the winner in the 1985 European Cup Final?
10. Which French side did Juve scrape past in the 1985 semi-final?
11. For how many years in a row did Platini finish top scorer in Serie A?
12. How many times has Platini been European Footballer of the Year?
13. True or false: Platini scored more than half of France's goals in their 1984 European Championship success?
14. Apart from scoring two, what was unusual about Platini's two hat-tricks in the 1984 Euros, which were scored against Belgium and Yugoslavia?
15. In what year did Platini become the UEFA President?

1. Three – 1978, 1982 and 1986 2. Nine 3. Officer of the Legion of Honour 4. The club doctor felt that he had breathing difficulties and a weak heart 5. Nancy 6. Saint-Étienne 7. 1982 8. 1984 and 1986 9. Liverpool 10. FC Girondins de Bordeaux 11. Three – 1982–3, 1983–4 and 1984–5 12. Three – 1982–3, 1983–4 and 1984–5 13. True. He scored nine out of 14 goals 14. They were both 'perfect' hat-tricks – one header and one goal with each foot 15. 2007.

Johann Cruyff

1. What is Cruyff's full name?
2. In which decade was he born?
3. How many times has Cruyff won European Footballer of the Year awards?
4. With which two players does he share the record for the number of European Footballer of the Year awards?
5. With which two clubs did Cruyff have a successful management career?
6. With which two US teams did Cruyff play for between 1979 and 1981?
7. How many European Cups did Cruff win with Ajax?
8. Cruyff won eight Dutch league titles with Ajax. With which other team did he win one?
9. How many La Liga titles did Cruyff pick up as a player with Barcelona?
10. By contrast, he was much more successful as a coach with Barca. How many consecutive titles did he win with them?
11. And in which of those years did he also pick up a European Cup as manager?
12. True or false: Cruyff played fewer than 50 matches for Holland?
13. How many goals did he get in those games, setting a great scoring rate?
14. What was unusual about Cruyff's second Dutch national team match, a friendly against Czechoslovakia?
15. In which year did Cruyff lead Holland to a runners-up place in the World Cup?

1. Hendrik Johannes Cruyff 2. 1940s 3. Three - 1971, 1973 and 1974 4. Michel Platini and Marco van Basten 5. Ajax and FC Barcelona 6. Los Angeles Aztecs and Washington Diplomats 7. Three - 1971, 1972 and 1973 8. Feyenoord, in 1984 9. One - 1974 10. Four - 1991, 1992, 1993 and 1994 11. 1992 12. True - he played 48 13. 33 goals 14. He was the first Dutch international to receive a red card 15. 1974.

Van Basten, Gullit, Rijkaard

1. How many times has Van Basten been European Footballer of the Year?
2. In which year was he FIFA World Footballer of the Year?
3. Van Basten scored on his Ajax debut. Who did he replace as a substitute during that game?
4. How many goals did Van Basten score for Ajax in his unbelievable period there?
5. In what year did Silvio Berlusconi's cash bring Van Basten to AC Milan?
6. Against which team did Van Basten score arguably the best goal ever in the 1988 European Championships Final?
7. Who did Van Basten score twice against to help win the 1989–90 European Cup?
8. Who scored the winner for AC Milan in the 1990–1 European Cup?
9. Which Ajax coach gave Rijkaard his debut at the age of just 17?
10. Under which coach did Rijkaard play when he returned to Ajax in 1993, where he helped win the first two of three consecutive Dutch Championships?
11. Against which side did Rijkaard help Ajax win the 1994–5 European Cup in which Patrick Kluivert scored the game's only goal?
12. In which year(s) has Ruud Gullit been named World Soccer Player of the Year?
13. Which side was managed by Gullit in 2008–9?
14. For which club did Gullit make his professional debut?
15. For which Englishman was Gullit widely regarded as a replacement when he joined AC Milan?

1. Three times – 1988, 1989 and 1992 2. 1992 3. Johan Cruyff 4. He scored 128 goals in 133 games and was top scorer in the league for four seasons in a row 5. 1987 6. USSR 7. FC Steaua Bucuresti 8. Frank Rijkaard 9. Leo Beenhakker 10. Louis van Gaal 11. Ironically, it was AC Milan 12. 1987 and 1989 13. Los Angeles Galaxy 14. HFC Haarlem 15. Ray Wilkins.

Best and Charlton

1. In which year did Best win European Footballer of the Year?
2. Fill in the missing sections of this Northern Ireland supporters' chant: '____ good; ____ better; ____ Best'.
3. With which youth club did Best begin playing in 1962?
4. Which football club rejected Best for being 'too small and light'?
5. Best made his Manchester United debut in 1963. How old was he?
6. After which match was Best dubbed 'The Fifth Beatle'?
7. What are Oscar's and Slack Alice's?
8. How old was Best when he quit Manchester United?
9. For how many seasons was Best Manchester United's top scorer?
10. Which teammate and drinking partner was cheekily tackled by Best in a 1976–7 FA Cup game while at Fulham?
11. Best once famously clipped the ball out of a goalkeeper's hands and then scored while playing for Northern Ireland. Who was the keeper and which team was he playing for?
12. In which year did Bobby Charlton win European Footballer of the Year?
13. How many goals did Charlton score in the victorious European Cup Final of 1968?
14. True or false: when Charlton retired he was both Manchester United's and England's most-capped player?
15. After leaving Manchester United, where did Charlton become player-manager?

1. 1968 2. 'Maradona good; Pelé better; George Best.' 3. Cregagh Boys Club 4. Glentoran 5. 17 6. The 1966 European Cup quarter-final against Benfica in which he scored two goals 7. Nighclubs opened by Best in Manchester 8. 27 9. Six 10. Rodney Marsh 11. Gordon Banks of England 12. 1966 13. Two 14. True 15. Preston North End.

Beckham, Bergkamp, Ceulemans

1. In which year did David Beckham win the Youth Cup with Manchester United?
2. Against which club did Beckham score his famous goal in 1996–7 from just inside the halfway line?
3. True or false: Beckham won the award for European Footballer of the Year and FIFA World Player of the Year in 1999?
4. How many league titles did Becks win with Manchester United?
5. In which year did Becks pick up a Spanish league title?
6. With which club did Dennis Bergkamp begin his professional career?
7. What are Bergkamp's unusual middle names?
8. After which famous footballer did Bergkamp's football-mad family supposedly name him?
9. Which Arsenal manager made a great move by signing Bergkamp in 1995?
10. In which year did Arsenal do the domestic Double, while Bergkamp was named PFA Player of the Year?
11. What was unusual about Bergkamp's goals in the BBC Match of the Day's Goal of the Month competition in September 1997?
12. Against which side did Bergkamp control a 60-yard pass and calmly finish to score one of the tournament's best goals and help Holland to a 2–1 win in the 1998 World Cup?
13. To which position did Jan Ceulemans captain the Belgian national side in the 1986 FIFA World Cup?
14. Ceulemans scored three goals in that tournament, the best being a beautiful diving header against which side in the quarter-finals?
15. Which Italian super-club did Ceulemans turn down in order to remain playing in Belgium?

1. 1992 2. Wimbledon 3. False. He was runner-up to Rivaldo in both awards 4. Six - 1995–6, 1996–7, 1998–9, 1999–00, 2000–01 and 2002–3 5. 2006–7 6. Ajax 7. Nicola Maria 8. Denis Law 9. Bruce Rioch 10. 1998 11. He was the first and only player to have come first, second and third in the competition. 12. Argentina 13. Fourth place 14. Spain 15. AC Milan

Romario, Rivaldo, Ronaldo

1. What is Romario's full name?
2. In which Brazilian World Cup winning side did he star?
3. How old was Romario when he officially anounced his retirement?
4. In which year did he win the FIFA World Player of the Year?
5. With which club did he begin his professional career?
6. When Romario returned to Brazil from Barcelona, who did he play for?
7. What amazing record did Romario set in the Brazilian league in 2005?
8. Against which side did Romario's self-claimed 1000th goal arrive on May 20 2007?
9. Which club signed Rivaldo in 2007?
10. With which Spanish side did Rivaldo have his first successful year in La Liga?
11. True or false: both Rivaldo and Ronaldo scored in the first four games of Brazil's 2002 World Cup campaign?
12. Against which side did Rivaldo infamously get hit on the thigh with a ball only to roll on the ground clutching his face?
13. Which Brazilian side first played Ronaldo?
14. True or false: despite all of his injuries Ronaldo has played in more than 100 international matches?
15. Ronaldo is the top scorer in World Cup history. How many goals does he have and whose record did he break?

1. Romário de Souza Faria 2. 1994 FIFA World Cup 3. 42 4. 1994 5. Vasco da Gama 6. Flamengo 7. At almost 40 years of age, Romario scored 22 goals in the Brazilian Championship, making him the league's top goalscorer 8. He scored against Sport Recife while playing for Vasco da Gama 9. AEK Athens 10. Deportivo La Coruña 11. True. Rivaldo actually scored in the fifth also 12. Turkey 13. Cruzeiro 14. True 15. He has 15 goals and broke Gert Muller's previous record of 14.

Other Stars

1. Which Italian legend played all of his 532 professional games with AC Milan between 1977 and 1997?
2. What was that player's nickname in Milan?
3. With which club did Franz Beckenbauer finish his professional career?
4. Which player played all 444 of his professional games between 1946 and 1961 at Juventus, where he picked up five Serie A titles?
5. Name the two Italian goalkeeping legends to have made the FIFA Top 100 Players.
6. A legendary Spaniard signed for Atletico Celaya in Mexico in 1995. After playing there for three years, where he was nicknamed the 'Gentleman of the Pitch', he retired. Who is he?
7. Finish the name of this French legend. Eric Daniel Pierre _____.
8. Name the Peruvian legend who helped his national side to the 1975 Copa America and the quarter-finals of the World Cups in 1970 and 1978. He was also South American Footballer of the Year in 1972.
9. Finish the name of the Scottish legend: Kenneth Mathieson _____.
10. Which great goalkeeper, born in Astrakhan, is considered the best USSR keeper ever alongside Lev Yashin?
11. In which country was Eusebio born?
12. True or false: Eusebio guided Portugal to the final of the 1966 World Cup?
13. Eusebio's goal-scoring record at Benfica was amazing. How many goals did he get in 301 games?
14. With which Uruguayan team did Enzo Francescoli make his professional debut?
15. What was Gheorghe Hagi's nickname?

1. Franco Baresi 2. 'Piscinin' – Milanese dialect for 'little one' 3. New York Cosmos, in 1983 4. Giampiero Boniperti 5. Gianluigi Buffon and Dino Zoff 6. Emilio Butragueño 7. Cantona 8. Teófilo Juan Cubillas Arizaga 9. Dalglish 10. Rinat Dasayev 11. Mozambique 12. False. They came third 13. 317 14. Montevideo Wanderers 15. The Maradona of the Carpathians

Other Stars

1. True or false: Roy Keane was told by Brian Clough just minutes before his debut that he was going to start?
2. How many league titles did Keane win with Manchester United?
3. Kevin Keegan won three league titles with Liverpool, but how many European Cups did he lift?
4. Which future Argentinian World Cup hero started his career with Instituto de Córdoba in 1970?
5. Name the brothers that were central to the Dutch World Cup runner-up side in 1974.
6. Which German legend won the 1995 Football Writers' Association Footballer of the Year award?
7. Which Frenchman was voted 1954 Best Young Player of the Tournament and 1958 Best Player of the Tournament during the World Cups in those years?
8. Name the two brothers that were key to Denmark's amazing run in the 1998 World Cup?
9. Which Englishman now lies second in numbers of goals scored for England, behind Bobby Charlton?
10. Which national side did Sepp Maier play for?
11. Which player is the most selected player in both the history of his club and Serie A?
12. Which Czech player was named European Footballer of the Year in 1962?
13. For which club did Lothar Matthaus play most of his games?
14. How many games, to within ten, did it take Gerd Müller to score his 398 goals for Bayern Munich?
15. How is free-kick specialist and trickster legend Arthur Antunes Coimbra better known?

1. True 2. Seven – 1994, 1996, 1997, 1999, 2000, 2001 and 2003 3. One, in 1977 4. Mario Kempes 5. Willy van de Kerkhof and René van de Kerkhof 6. Jürgen Klinsmann 7. Raymond Kopa 8. Michael Laudrup and Brian Laudrup 9. Gary Lineker, who can also claim to have done it in far fewer games 10. Germany 11. Paolo Maldini 12. Josef Masopust 13. Bayern Munich 14. 453 15. Zico.

Other Stars

1. For which Spanish club did Hugo Sanchez score 164 goals in 283 games?
2. True or false: Hugo Sanchez is second highest ever scorer in La Liga, behind Telmo Zarra and ahead of Alfredo Di Stefano?
3. With which two Italian clubs has Alessandro Nesta played out most of his career?
4. Which legendary Nigerian's first two names are Augustine Azuka?
5. Which French striker scored 30 goals in 54 games for France between 1986 and 1995?
6. Which Argentinian World Cup winning player is known as 'El Gran Capitan'?
7. Which Italian footballer won the European Footballer of the Year prize in 1969, while playing for AC Milan?
8. How is Ronaldo de Assis Moreira better known?
9. Which Italian player scored three great goals to defeat Brazil in the 1982 World Cup?
10. With which Italian club did Karl-Heinz Rummenigge excel after leaving Bayern Munich?
11. What nationality is Rustu Reçber?
12. Which Dutch star has four European Cup medals as a winner, with three different clubs?
13. With which US team did Hristo Stoichkov finish his career?
14. For which two English sides did Davor Suker play?
15. Which footballing great's first few professional clubs were Young Survivors, Bongrange Company, Mighty Barolle, Invincible Eleven, Tonnerre Yaounde and AS Monaco?

1. Real Madrid 2. True 3. Lazio and AC Milan 4. Jay-Jay Okocha 5. Jean-Pierre Papin 6. Daniel Passarella 7. Gianni Rivera 8. Ronaldinho 9. Paolo Rossi 10. Internazionale 11. Turkish 12. Clarence Seedorf – 1995 (Ajax); 1998 (Real Madrid); 2003 (AC Milan); 2007 (AC Milan) 13. DC United 14. Arsenal and West Ham United 15. George Weah

Other Stars

1. Which Polish player, in 1982, became part of Juventus' famous team of the 1980s and alongside Platini helped transform the side's playing style?
2. Boniek helped Poland to their best ever finish in the World Cup in 1982. What round did they get to?
3. Juve beat Liverpool in the 1984–5 European Super Cup Final. How many goals did Boniek score that day?
4. What nickname did the Juve president give Zbigniew Boniek?
5. Prior to the 2010 World Cup, which Italian player was the only player to have scored in three different World Cups?
6. In which year did the same Italian player win European Footballer of the Year (Ballon d'Or) and the FIFA World Player of the Year?
7. True or false: Roberto Baggio had a goal rate of more than one goal every two games while at Juve?
8. With which club did Roberto Baggio begin his professional career?
9. True or false: in 1992–3, Juve won the UEFA Cup 6–0 on aggregate. The records show five goals by Baggio and one by Möller?
10. Baggio has nine World Cup goals. That puts him equal with which two Italians as their country's top scorers in World Cups?
11. Baggio was Italy's penalty taker, so why did he refuse to take one in the third place play-off in Italia 90?
12. With which club did Giuseppe Bergomi play all 519 of his professional games between 1980 and 1999?
13. In which year did Bergomi help Inter win their only Serie A title during his time there?
14. Bergomi had a much better record in the UEFA Cup. In which years did he help Inter win it?
15. Name either of Bergomi's affectionate nicknames.

1. Zbigniew Boniek 2. Italy knocked them out in the semis. They won the third place play-off against France 3. Two 4. Bello di notte ('Beauty at night') because he seemed to perform very well in evening kick-offs 5. Roberto Baggio 6. 1993 7. True. He scored 115 goals in 201 games 8. Vicenza 9. True, but Dino Baggio scored three and Roberto Baggio scored two 10. Christian Vieri and Paolo Rossi 11. He let Schillaci take it thus helping him win the Golden Boot as the tournament's top scorer 12. Inter Milan 13. 1989 14. 1991, 1994 and 1998 15. 'Lo zio' ('the uncle') or 'Il Capitano' ('the captain').

Extra-Time

Hungary – World Cup

True or False?

1. Hungary met Wales twice in 1958 in Sweden.
2. John Charles and Ivor Allchurch each scored in those matches.
3. Wales won one and drew one with Hungary in 1958.
4. Lajos Tichy, a goal-scoring giant for Hungary, scored in all four of their finals matches in 1958.
5. Sandor Kocsis scored ten goals for Hungary in the 1954 finals.
6. Kocsis had hat-tricks in the first two games of 1954.
7. Sandor Kocsis and Ferenc Puskas scored Hungary's goals in the 3–2 final defeat by West Germany in 1954.
8. Hungary scored 27 times in the 1954 finals.
9. Lajos Tichy was on target with both goals against England in their first group match of the 1962 finals.
10. Tichy scored three goals and Florian Albert two in the 6–1 defeat of Bulgaria in 1962.
11. Tichy got two and Albert three in that match.
12. Nobody scored for Hungary against Argentina and Czechoslovakia in 1962.
13. Nandor Hidegkuti scored in three of Hungary's five matches in 1954.
14. Hungary won three matches in the Argentinian World Cup Finals of 1978.
15. Hungary scored once in each of those matches.

1. True 2. True 3. True 4. False – he got four in three matches 5. True 6. True 7. False – Ferenc Puskas and Zoltan Czibor scored Hungary's goals 8. True 9. False – he scored one goal 10. False 11. True 12. True 13. True 14. False – they lost all three matches 15. True.

Russia – World Cup

True or False?

1. The Soviet Union played in seven World Cup Finals tournaments before competing as Russia in 1994.
2. The Soviets first played in the finals in Sweden in 1962.
3. Their first World Cup Finals match was against England.
4. They drew 2–2 in that match after leading 1–0 at half-time.
5. Derek Kevan scored from the penalty spot for England against the Soviets in 1958.
6. Johnny Haynes captained England in that match.
7. England's last match before the World Cup of 1958 was also against the Soviet Union.
8. England's captain in that friendly match with the Soviets was Stanley Matthews.
9. The Soviets played six times in the England 1966 finals.
10. They lost 2–1 to West Germany in the semi-finals that year.
11. That was the Soviets' only defeat in the finals of 1966.
12. The Soviet Union scored 49 goals in all in the World Cup Finals up to and including Italia 90.
13. Igor Belanov's four goals in the Mexico 1986 finals included two from the penalty spot.
14. Russia's bid for the 2018 World Cup is being financed by the owner of an English Premiership club.
15. Goalkeeper Lev Yashin, who played from 1949 to 1971, was known as the Black Spider and used to be told off by his wife for yelling too much on the pitch as he organized his defense.

1. True 2. False – the year was 1958 3. True 4. True 5. False – it was Tom Finney 6. False – Billy Wright 7. True 8. False – Billy Wright again 9. True 10. True 11. False – they lost the third-place play-off 12. True 13.True 14. True – Chelsea's Roman Abramovich 15. True

World Cup Officials

1. What is the maximum age set by FIFA for a World Cup referee?
2. How many referees officiated in the 1994 World Cup Finals in the United States?
3. England had one representative on the referees' list for 1994. Who was he?
4. Who was the last English referee to oversee a World Cup Final?
5. Where and when was that final?
6. Who captained West Germany in the 1974 World Cup Final?
7. Who was the English referee of the World Cup–deciding match in 1950 between Uruguay and Brazil?
8. What was the name of the English referee chosen to officiate in the 1954 World Cup Final?
9. Apart from England, how many other countries have supplied three referees for the World Cup Final?
10. Who was presented with the Jules Rimet trophy as captain of the winning team in the 1954 final?
11. Who, as retiring president of FIFA, made the presentation of the trophy in that final?
12. Who was the captain of the losing nation in the 1954 final?
13. Who coached the German squad in that 1954 tournament?
14. Who was the Welsh referee with the job of linesman in that final?
15. Who was the Hungarian Deputy Minister of Sport in supreme control of the Hungarians in 1954?

1. 45 2. 24 3. Philip Don 4. Jack Taylor 5. Munich, 1974 6. Franz Beckenbauer 7. George Reader of Southampton 8. Bill Ling 9. None 10. Fritz Walter of Germany 11. Jules Rimet 12. Ferenc Puskas of Hungary 13. Sepp Herberger 14. Mervyn Griffiths 15. Gustav Sebes.

 Captains and Officials I 

1. Who was coach to the Hungarian finalists of 1954?
2. Who was captain in England's first ever World Cup qualifying match in October 1949?
3. Who was England's team manager for the 1950 World Cup Finals?
4. Who was the English referee knighted for his services to football in 1949?
5. Who was president of FIFA for 13 years from 1961?
6. Who was team manager of England for four World Cup campaigns?
7. Which former England team manager became FA Director of Coaching and was knighted for his services?
8. England played three qualifying matches and three finals games in the Switzerland 1954 series. Who was captain for all six matches?
9. England played four qualifiers and four finals matches in the 1958 World Cup. Who was captain for all these?
10. In which year did Alf Ramsey become England's manager?
11. Whom did he succeed?
12. What was Ramsey's job before he took over England?
13. Who was England's first World Cup team captain after Billy Wright?
14. That player's first World Cup match as England captain was played in the qualifying round for the 1962 finals in Chile. Who were England's opponents in that match?
15. England won that match 9–0. Was the new skipper among the goalscorers?

1. Gyula Mandi 2. Billy Wright 3. Walter Winterbottom 4. Sir Stanley Rous 5. Sir Stanley Rous 6. Walter Winterbottom 7. Sir Walter Winterbottom 8. Billy Wright 9. Billy Wright 10. 1963 11. Walter Winterbottom 12. Ipswich Town manager 13. Johnny Haynes 14. Luxembourg 15. Yes, Haynes scored one goal.

Captains and Officials 2

1. England had the same captain for seven of their eight matches – qualifiers and finals – in the 1962 series. Who took over just once?
2. Which club did he play for in the Football League?
3. That player won 43 England caps. How many times was he skipper in a World Cup match?
4. In how many qualifying matches was Alf Ramsey the manager of England during the 1966 series?
5. Who took over as England's captain in May 1964 before the run–up to the 1966 series?
6. From whom did he take over the captaincy?
7. Who was the secretary of FIFA at the same time?
8. Who was the president of FIFA at the same time?
9. Who was the first captain presented with the World Cup in 1930?
10. From which country was the first World Cup Final referee John Langenus?
11. The 1954 quarter–final match between Hungary and Brazil was called the 'Battle of Berne'. Who was the referee?
12. How many players were sent off in that match?
13. The 1954 quarter–final between Hungary and Brazil prepared the match's referee for a much tougher TV refereeing assignment on which popular programme?
14. Who captained the Austrian team beaten in the 1954 semi–finals by Germany?
15. Italian players chased referee Mario Viani off the pitch after losing to the Swiss in a 1954 group match. What nationality was he?

1. Jimmy Armfield 2. Blackpool 3. Once 4. None – England qualified as hosts 5. Bobby Moore 6. Jimmy Armfield 7. Henri Delaunay 8. Jules Rimet 9. Nasazzi of Uruguay 10. Belgium 11. Arthur Ellis of England 12. Three 13. It's A Knockout 14. Ernst Ocwirk 15. Brazilian.

Belgium, Austria – World Cup

True or False?

1. USA beat Belgium 3–0 in the first World Cup Finals match between the two teams.
2. Brazil's Pele is the only player to hold three World Cup winners' medals.
3. Jean Nicolas scored a hat-trick for France against Belgium in the 1938 finals in France.
4. That was Belgium's only match in the 1938 finals.
5. Belgium conceded five goals against Germany in the Italy 1934 finals.
6. That was Belgium's only match in the 1934 finals.
7. Germany's scorers in that match were Stanislaus Kobierski (three goals) and Conen (two goals).
8. Austria qualified for their seventh World Cup Finals in winning through to France 1998.
9. Austria's best World Cup performance was in 1954 when they reached the quarter-finals.
10. Twelve goals were scored in their quarter-final match of 1954.
11. The result of that match was Austria 8–4 Switzerland.
12. Austria's first finals match in 1954 was a 1–0 defeat of Scotland.
13. Their last match in the 1954 finals was against West Germany.
14. Their last match was against Uruguay in a third-place play-off.
15. Austria were beaten 3–1 in the third-place match.

1. True 2. True 3. False – he scored only two goals 4. True 5. True 6. True 7. False – Conen scored three, Kobierski two 8. True 9. False – they reached the semi-finals 10. True 11. False – Austria won 7–5 12. True 13. False 14. True 15. False – Austria won 3–1.

Belgium at the World Cup

True or False?

1. Belgium's entry to the World Cup Finals of 2002 was their sixth consecutive qualification for the finals.
2. Korea/Japan 2002 was Belgium's ninth World Cup Finals.
3. Belgium's best World Cup achievement was to reach the semi-finals in 1986.
4. They played seven matches in that tournament.
5. Two of their matches in Mexico 1986 went to extra time.
6. Two of their matches went to penalty shoot-outs.
7. Belgium won a penalty shoot-out against Spain 5–4.
8. Diego Maradona scored all three of Argentina's goals against Belgium in the semi-finals.
9. Franz Beckenbauer is the only person to win the World Cup as both captain and head coach.
10. France scored four goals to take third place in 1986.
11. England eliminated Belgium in the second round in Italia 90.
12. David Platt scored the only goal in extra time in that match.
13. Saudi Arabia drew 1–1 with Belgium in the 1994 finals.
14. The Belgians beat Morocco and Holland 1–0 in 1994 group matches.
15. Rudi Voller and Jurgen Klinsmann (two goals) scored in Germany's 3–2 defeat of Belgium in 1994.

1. True. 2. False – it was their 11th. 3. True 4. True 5. False – three of their matches went to extra time 6. False – only one went to penalty shoot-outs 7. True 8. False – the score was 2–0 9. True 10. True – the score was Belgium 2–4 France 11. True 12. True 13. False – Belgium lost 1–0 14. True 15. False – Voller scored two goals, Jurgen Klinsmann one.

World Cup I

True or False?

1. El Salvador conceded 22 goals in their six World Cup Finals matches.
2. Belgium have beaten El Salvador twice in the World Cup.
3. Hungary were the kiss of death for El Salvador in a 10–1 defeat where Laszlo Kiss scored four goals.
4. England beat El Salvador 4–1 in the 1970 finals in Mexico.
5. France's appearance in the 2002 World Cup was their 11th, but first as holders.
6. Mexico made their tenth finals appearance in 2002.
7. Spain made their 12th finals appearance in 2006.
8. Slovenia made their second appearance in the finals in 2002.
9. England made their 11th World Cup appearance in 2002.
10. Romania did not make their eighth finals appearance in 2002.
11. France appeared in all three pre–Second World War finals.
12. They played six times in pre–war finals matches, winning three.
13. France's first British opponents in a finals series were England in Sweden 1958.
14. France's second British opponents in the next match in Sweden were Wales.
15. France were beaten in the semi–finals in Sweden by Brazil, for whom Pelé scored a hat–trick, with Vava and Didi also scoring. Just Fontaine and Roger Piantoni scored for France, who lost 5–2. The match took place on 24 June 1958 and Brazil led 2–1 at half–time.

1. True 2. True 3. False – he scored three goals 4. False – they never met 5. True 6. False – it was their 12th appearance 7. True 8. False, it was their first appearance, having impressed at Euro 2000 9. True. 10. True – they failed to qualify in 2002 11. True 12. False – they won two matches 13. False – Scotland 14. False – Northern Ireland 15. True – every word!

World Cup 2

True or False?

1. France's manager in Sweden 1958 was Paul Nicolas. (He was not known for his singing, unlike his namesake who has appeared on the West End stage.)
2. They won third place in those 1958 finals by beating West Germany.
3. The result was France 6–3 West Germany.
4. Just Fontaine scored four goals including a penalty.
5. Raymond Kopa scored from the penalty spot in that match.
6. France beat Argentina 2–1 in the Argentina finals of 1978.
7. France were beaten in the quarter-finals in 1978.
8. France were beaten by England in 1966 with goals from Roger Hunt and Bobby Charlton.
9. France lost 3–2 to Poland in the third-place play-off match in 1982.
10. Jean-Pierre Papin scored the only goal of the match with Canada in the 1982 finals.
11. France had never played in a World Cup Final before 1998, but have won third place twice.
12. Germany's pre-war teams played six times in two tournaments.
13. They drew with Switzerland and lost the replay in 1938.
14. Unified Germany went out after four matches in USA 94.
15. Jurgen Klinsmann scored in every match in the USA.

1. True 2. True 3. True 4. False 5. True 6. False – they lost 1–2 7. False – they went out after the group games 8. False – Hunt scored both goals 9. True 10. True 11. True. 12. True 13. True 14. False – they played five matches 15. False – he scored only in the first four matches.

World Cup 3

True or False?

1. Paraguay played in their third World Cup Finals in Mexico in 1986.
2. Paraguay won three points in their three group games in Mexico in 1986.
3. Paraguay won four points in their group games in Sweden in 1958.
4. Scotland beat Paraguay 3–2 in their group match in 1958.
5. Just Fontaine scored two of the seven French goals against Paraguay in 1958.
6. Paraguay have won four of their 15 matches in the World Cup Finals.
7. Paraguay have lost only five of their 15 matches in the World Cup Finals.
8. Gary Lineker scored twice for England in a 4–0 win against Paraguay in the 1986 World Cup Finals.
9. Peter Beardsley scored for England in that match with Paraguay in Mexico in 1986.
10. Jackie Mudie, one of the Scotland scorers in 1958 against Paraguay, was a Blackburn player.
11. Poland lost their only match in their first finals appearance.
12. One Polish player scored four goals in that match.
13. A Brazilian player scored four goals in that match.
14. Brazil beat Poland 7–5 in that match.
15. They played extra time in that match.

1. False – it was their fourth 2. False – they won four points 3. False – they won three points 4. False – Paraguay won 3–2 5. False – he scored a hat-trick 6. True 7. True 8. False – it was 3–0 9. True 10. False – he was playing for Blackpool 11. True 12. True – the player was Ernst Wilimowski 13. True – the player was Leonidas 14. False – Brazil won 6–5 15. True.

Australia – World Cup

True or False?

1. Australia won one point in their first World Cup Finals.
2. Australia were eliminated in the qualifying rounds for the 1998 World Cup.
3. They were beaten by Iran at Melbourne on a penalty shoot-out.
4. Australia were again beaten in a play-off attempting to qualify for the 2002 World Cup.
5. The first goal against Australia in the 1974 finals was scored by an East German.
6. West Germany scored twice in the first half against Australia in the 1974 finals.
7. Gerd Müller made it 3–0 in the second half.
8. Australia were unbeaten in their 11 matches in the 1974 qualifying rounds.
9. Australia lost twice in the 1974 qualifiers.
10. Iran beat Australia in one of the 1974 qualifying rounds.
11. Australia beat Iran in one of the 1974 qualifying rounds.
12. Australia played South Korea three times in the group final in October and November 1973.
13. Australia lost one and won two against South Korea.
14. The highest score in a World Cup qualifying-round match is 31–0 by Australia against American Samoa in 2001.
15. The previous best was set in the same qualifiers.

1. True – in a 0–0 draw with Chile 2. True 3. False – Iran went through on away goals 4. True – they lost 3–1 on aggregate to Uruguay. 5. False – it was an own goal by Colin Curran. 6. True 7. True 8. False 9. False 10. True – by 2–0 11. True – by 3–0 in the first leg 12. True 13. False – Australia drew two, won one 14. True 15. True – Australia beat Tonga 22–0 in the same year.

England, Scotland – World Cup

True or False?

1. The first goal in England's qualifying matches for the 1998 finals was scored by Paul Gascoigne.
2. Nick Barmby played in only one of England's eight qualifying matches for the 1998 World Cup.
3. Scotland's first qualifying match for 1998 ended 0–0.
4. Their opponents in this match were Belarus.
5. Scotland beat Latvia 2–1 in their second qualifier for 1998.
6. Craig Brown was appointed as manager of Scotland in 1993.
7. Kevin Gallacher scored six goals in Scotland's ten qualifying matches for 1998.
8. Gary McAllister captained Scotland in all their ten qualifying matches for 1998.
9. Alan Shearer was England's leading scorer in the 1998 qualifiers.
10. Shearer scored four goals in the 1998 qualifying games.
11. Paul Gascoigne scored three times in the 1998 qualifiers.
12. Ian Wright scored three in the 1998 qualifiers.
13. David Seaman missed only one of England's eight qualifying games for 1998.
14. David Beckham also missed only one of those eight matches.
15. Geoff Hurst played three times in England's six matches in the 1966 finals.

1. False – it was scored by Nick Barmby 2. True 3. True 4. False – their opponents were Austria 5. False – they won 2–0 6. True 7. True 8. False – he missed one match 9. True 10. False – he scored five goals 11. False – he scored twice 12. False – he scored twice 13. True 14. False – he played in all eight matches 15. True.

World Cup 4

1. True or false?: Iran have never qualified for the finals stage.
2. True or false?: Iraq have never qualified for the finals stage.
3. True or false?: Scotland have never progressed beyond the first round in the World Cup.
4. True or false?: Germany/West Germany have missed the finals only once.
5. True or false?: England have qualified for the finals stage 11 times.
6. True or false?: England have never met South Africa in the World Cup.
7. True or false?: England have beaten Iran once in the World Cup.
8. Who, on being appointed a national manager, said 'England will win the World Cup'?
9. In how many World Cup Finals stages was he the manager?
10. Alf Ramsey named 41 players in his preliminary list for the World Cup of 1966, with seven from each of two clubs. Which two clubs?
11. In the 1966 quarter–finals, an English referee sent off two Uruguayans in their match with West Germany. Who was he?
12. How were those two players punished?
13. What happened to the Uruguayan player who kicked the referee after the match?
14. Two British referees officiated in Brazil's group games in 1966 against Bulgaria and Portugal, after which Pelé swore never to play in the World Cup again. Who were the referees?
15. Name the Italian manager who was sacked after his team failed to get beyond the group stage of the 1966 finals.

1. False – they qualified in 1978 and 1998 2. False – they qualified in 1986 3. True 4. False – they have missed them twice 5. False - they've qualified 12 times 6. True 7. False - they have never met 8. Alf Ramsey 9. Two (1966, 1970) 10. Chelsea and Liverpool 11. Jim Finney 12. Each was suspended for three matches 13. He got a six-match suspension 14. Jim Finney and George McCabe 15. Edmondo Fabbri.

World Cup 5

True or False?

1. The World Cup trophy won outright by Brazil was named after a Frenchman.
2. His name was Jules Verne.
3. The first European country to stage the World Cup Finals was France in 1934.
4. The second European country to stage the finals was France in 1938.
5. Italy won the 1934 World Cup Final.
6. France won the 1938 World Cup Final.
7. Just Fontaine scored 13 goals for France in the 1958 finals in Sweden.
8. Kevin Keegan captained England in the 1977 qualifying match with Italy at Wembley.
9. Kevin Keegan scored a goal in that match.
10. Michel Platini was president of the Organising Committee for the 1998 World Cup.
11. Platini was a captain and also a coach of France in World Cup tournaments (including qualifiers).
12. Romania beat Sweden 5–4 in a penalty shoot-out in a quarter-final match in 1994.
13. Romania have qualified seven times for the finals stage.
14. Scotland have qualified seven times for the finals stage.
15. Holland have qualified eight times for the finals stage.

1. True 2. False – it was Jules Rimet 3. False – it was Italy 4. True 5. True 6. False – Italy won again 7. True 8. False – Emlyn Hughes was the captain 9. True 10. True 11. True 12. False – Sweden won 5–4 13. True 14. False – they have qualified eight times 15. True.

World Cup 6

True or False?

1. Eusebio of Portugal was the top scorer in the 1966 World Cup tournament in England.
2. A dog called Pickles found the stolen World Cup trophy in a London garden in 1966.
3. The fastest goal to be scored in a finals tournament was by Bryan Robson in Spain in 1982.
4. Ray Wilkins was sent off in a World Cup match.
5. Diego Maradona scored three goals against England in 1986.
6. Wales have never played in a World Cup Finals series.
7. Brazil beat West Germany in the final of 1970.
8. Gerd Muller scored two hat-tricks for West Germany in the 1970 World Cup finals.
9. How many of their four matches in the 1950 finals in Brazil did Uruguay lose?
10. Argentina won their second World Cup Final in eight years in 1986.
11. Argentina played in three World Cup Finals in four consecutive tournaments.
12. Alf Ramsey was knighted before the 1966 final.
13. Martin Peters played county cricket once for Essex.
14. Belgium played in three World Cup Finals series before the outbreak of the Second World War.
15. Belgium lost all their World Cup Finals matches before the war.

1. True – he scored nine goals 2. True 3. False – the fastest goal was scored by Vaclav Masek of Czechoslovakia in Mexico 1962 (16 seconds) 4. True – against Morocco in 1986 5. False – he scored two goals 6. False – they have played once in 1958 7. False – they beat Italy 8. True 9. None 10. True 11. True – in 1978, 1986 and 1990 12. False 13. False 14. True 15. True.